300 words
30/11/65

Logic
192   A R

Ed
Phil Q
Queen's Coll
Dundee

Check Herbert L. Searles' Logic & Scientific Methods ch. 2
        JSL Sept '57 (pp 233-6 Vol 22)

p. 122
        Kanger
        Rosser   L for M   ch II

PAUL L. BROWN, Th.D., Victoria University, Toronto, is
Associate Professor of Philosophy at the University of
Tulsa, where he has been teaching since 1949. Dr. Brown
is a member of the American Philosophical Association and
the American Association of University Professors, and the
author of articles in scholarly journals.

WALTER E. STUERMANN, Ph.D., University of Chicago,
is Professor of Philosophy at the University of Tulsa, where
he has been teaching since 1947. Dr. Stuermann also
taught mathematics at the Illinois Institute of Technology
and was Professor of Philosophy and Religion at Missouri
Valley College. He is the author of a book on faith and
logic.

ELEMENTARY MODERN LOGIC

PAUL L. BROWN
UNIVERSITY OF TULSA

and
WALTER E. STUERMANN
UNIVERSITY OF TULSA

THE RONALD PRESS COMPANY • NEW YORK

Library of Congress Catalog Card Number: 65-12743

PRINTED IN THE UNITED STATES OF AMERICA

Preface

This textbook provides an introduction to logic that will not only help the student to recognize and draw correct inferences in words, but will also orient him to the important realm of symbolic logic. Increasingly, the understanding and use of the literature and methods of the social sciences, law, modern mathematics, and the various physical sciences depend upon an understanding of the formulations and principles of symbolic logic.

The study of logic is made easier when it is presented in a modern idiom than when it is offered in the categories and techniques of classical logic. Furthermore, students can be brought along much further in their mastery of the subject, arriving at a point where they can analyze complex and extended arguments that are beyond the competence of classical techniques.

This book contains enough material to permit the selection of topics to meet the various needs of different groups of students. The three major subdivisions of topics, Language and Logic, Logic in Argument, and Deductive Logic and Science, provide a broad coverage of material taught in modern deductive logic. Exercises 135, 141-2, 145 [(No answers)] 152-3, 160-2, 164-5

Some of the features of the book that are distinctive for an elementary textbook are: (1) the extent to which the text goes to lead the student to master techniques of analysis and proof for extended and complex arguments; (2) a treatment of the topic of making valid inferences from sets of premises, no conclusions being given; (3) an introduction to the analysis of arguments containing quantified statements; (4) a brief discussion of relations, n-valued logics, and postulates; and (5) a discussion of the uses of deductive logic in modern scientific processes, in place of what is traditionally known as "inductive logic." The text also advances other more technical departures, such as its treatment of "equivalence" and the "algebraic method of proof." — Reduction to deg^n of p.l. s and negated p.l.s

In exercise sets the problems are classified in three groups according to their difficulty. Exercises in group "A" are elementary and should be easily solved by almost all students. Those in group "B" are of a medium level of difficulty. In group "C" are exercises that require a greater depth of analysis, some special study, or an ability to anticipate topics that are to appear later in the book. Where no letter designation appears, all problems are understood to be of a group "A" difficulty.

PREFACE iv

The authors express their gratitude to Cambridge University Press and W. W. Norton and Company, Inc., for permission to use several quotations appearing in this book. They also acknowledge their indebtedness for the aid of Louise E. Larrabee of the staff of the University of Tulsa.

PAUL L. BROWN
WALTER E. STUERMANN

Tulsa, Oklahoma
January, 1965

Contents

Part II: LOGIC IN ARGUMENT   132. ff

Part I
LANGUAGE AND LOGIC

1

Language and Its Uses

1-1. MAN AND LANGUAGE

Man is frequently described as the language-using animal. Word-languages, mathematics, music, and painting are a few of the "languages" that man has devised for expression and communication. If other animals employ a genuine language, its form is rudimentary.

No satisfactory explanation has as yet been advanced to clarify the origins and early development of this amazing and pregnant achievement of the human organism. The birth of language is certainly very ancient, and it may mark the appearance of man in nature. Perhaps in other animals than man we may find the beginnings of primitive language forms that are not discovered among peoples of an ancient or primitive culture. For, even the ancient Ugaritic or the Micronesian and Polynesian languages display a subtlety of form and an intricacy of structure that approach the languages of advanced civilizations.

Since word-languages constitute one of the very obvious sorts of language, the term "language" is often equated with such tongues as written or spoken German, Greek, or English. Accompanying this limited conception of language, we frequently discover the view that communication is the basic function of language. The term "language" certainly can be stipulated to mean the process of written or vocal communication through words. But the languages that man develops and uses are not all word-languages, and he uses his various languages for purposes other than communication. For example, if the babbling and non-communicative "talk" of the small child is recognized as one of the embryonic uses of language, the expressive function of language is equally as important and basic as the desire to communicate. The suggestion that language was developed as a means of communication is challenged by those who contend that the expression of intense feeling is the mother of language.

In addition to word-languages, man has devised gesture- and finger-languages; mathematical languages, such as algebra and arithmetic; and languages of art, such as music and dance. These languages are used

3

both for communication and the expression of feeling, although sometimes one function or the other will be dominant. Ceremonial and ritual acts, insofar as they are mediums for expressing, fixing, and transferring certain emotional attitudes and needs, also constitute a language form. In face of the wide variety of devices that men employ for the communication of meaning and the expression of feeling, the term "language" can rightfully be used to designate all these mediums.

The building blocks of languages are symbols. Certain gestures of the hands and fingers, notes and tones, words and sounds, and dances and icons may all serve as symbols. Of course, symbols may be selected and used by a single individual, irrespective of other persons, in order to express feelings or to note information. But they cannot be devised and employed in such a way as to *communicate*, apart from their acceptance by others. A single individual cannot establish a language of communication. Symbols for the communication of meanings or feelings within a group must be accepted and understood by at least two parties. In a word-language such as English or Greek, the alphabets, vocabularies, and grammatical rules are in some measure common possessions of a group of persons.

Languages are dynamic. They change, expand, or develop. They mirror the changes and developments, the interchanges and conflicts, and the characters and creative achievements of the persons in the groups that use them. Certain languages have had a greater stability than others, due to their own characteristics or due to the natures of the groups that have employed them. Mathematical languages, for instance, have displayed a greater degree of stability than have the languages of art and music.

Word-languages have a life of their own. Changes occur in the sounding of syllables, in the meanings of words, in grammatical structures, or in the use of idioms. A tense or mood of the verb disappears. New words are created, while others become archaic or are lost. Occasionally a word-language will cease to be used.

Man is the creator and manipulator of his languages. But, once they are created and used, they modify and condition the outlook and behavior of man himself. In some sense, a word-language forces its users to "see" the world in certain ways. For example, among men who use English or other Indo-European languages, the world is generally understood as made up of things (subjects) that possess properties (predicates) and as a domain where statements are generally "true" or "false" (two-valued).

1–2. SIGNS OR SYMBOLS

What are signs? What are symbols? What is the relation of the one to the other? How do we distinguish between them? The natures and relations among signs and symbols are matters that continue to demand investigation by linguists, semeiologists, and philosophers. Only a few simple things will be said about these matters.

The word "sign," which has French and Latin roots, appears to have the same basic meanings as "symbol," which has a Greek root. Attempts have been made to establish fundamental differences between the meanings of the two words. These efforts have enjoyed only limited success. For our purposes, we shall understand the two terms to have the same meaning. *Are syncategorematic words then not symbols?*

A symbol (sign) is a physical thing that stands for or represents some other object or action. Symbols are physical things, such as a set of sound waves striking the ear, a particular movement of the hand, or visible marks or objects. The man or animal who receives the symbol recognizes that this physical thing represents something else. A symbol may be relatively simple, such as the hand's pressure on the back of a dog (a signal for it to lie down). Or, it may be more complex—for example, a traffic light or an algebraic formula.

Man's uses of symbols vary. A symbol may be primarily an object for reaction and response. Hearing the sound of the vocalized "Sit!" the dog reacts by taking a sitting posture. A driver upon seeing a red light or stop sign quickly and automatically responds by depressing the brake pedal. In the actual uses of symbols in this way, which are often cases of conditioned reflexes, no grasp of the relational significance of the symbol is needed. No conceptualization is necessarily required. Both men and animals have the ability to utilize symbols in this way. The organism need only accept the symbol as a representative of some other thing or act.

Symbols may also be utilized as vehicles of feeling and desire. The notes of a Chopin composition struck on a piano can express human anguish or despair. A mysterious mark or charm can be a device for communicating hope or confidence. Quite apart from any logical or conceptual meaning, words can be used in college yells or songs for the expression of feeling or passion.

A third use of symbols is their employment in thought and conceptualization. Here the symbol is accompanied by an *idea* of the thing or action for which it stands. A red light or stop sign in this particular use is accompanied by a conceptualization of the act or process of stopping. This *thinking about* the thing symbolized makes possible the wide range of intellectual and cultural activities among men. In this function, symbols enable us to think about objects. To what extent other animals have the ability to use symbols in this way is a question not fully answered. It is clear, however, that human life and culture are distinguished by such a use of symbols.

For purposes of classification, these three ways in which symbols are utilized may be kept separate. In actual usage, however, there is a continual shifting from one function to another and often a simultaneous occurrence of different functions. A holy symbol at one time may evoke a response of reverence; another time it may be an avenue for the expression of deep feeling; and at yet another time it may be accompanied by thought. A common case of the use of a symbol with simultaneous but different functions is in the reaction of stopping and in the flow of thoughts when we confront a flashing red light or a signpost saying, "Danger!" A particular symbol may have its genesis and a brief life in one of the several roles and then be utilized regularly, occasionally, or predominantly in another.

The variety of symbols is very great. Anything may, given man's intent to utilize it in one of the ways indicated, become a symbol. Some things become symbols as a result of a causal connection. Thus, smoke is a symbol of fire for both man and beast. A flash of lightning becomes a symbol of a storm in the offing. Such symbols are called *indexical signs or symbols*. *Iconic signs or symbols* are ones in which the symbol possesses a similarity in appearance to the object or action indicated. Photographs, pictures, or drawings are common iconic signs or symbols. There are other symbols where the designation of the entity indicated is purely conventional. Such *conventional signs or symbols* may be established due to a certain fitness, convenience, or appeal. The football official's upraised arms indicate that a touchdown has been scored. "π" symbolizes the relation of the circumference to the diameter of a circle. The establishment of conventional symbols can be entirely arbitrary. A laundry symbol or a brand in certain instances may be quite arbitrarily chosen or assigned.

1–3. THE FUNCTIONS OF WORD-LANGUAGES

The use of symbols is one of man's distinctive characteristics. The production and use of word-languages is one of the common ways in which man's symbolic activities manifest themselves. The uses to which a word-language is put are many. Logic is related to only one of these uses or functions. An understanding of some of the other functions of word-languages is necessary, however, if the study of logic is to proceed satisfactorily.

The Expressive Function. One use we make of word-languages is simply to give verbal expression to our feelings. This expression of feeling is often made without any intent to inform others of our feeling or to communicate information to them. An intense feeling builds up within us, demands expression, and finds its release in words. Swearing is one of the purer examples of the expressive function of a word-language.

Stumbling across a chair or toy in the dark, we feel angry or hurt and cry out, "Damn that chair!" This is said too vociferously to be considered merely a ceremonial utterance, such as "How do you do?" Moreover, our intention is not to communicate or to give directions to the chair or toy. Intense feelings or emotions have arisen within, which stream forth through the medium of words. The expressive function often serves a therapeutic purpose—in a sense we are cleansed by the utterance: tension is relieved and the normal equilibriums of body and mind are restored.

The expressive function of a word-language reveals itself in a different manner in ceremonial utterances, such as conventional forms of address and "small talk." Poetic discourse is a highly developed use of expressive language in which we also attempt by the use of esthetic forms to communicate as well as to express feeling. The use of emotionally loaded words can also add an expressive dimension to utterances that try to communicate information or to direct actions. Frequently, editorials, political speeches, and sermons employ terms and phrases charged with feeling, so that we must judge that, whatever else the speaker or writer is doing, he is revealing how he *feels* about the issues under consideration.

The Directive Function. Very often we use words in a sentence such as "Close the window!" or "Open your textbooks to the beginning of Chapter III." In such cases, the function of the language is not primarily to express how the speaker or writer feels about a situation. The function is to evoke or call forth a certain type of behavior in the listener or reader. We suggested earlier that the expressive function of word-languages takes many forms. The directive function of discourse is equally complex. Our purposes do not, however, require a fastidious examination of the different modes of directive discourse. Orders, commands, and exhortations are common examples.

The principles of logical criticism and analysis are not properly applied to expressive or directive discourse. When a student of logic undertakes to apply logical criteria of criticism to poetry, to invectives, to "small talk," or to other modes of these functions of word-languages, the fault lies with him. He has misconstrued the nature of the texts or discourses with which he is dealing. His sophistic "logical" maneuvers tell us little about the texts or discourses, but much about his ignorance of the functions of word-languages and his lack of comprehension of the tasks of logic.

The Informative Function. Among its other uses, word-language has an informative function. Here is where the principles we shall be studying find their applications.

In brief, the informative function of a word-language is exhibited whenever the speaker's or writer's intent is primarily to communicate information, either in a single statement or in a complex argument. Simple examples of the informative function are: "There is a book on the floor"; "The United Nations' building overlooks the East River"; "Carrots are vegetables"; and "Since Carpenter is an insurance salesman, he is a Republican; for all insurance salesmen are Republicans."

As a result of ignoring the expressive and directive functions of word-languages, many people assume all discourse is meant to inform or to communicate logical meaning. Often the tide of emotion or strong feeling in the speaker or writer deceives him and his audience into believing that he is informing them when as a matter of fact he is expressing his feelings on the subject under consideration. The student of logic must be alert to and develop a sensitivity to the various uses and functions of word-languages, so that he may ferret out discourse that is truly informative in character.

Language with Mixed Functions. Many speeches and pieces of writing serve, of course, multiple functions, especially if they are extended discourses. A paragraph from the speech of a politician running for office may simultaneously communicate certain information, express the candidate's feelings, and serve to call upon the listener to cast his vote for the speaker. In such cases, the student of logic must separate the informative content of the speech from those aspects that are expressive or directive. This is, of course, not always an easy task.

In long and complex speeches or writings, one may find it necessary to determine the functions served by each sentence or paragraph, or each set of related paragraphs, and then determine the functions served by the discourse as a whole. Thus, a sermon may contain certain ceremonial phrases of an ecclesiastical nature, descriptions of situations or problems in the community, quotations of poetry, deprecations, exhortations, and so on. As a whole, it may, however, weave these parts together in such a way that the chief function of the sermon is directive.

1–4. CRITERIA FOR LANGUAGE

Understood as a means of communication and expression, language includes word-languages, ritual, music, art, and so forth. The criteria used for the evaluation of these different languages will vary. The music lover and the musician employ such criteria as harmonic structure and movement as bases for the evaluation of music. Those who are specialists in other language areas devise suitable criteria for making their evaluations. Our purposes and interests preclude, of course, a consideration of the criteria useful in all the various language areas. Students of logic, however, need to study the criteria for making judgments about word-languages.

Our consideration of the functions of word-languages has already indicated that most discourse is not a simple piece of cloth, but a tapestry of many complex forms and functions. A discriminating mind will respond to the sentences and words as they function in various ways. But confusion and misunderstanding often arise from another quarter. Many people are unaware that differing criteria must be employed, if discourses serving different functions are to be properly evaluated. The different functions of word-languages demand different criteria for evaluation.

Mistakes frequently occur as a result of too extensive a use of the criterion of truth and falsity for assessing word-languages. Poetry has been judged true; commands have been called false. The "truth-or-falsity obsession" that moves many people to judge all word usages from this perspective is no doubt the result in part of the presence in the Western world of certain major religious and philosophical views that think of themselves as the final authorities, as holding the genuinely correct positions, or as embodying ultimate principles of judgment. The biases introduced by the views of truth among these philosophies and theologies result in distorted or confused uses of words and in improper judgments about the uses of words.

The various functions of word-languages provide us with certain clues to the criteria that may be employed in evaluation. When in the dark one falls over a bicycle on the sidewalk and cries out, "You stupid idiot!" a strong feeling of disgust or anger is expressed. It hardly makes sense to judge this expression as true or false. The command by a general for his troops to advance or the test instructions given by a professor call for some other criteria of judgment than "true" or "false."

Whenever we express hope, conviction, love, hate, or any other of the many feelings of man, other criteria than truth are demanded. A poem may be esthetically satisfying. An expressive word, either spoken or written, may be judged as morally acceptable or unacceptable. Other criteria of judgment—from psychological ones to religious ones—can be employed. Perhaps the common element in all of them is that expressive words are viewed as in some sense satisfying our feelings or needs. A judgment that certain expressive words are or are not satisfying will have subjective and objective aspects. Thus, the user of a curse may judge his expression to have been satisfying, although the public may not concur. Many will judge the love exchanges of Romeo and Juliet, the expressions of suffering and hope by Job, and the agonies of Oedipus as satisfying expressions of certain human needs and feelings. He who approaches such utterances with the bias that they must be "true" or "false" is insensitive to language and to human feelings.

Although the criterion of true and false is justifiably applied to word-languages used for communicating information, it is not the only criterion that can be employed.   Statements of information can also be judged as useful or not useful.   They can be assessed as significant or insignificant. The layman may assume that the criterion of true and false is simple in nature and easy of application to statements of information.   This presumed simplicity is belied by the various conceptions of truth that scientists and philosophers have advanced.   Whether consistency and coherence, correspondence, or workability is the mark of the true is still an open issue.   The understanding of truth as something fixed and absolute has been dealt severe blows by scientific and philosophical thought in the twentieth century.   The severe difficulties in the application of the criterion of truth in any but the simplest situations make it clear that most statements of information are judged true or false only within a specific, limited frame of reference.   When later we use "true" and "false" in logical analysis, it will be done in such a way as not to commit ourselves implicitly to some one side of the philosophers' debates over the coherence, correspondence, or pragmatic theories of truth.   Actually, "true" and "false" in logic have very special meanings.

In spite of the problems that surround the use of the criterion of true and false, it is one of the important criteria that concern the logician as he deals with languages that communicate information and argument. Since this criterion is used by the logician and by all who desire to reason correctly, it is important to note the domains in which it is not applicable, lest its misuse leads to errors.

There are no simple and sure rules that can be followed to identify the function of a word, a sentence, a paragraph, or a discourse.   Mixed functions further complicate the decision as to what criteria for judgment should be applied at any point.   Sensitivity to the writer's or speaker's intention is essential.   Often the context of the material being assessed will indicate the basis for judgment.   Certainly no judgment about a statement should be made apart from its context.   "I murdered them" may be an informative confession or a victor's expression of satisfaction. The judgments of "true" or "false," "satisfying" or "unsatisfying," and so on, can only be applied with some measure of confidence after an examination of the context reveals the function intended by the user.

RECOMMENDED FOR FURTHER STUDY

Susanne K. Langer's *Philosophy in a New Key* (New York, 1948) discusses in a lively manner man's role as a maker and user of symbols—the symbols of word-languages, logic and mathematics, sacraments and rituals, myths and music, and so forth.

C. W. Morris' *Signs, Language and Behavior* (New York, 1946) will also serve as a more elaborate introduction to this area of concern.   Ernst Cassirer's *Language and Myth* (New York, 1946) indicates another aspect of man as the symbolizing animal.

Chapter 4, "Proper Names, Adjectives, and Verbs," of Bertrand Russell's *The Principles of Mathematics* (2d ed.; New York, 1937) may be relevant and stimulating for those students who found our Chapter 1 entirely too easy. L. S. Stebbing's *A Modern Introduction to Logic* (6th ed.; London, 1948), Chapters 1 and 2, also includes a more sophisticated treatment of signs and symbols than we have given.

Herbert L. Searles' *Logic and Scientific Methods* (2d ed.; New York, 1956) *check* discusses in Chapter 2, "Logic and Language," the "triangle of meaning" (word, meaning, referent) as well as some of the functions of language. Among other books that discuss the functions of language, we mention Lionel Ruby's *Logic, An Introduction* (2d ed.; Chicago, 1960), Chapter 4; A. M. Frye and A. W. Levi's *Rational Belief* (New York, 1941), Chapters 1 and 2; and S. I. Hayakawa's *Language in Thought and Action* (2d ed.; New York, 1949), which is an extended, informal discussion, with many examples, of the uses of language and the meanings of symbols.

2

Meaning

2–1. FUNCTIONAL WORDS

Whether meanings always precede words or words always precede meanings is an argument that appears to be largely fruitless. In actual experience, meanings sometimes precede words, while on other occasions words are employed that later acquire meanings. The argument about precedence, however, should not be confused with the issue of *priority or order of importance*. With respect to importance, meaning is prior; for any word can be surrendered and be replaced by another. We do this repeatedly when we move from one word-language to another, or when we modify our native tongue by dropping out words that were used for particular objects and activities and replacing them with others. Generally speaking, in the developing life of a word-language, meanings will be preserved but the word-symbols used for them will change.

To infer from what we have said that there is a concept corresponding to every word would be an error. In certain instances, a word-symbol is used solely as a means for the expression of feeling. The word functions in a psychological role rather than a logical or conceptual one. As we have already indicated, symbols, including word-symbols, can be utilized both as avenues for the expression of feeling and as mediums for thought. In such instances, words have both a psychological and a logical significance. To distinguish between the logical and psychological dimensions of a word is an initial step in avoiding confusion.

When words are used without or primarily apart from any logical or conceptual meaning, they may be called functional words. Children certainly use words functionally. They add to their vocabularies words that they can pronounce, although conceptual meanings are absent. They will use these words with considerable delight, pleased with their sounds or the approval that their use evokes from adults. Parents and educators realize that such a functional use is regularly a forerunner to a later logical and conceptual use.

Words are used as functional words when they serve to convey feeling. "Hell!" mutters the man who breaks his shoelace. "Hell" functions as the vehicle of feeling. Any conceptual or logical meanings that may be attached to "hell" in other contexts are not relevant at this juncture. This is clear because others in the same frustrating circumstance utter, "Damn!" "Tarnation!" "Heavenly days!" or "Ugh!" A long list of functional expressions, such as "Faith and begorra!" and "Heavens to Betsy!" could be compiled in which the words function as mediums of psychological significance without regard to logical or conceptual meanings.

A functional use of words is present in "potent" or "magical" words. That ancient peoples employed certain words of power or magic is clearly evident. But we need not speak solely of the past, for "potent" or "magical" words are still with us. There are people who still contend that, unless a prayer is closed with certain precise words, such as "in the name of Jesus Christ," one does not have an efficacious prayer. Others employ the phrase "in the name of Allah" as a set of words carrying power. The use of divine or satanic names in curses was originally, and continues to be for many persons, the invocation of "potent" or "magical" words. That such words may occasionally possess, either for the user or others, conceptual meanings does not nullify the contention that on many occasions they are primarily or exclusively used as words of potency or magic.

Closely related to "potent" or "magical" words are "ceremonial" words. Many "ceremonial" terms have their origin in "potent" or "magical" words, although they have often lost that significance for the contemporary user. Other "ceremonial" words have their genesis in a patriotic or social context. In certain instances, these "ceremonial" words may be accompanied by logical or conceptual meanings, but their primary intent is other than the communication of logical or conceptual meanings. The passwords and initiation words of fraternal orders are instances of ceremonial utterances. The cheers and yells of schools are functional words of a ceremonial sort.

2–2. OBJECT WORDS

In contrast to a functional use of words, words may be established or employed to express or communicate logical or conceptual meanings. We shall call them *object words*. Very few words become exclusively the vehicles of logical or conceptual meanings. Being an emotionally responsive organism, man is inclined to associate feelings and personal experiences with virtually everything he encounters or uses. Hence, words designating logical or conceptual meanings are generally encumbered with emotional overtones. Such emotional overtones may be those of an individual or of a group. The word "horse" may arouse in Jane fears and unpleasant memories as a result of her fall from a horse. The word "Texas" symbolizes a given geographical and political entity, but the emotional overtones associated with the word will vary from group to group.

Although the association of emotive dimensions with object words has significant value when we assess poetry, religion, and human values, these emotive factors frequently make communication difficult and hide or destroy the logical or conceptual meanings of the words. For this reason, one of the prerequisites for logical thinking is to handle object words in such a manner that the emotive dimensions associated with them do not cloud the logical or conceptual meanings intended. Later, some formal steps will be suggested for achieving this objective.

There is not an object word for every entity, feeling, state, or idea. When man encounters new entities, feelings, or conditions, he attempts as quickly as possible to form new words for them or to restructure his old words to handle the new factors. But, applying satisfactory words to them depends upon an adequate acquaintance with and understanding of the nature of these new factors. In some areas, this understanding comes slowly. Meanwhile, no word is employed or some inadequate word is applied.

Object words are distinguished by the fact that they designate or name some form or kind of being. They are not confined to one form of being, such as physically existing entities; but they are used to symbolize any type or form of being that is an object of our awareness (for example, triangle, god, or valence). Object words fall into a number of categories. For convenience, we may distinguish among those that are applied to entities; those that are applied to events, interactions, and relations; and those that are applied to conditions, states, or qualities of entities.

Object words that are applied to entities may be general or individual. Thus, "man" is the common name for the group of bipeds of which we all are members. In this case, the object word is general, inasmuch as numerous humans are encompassed by the term "man." "Man" can be employed in an individual sense to mean "this man"; but most often an individual man is designated by a proper name, such as "Abraham," "James," or "Irving." Imaginary objects may also be named as in the cases of "gremlin" and "unicorn." "Horse," "centaur," "oxygen," "electricity," and many other similar terms are all object names or words applied to various entities.

Object words are also applied to events, interactions, and relations. "Birth" and "death" are typical words referring to events; "gravity" and "force" are typical instances of references to relations. The extent to which object words are employed in this domain depends, not only upon the events, relations, and interactions that occur outside man's thought, but also upon the creative thought of man himself as he interprets aspects of being in new ways and introduces and establishes new relations.

Object terms applied to conditions, states, or qualities of entities specify some quality or property that may not reside *exclusively* in the entity under consideration but that is clearly tied to, related to, or found in that entity. Hence, "green" trees, "unhappy" boy, and "sick" organism are typical examples of the use of object terms of this sort.

The use of symbols in general and in their roles as functional and object words can be simply displayed in this diagram:

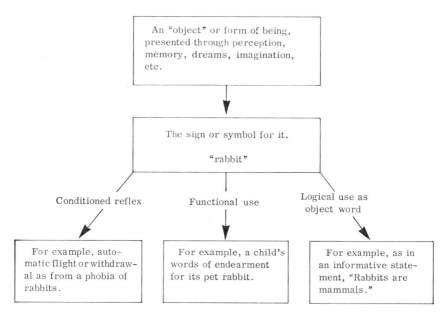

Logical inference and argument in a word-language employ object words. Object words involve some "object" of our awareness, the name or word for the object, and our conceptualization of it. These three elements need to be clearly distinguished in the interest of clarity and accuracy of thought.

2–3. LOGICAL CONNOTATION AND DENOTATION

We have remarked that object words may be general or individual in reference. Thus, the word "element" may be used to designate, not just the element oxygen, but also hydrogen, nitrogen, sulfur, chlorine, and so on. There is a sense in which the word "element" means any of the various basic elements that have been discovered or that appear in the periodic table. *This form of meaning, by which the various objects are referred to or denoted, is called the denotative or extensional meaning of the term.* "Extensional meaning" refers to the coverage of the term, that is, to the enumeration of the objects to which the term may be applied. In terms of aggregations or sets, the denotation of a word means all those entities that can be enumerated or considered to be included in the specified aggregation or set.

An individual object word is a word with a denotative meaning limited to a single entity. The denotative meaning of "Julius Caesar" is that single person in history to whom this term is applied. "Mars," "Venus," and "Jupiter," object words referring to planets, have meanings that extend in each case to an individual planet. To speak again in terms of sets or groups, in the set "Earth" there is only one member.

Obviously the meaning of a term can be understood in other ways than as the enumeration of the entities denoted by the term. Whether the term be individual as "Venus" or general as "man," *the objects designated have properties that are in some sense intended when we use a term. This reference to the properties is called the connotative or intensional meaning of a term.* All the common properties of the individuals denoted by an object word are the connotative meaning of that word. All the common properties of the various elements constitute the intensional meaning of the word "element."

The logical senses of the words "connotative" and "connotation" are subject to misunderstanding because of a commonplace use of "connotation." "Connotation" is often popularly employed to indicate the emotive meanings that an individual or a group may have associated with a term or the total significance of a term. In the field of logic, however, *the term "connotation" or "logical connotation" is used in the narrower sense to indicate the common properties of the objects that are denoted by the term.*

The question as to what properties are connoted by a term is not a simple one to answer. The term "pen" connotes one set of properties to the man on the street and another set to the physicist. We can also conceive that existing pens possess properties that have not been discovered by man or are beyond man's capacity to grasp. What properties, therefore, are encompassed in the logical connotation of a term? This question is answered in some measure by indicating various types of logical connotation—the subjective connotation, the objective connotation, and the conventional connotation.

The subjective logical connotation refers to those properties that an individual has discovered or intends by his use of a term. The subjective logical connotation of a term will vary, depending upon whether the individual using it is a schoolchild or a physicist; for, through his years of investigation the physicist has discovered properties of the pen of which the child is unaware. This sort of difference among subjective logical connotations is something quite different from the subjective feelings and associations that the child or the physicist attaches to the pen.

The conventional logical connotation refers to those properties that a group commonly understands to be the properties of the objects designated by a term. The child may not as yet have discovered or encountered all the properties that a given group understands to be the characteristics of a pen. On the other hand, this group, whether it is a group of citizens or university students, may not as yet have discovered or understood all the properties that the physicist has discerned in the pen. Nevertheless, there is a conventional intension of the term "pen" as it is ordinarily used in communication within a group.

There remains, then, the objective logical connotation of a term. There may be properties of an object beyond man's capacity to grasp. Other properties of the object may be known; some, not as yet discovered. The term *"objective logical connotation" refers to all the properties of an object—those known, those yet to be discovered, and those beyond man's capacity to grasp or understand.* Research and investigation advance to new discoveries and definitions as they probe into the objective properties of an object. Granted that the objective logical connotation may in certain cases be the same as the conventional logical connotation or the subjective logical connotation, nevertheless we cannot be certain of this, as long as human perception is limited and structured as it presently is.

[margin note: So science tries to discover the meanings of words]

2–4. INFERENCE OF MEANING

Although students who are perplexed by the philosophy of Immanuel Kant, or the poetry of T. S. Eliot, are quick to acknowledge their difficulties in understanding many things said and written by these men, many of them conclude too quickly that the difficulty lies solely in the natures of the subject matters. They assume that communication itself is simple and straightforward.

The young lover who misunderstands his beloved's phone call, the new business partner who misinterprets a telephone order, and the young officer who attempts to carry out his battle orders may discover that communication about very practical, concrete, or simple matters is a most complex and subtle thing. In a moment of confusion or frustration, they may cry out resentfully, "Well, I can't read another person's mind!" In communication, we never deal directly with another's mind. By means of a collection or series of mediate processes and entities, we indicate to one another, with greater or lesser degrees of success, our meanings. A great deal of the process of education, both formal and informal, is directed to developing through such studies as speech, grammar, composition, and literature greater skill in employing the processes and devices of communication.

Communication involves a communicator, who endeavors to impart some meaning, and a receiver, who endeavors to understand it. The communicator usually has in mind some referent, which he ordinarily symbolizes by spoken or written words. He assigns or accepts a symbol for the referent. This assignment or stipulation is not a mechanical act. Although customary or conventional usages significantly condition this stipulation, they by no means constitute a complete determination of the meaning of the symbol. Within the bounds of conventional usage, there is a wide variety of symbols that may be employed; and the communicator may, for various reasons, stipulate a meaning for a symbol that is not in keeping with customary usage. The receiver endeavors to infer from the symbol *the real or intended meaning, which we may call the authentic meaning.* How successful the receiver is in inferring the authentic meaning is always open to question. The inference of meaning is fraught with difficulties, just as is the assigning of symbols to referents. Among other things, the receiver must decide whether or not the denotation or logical connotation of the term is meant, and, if the logical connotation, whether the subjective, objective, or conventional logical connotation is being employed.

When we endeavor to infer meaning from the symbol, we must be aware of certain failures and corruptions that may have been introduced when the particular symbol was stipulated for the referent. The stipulation may be unsatisfactory due to the communicator's lack of familiarity with the language being used, or due to the peculiar framework and perspective out of which he speaks. Carelessness, self-deception, and lack of integrity are other conditions that may result in stipulations for symbols that make the satisfactory inference of meanings difficult, if not impossible. The dynamic, developing character of living languages, in which groups and individuals are repeatedly stipulating meanings for new symbols, makes them interesting and colorful. But the interpreter of symbols must be ever alert to the appearance of these new or unique stipulations.

Even after appraising in some measure the factors that may have conditioned a stipulation, the receiver still may be uncertain as to what precisely can be inferred from the symbol. Frequently, the method of trial and error must be employed. The young child who is learning a language uses this method when he points, in response to his parents' use of the word "tree," to an object and calls it "tree," only to be corrected by being given the word "bush" as a substitute. Adults also employ the trial-and-error method in their endeavors to infer the meanings of many symbols that they see and hear.

The inference of meaning from the context is a method commonly employed. In case of the written word, the sentence, paragraph, or larger context in which the word occurs is the basis for judging its meaning. Often, however, the context proves inadequate; and we cannot be sure that the inferred meaning is exactly what the communicator intended. When the symbol is a spoken word, the receiver usually has other aids, such as the inflections and facial expressions of the speaker. In many forms of oral expression, there is also an opportunity for questioning in regard to the meaning of the word at the very time that it is used.

We are generally disposed to assume that a symbol is used with its conventional logical connotation. If the symbol-stipulator has deviated from the conventional logical connotation, he has a responsibility to alert us to the special meaning he intends. Hence, we employ the dictionary, which is a summary of the conventional logical connotation of words. Smaller dictionaries concentrate on contemporary conventional connotations, while more scholarly ones record the conventional connotations of the past as well as the present. Although they are descriptive of the meanings of symbols, dictionaries usually are *prescriptive* only for dead languages. Thus, they cannot be taken as final authorities for inferring the meaning of any particular use of a symbol.

Often the communicator will name specifically some of the objects denoted by the symbol. By means of this specification of part of the extensional meaning of the symbol, aid is given to the receiver in inferring the meaning. Again, a definition may be given that is based on the logical connotation of the symbol. Whenever interchange is possible between communicator and receiver, disagreement over meaning can frequently be eliminated by an appeal to denotation or to some form of definition based on the logical connotation.

In certain instances, the meaning of the communicator can be properly inferred only as the receiver undertakes some action. In the act of assembling some device according to the instructions, the meaning of a word, which was previously obscure, becomes clear. Successful cooperation in a project may provide the context for the receiver's correct inference of the communicator's meaning. Trial actions by the receiver, followed by success or error, are often a painful but useful and forceful means of discovering the communicator's meaning.

Enough of the factors and difficulties in inference have been noted to indicate that the inferring of the meaning of any spoken or written symbol is not a mechanical process. Sensitivity to the perspective and the language techniques of the communicator, alertness to the given context and the framework in which the symbol appears, and patient understanding are all necessary if the authentic meanings of symbols are to be inferred.

2-5. THE ROLE OF THE INDIVIDUAL IN MAKING WORDS MEANINGFUL

We have suggested a number of problems and difficulties that appear whenever we endeavor to infer the authentic meaning of a symbol. One factor to which we have alluded needs to be specifically considered—the role of the individual as receiver in making words and other symbols meaningful.

Ideally, the receiver should sensitively and patiently pursue the task of inferring meaning, without permitting his personal biases or emotions to influence his task. But he is a human being; and his temperament, frame of reference, biases, and emotions cannot be completely pushed aside or ignored. Just as we need to be sensitive to the framework and possible biases out of which the communicator selects a given symbol, so as receivers we also need to be alert to our own involvement, framework, and possible biases. We do not merely receive symbols, but we interpret them. Consequently, subjective factors usually influence the process of inferring meaning.

Human beings are not passive when they hear or see symbols. The thesis that man is a "blank tablet," upon which words mechanically leave their impressions, is quite inadequate. Any theory that emphasizes the passive receptivity of man to the neglect of his active role in this matter does an injustice to him. Man "attacks" symbols, not only from a desire to know and understand, but in order to control and manipulate his world. He endeavors to control other persons and things by means of words and other symbols. Any new symbol he grasps gives him further understanding and provides him with another instrument by which he can attempt to control his environment.

We attack the symbol we hear or see, and in this movement we try to grasp its meaning. New symbols and unusual uses of words do not become meaningful for us unless in some measure we actively approach and manipulate them. We want to understand. We wrestle and probe for meaning. We *make* the word meaningful in some sense, even if we do not grasp its authentic meaning. This disposition to attack symbols and to make meaning should not be condemned, for it is part of the process by which man makes and uses knowledge. It should, however, be carefully appraised.

Whenever we attack a symbol, we do so from a milieu of past experiences, ideas, and assumptions. These conditions of our intellectual life not only limit our possible understanding of the symbol, but they also predispose us to sense the symbol's meaning in certain ways. This is particularly true when we are dealing with abstract matters. The word "freedom" as it appears in a political discussion means one thing to a student in the United States, raised and trained apart from Marxist philosophy, while to the Soviet student, steeped in a Marxist heritage, it takes on quite different meanings. The authentic meaning of the term "freedom" in the sentences in which it appears may be quite different from what some students make it out to be. Their experiential and intellectual frameworks have predisposed them to make "freedom" mean what their backgrounds and expectations dictate.

Man has rational capacities unequaled on the earth by any other animal. But they do not function in a pure manner, apart from emotional influences, for long periods of time. Schopenhauer, Nietzsche, Freud, and others have called our attention to the non-rational aspects of our lives and to how these features influence reason in various ways. As finders of meanings among symbols, we are emotionally biased readers and hearers. The student who is angered by not finding "pragmaticism" in the dictionary may be led more easily to assume that Peirce's "pragmaticism" was just another word for James' "pragmatism." The Christian's emotional commitments may be a factor in his failing to infer the authentic meaning of his Jewish friend's utterance, "My Lord and my God!"

The framework from which we attack symbols, our emotional involvements, and our non-rational commitments are often the basis for misunderstanding or for failing to infer the authentic meanings of symbols. The importance of knowledge and studied effort in keeping our emotions and predispositions from misleading us about authentic meanings need not be labored. The whole educational process, including this course in logic, is in no small measure dedicated to the task of orienting people so that they can more correctly infer the authentic meanings of symbols.

In general, what does logic do to aid in achieving this objective? One thing it does is to *mechanize* the processes for analyzing lines of thought or argument. A mechanical process is impersonal, or nearly so. Mechanical techniques reduce to a minimum the perils that arise when emotional factors or other biases influence meaning and thought. Thus, logic advances scientific attitudes and techniques in the treatment of problems of communication and argument. Precisely how this is accomplished in logic will become clear as we study Part II "Logic in Argument."

Although great strides can be taken to diminish the role of our emotions and frames of reference as we approach the use of symbols in communication, we should not assume that even the best scholars are able to detach themselves completely from their established frames of reference or to eliminate altogether the role of emotions. To be able to do so would be more than human—or perhaps less so. We must be alert, then, to our own roles in making symbols meaningful. Often, we find it difficult to recognize how much we have actually contributed to *making* the meaning of a symbol. It is easier to see this happening in the cases of others. The biases of our friends, fellow students, and professors are often quickly spotted. Increased knowledge, the use of logical methods, and constant self-criticism are important, if the role of the individual in inference is to be understood and to be properly assessed.

RECOMMENDED FOR FURTHER STUDY

A general philosophical presentation of ideas in relation to symbols and of the kinds of meaning can be found in Ralph M. Eaton's *Symbolism and Truth* (Cambridge, Mass., 1925).

For a more advanced study of the topics in this chapter, the student can begin with Chapter 13, "The Analysis of Meaning," in Arthur Pap's *Elements of Analytic Philosophy* (New York, 1949).

The chapter from Bertrand Russell's *The Principles of Mathematics* (2d ed.; New York, 1937) that was cited after Chapter 1 is also relevant here. Certain students may also find his Chapter 5, "Denoting," from the same book, to be valuable. Similarly, his "Knowledge by Acquaintance and Knowledge by Description," Chapter 5 of *The Problems of Philosophy* (New York, 1959), is a worthwhile treatment of certain aspects of the meanings of terms.

W. H. Werkmeister's *An Introduction to Critical Thinking* (rev. ed.; Lincoln, Neb., 1957), Chapter 7, "Terms and the Classification of Terms," gives a further discussion of extension and intension of terms, as well as a treatment of the classification of different sorts of words.

3

Definition

3–1. THE ROLE OF DEFINITION

To state or stipulate a relation between a symbol and its meaning is to give a definition. Sometimes the use to which we put a particular symbol is new or unusual. At other times the situations and needs of the persons with whom we are communicating are such that we assume they will not immediately understand a term or symbol that we use. In such cases, we should give an explanation of the meaning of the symbol. That is, we should *define* the symbol.

At one time, every symbol was new and its meaning was stipulated for the first time. The stipulation related the symbol to some form of being. Definitions are used to make words and other symbols of communication meaningful. Apart from adequate definitions, our statements would be of limited value, practically and theoretically.

Since man starts life in a community in which a language is already functioning, definition is employed to introduce the meanings of words already in use. The student is given the definitions of words to increase his vocabulary. To this end, the dictionary is a useful instrument. Through it, the student is introduced to the different meanings of various words as they are known and used now and in the past. Such *dictionary definitions are called lexical definitions.* Although lexical definitions are valuable in helping us to understand how words are presently used and how they have been used in the past by the majority of people, dictionaries can never guarantee the meaning of a word in any specific instance.

Definitions, or perhaps redefinitions, also serve to clarify ambiguous terms. An examination of the contents of a dictionary reveals that words generally have several distinct meanings or senses. Which of these meanings is to be employed? Usually the context of the sentence, the subject matter under study, or auxiliary considerations will indicate which of the several meanings is intended. This is not, however, always the case. *Whenever it is not clear which meaning of a word is intended, the word is ambiguous.* Ambiguity extends beyond single words, for sentences and paragraphs may also be ambiguous in character.

When ambiguous words are present in a discourse, misunderstanding and useless arguments may arise. The user of an ambiguous term can easily shift from one meaning to another, and thus devise or advance a faulty argument. Definition is essential in order to indicate clearly which of several possible meanings of a word the communicator has in mind. The old argument about whether there is "sound" if a tree falls in an area where no hearing organism or device is present is a vain argument based on an ambiguity. The question is answered differently, depending upon which meaning of "sound" is employed. If the definition of "sound" includes, not only waves and vibrations of a particular character, but a receptor in terms of some hearing organism or device, then no sound is present when the tree falls. If the definition of "sound" does not include such a hearing agent or device, then there is sound when the tree falls. Since disagreements frequently rest upon some ambiguous term, correct thinking demands that we clarify any possible ambiguous terms before we proceed in discussion or argument.

Another role of definition is to eliminate vagueness that may be present in the use of terms. Vagueness is not to be confused with ambiguity. *A term is vague when the collection of objects or properties it is supposed to designate is not clearly delineated or is not precisely understood.* In the statement, "This room is cold," the word "cold" is vague. Is it "cold" relative to the temperature of a furnace-room or relative to the temperature of a refrigerator? Does "cold" mean below 32° F. or between 50° F. and 72° F.? Is the room "cold" in terms of its being the site of a Ping-pong game or in terms of being the site for a chess game? To remove the vagueness that attaches to the use of "cold" in this sentence, we must define the word in terms of a temperature scale, in terms that relate the room's temperature to the temperatures of other places, or in terms of an activity or function that is to occur in the room. Out of a recognition that certain terms are vague, new words and terms are often devised in order to meet more precise demands. Of course, most words are vague to a greater or lesser degree. In particular circumstances, they must be accurately defined in order to eliminate the faults and errors in communication and argument that result from vagueness.

3–2. TYPES AND TECHNIQUES OF DEFINITION

The most primitive or basic type of definition is the demonstrative or ostensive definition. *In the demonstrative definition, the meaning of the term being defined is established by a gesture that points to the object or objects intended.*

A father utters "ball" and hands the actual ball to the small child. The mother says "bus" and points to the passing bus. Frequently, demonstrative pronouns, demonstrative adjectives, or "indicator" sentences accompany the appropriate gesture. The teacher points to a yellow substance and says, "This is sulphur."

Our developed skill in using our language and our inability to recall our entrance into the world of language obscure the fundamental importance of the demonstrative definition. This type of definition connects our symbols to the non-verbal world of objects and entities. Scientific demonstrations are often highly refined and systematic forms of demonstrative definitions.

Other definitions use a symbol or set of symbols to explain the term being defined. As a form of gesturing, pointing, or manipulating, the demonstrative definition does not employ a set of symbols. When words such as "This is a _____" do accompany the gesture, they serve an announcing or demonstrative role. The demonstrative definition permits us to break out of the endless circle of words to things and non-symbolic reality. Other forms of definition, apart from demonstrative definition, are in a sense "circular" or are a part of a great arc of symbolic definitions. These "circular" definitions can be broken by introducing demonstrative definitions. In fact, without demonstrative definitions children would not learn a meaningful or usable language, for there would be no way of relating some symbols to objects. The account of Helen Keller's breaking into the symbolic realm of language through demonstrative definition vividly portrays what takes place in the lives of all of us.

Other definitions than demonstrative ones tend to become increasingly abstract. As symbols are built upon symbols, we generally either become uncertain as to the meanings of our abstract terms or we misuse them. In such cases, we should move from the abstractions to demonstrative definitions. One of the practical and beneficial contentions of modern empirical science has been that abstract symbols must have their renewal in experimental demonstration. The failure of certain disciplines to do this has been a factor in their inability to adequately understand that aspect of reality that they examine. Of course, there are systems that by their nature and interests do not employ demonstrative definitions. Systems of abstract logic and mathematics are examples; but they do not, as such, concern themselves with the universe of physical things.

A type of definition closely related to the demonstrative definition is the denotative definition. *In the denotative definition, the term being defined is explained by enumerating objects to which it may be applied.* Hence, the definition is generally a list of examples of the objects that are to be designated by the term. "Nation" is defined by listing such examples as the United States of America, France, Italy, Brazil, etc. "By a number, I mean 1, 3, 60, 700, or 1,000,000" expresses a denotative definition. Such a definition may have a lengthy or indirect form, as in the case of a parable. "Justice" may be defined by relating several stories that display what the user means by "justice."

The denotative definition has its limitations. The enumeration of examples may fail to call attention to certain distinctive aspects of the objects intended by the term. Nonetheless, this type of definition has a vividness and pedagogical value that has been recognized by many teachers and writers. Stories or historical reports of men of courage can often explain the meaning of "courage" in a clear and unforgettable manner. The meaning of "neighbor" was dramatically defined by the parable of the Good Samaritan in Luke 10.

A third type of definition is the synonymous definition. *In the synonymous definition, one gives a term that has the same meaning as the term being defined.* This type of definition is very frequently used in interlanguage dictionaries. The German *Abend* means "evening." A professor of English defines "infamous" as "scandalous." Another technique of definition that is related to the synonymous definition is one in which the antonym is cited. Thus, "infamous" is defined as "not praiseworthy." Although it is a quick method of definition, the synonymous definition is limited, inasmuch as often in a given context there is no synonym for a particular word.

A related type of definition, which may be considered as a form of synonymous definition, is the transcriptional definition. *In the transcriptional definition, a compact and simple symbol or term is substituted for a cumbersome or complicated one.* A teacher's record-book may have a series of figures or terms that indicate that a student is doing excellent work. These symbols are transcribed on the student's grade record as an "A." The student of geometry employs a transcriptional definition when he uses "π" for the ratio of the circumference to the diameter of a circle, c/d. Music, mathematics, and science regularly employ complex transcriptional definitions. We shall discover later that logic makes extensive use of this type of definition.

Probably the most advanced and abstract form of definition is the connotative definition. *In the connotative definition, the meaning of the term being defined is expressed by citing the characteristics or properties that are possessed by all members of the set designated by the term.* The properties so specified may constitute the subjective logical connotation or the conventional logical connotation of the term. Whether from the perspective of the subjective logical connotation or that of the conventional logical connotation, the definer selects and names distinctive characteristics or properties possessed by all members of the set intended. In most cases, to enumerate all the properties will be impractical or unnecessary, if it is not impossible. To select and name random characteristics would fail to express the proper meaning of the term. If "barn" is defined as a building with a roof, the definition fails to express some of the distinctive properties of barns.

One of the common techniques for giving a connotative definition is to state the distinctive characteristics or properties in terms of *genus* and *differentia.* "Genus" refers to a group that is subdivided into species of different kinds. All members of a genus will have certain properties in common. A species within the genus displays properties that are unique to it, that is, that distinguish its members from the members of other species within the genus. Thus, in the definition, "Man is the animal that uses symbols," the genus is animal. Man shares certain properties with other animals. But he is a species within that genus insofar as he possesses at least the distinctive characteristic of being a user of symbols. Often the *genus* and *differentia* technique must be employed more than once to adequately and precisely specify the meaning of a term. Consider, "Square means a polygon having four equal sides." To mention the genus polygon and the difference of four equal sides is not a sufficiently accurate definition, inasmuch as there are other equilateral quadrilaterals besides squares (e.g., the rhombus). In the genus equilateral quadrilaterals, the difference of four right angles must be specified, if a square is to be defined.

Although the technique of *genus* and *differentia* is commonly employed in giving connotative definitions, other techniques are just as useful. A perusal of a dictionary will indicate that connotative definitions are often based on cause, composition, construction, function, purpose, origin, relation, or structure. No doubt other bases for such definitions can be specified. An example or two of such techniques for giving connotative definitions may be helpful. Employing the technique of composition, "sulphuric acid" is defined as "consisting of two parts hydrogen, one part sulphur, and four parts oxygen." The purpose of the object denoted by the term is used in, "A scythe is an instrument for mowing grass, grain, etc." The technique of defining by citing a cause is displayed in, "Seasickness is a nausea caused by the rolling and pitching of a ship." Origin is specified in, "A straw is the stem or stalk of grains, such as wheat, oats, and barley." In similar manner, the other techniques may be employed.

3–3. CRITERIA FOR DEFINITIONS

By what criteria are definitions to be judged? Students frequently respond that a good definition is a true one. When one considers the nature and purpose of a definition, he can understand that the tendency to judge definitions as true or false is ill-conceived or erroneous. When Marie Curie first used the term "radioactivity" to describe the phenomenon of radiation from an element, on what basis could this definition of "radioactivity" be called "true" or "false"? Whether or not uranium, or any other element, does emit radiations is a meaningful question; but this is something quite different from the definition or stipulation of the meaning of the term "radioactivity." In fact, "radioactivity" could have this meaning even if uranium, thorium, radium, and so on, did not display the properties cited in the definition. Are the definitions of "unicorn" and "gremlin" true or false? We can stipulate the word "Martian" to mean any human-like being who inhabits Mars, regardless of the fact that such beings exist or do not exist. In a definition, we do not raise the question of truth. But whenever we assert, "*There are Martians*," we have made a statement that may be judged, if the appropriate information is available, to be true or false.

The nature of a statement and the question of its truth or falsity are matters of importance that will be discussed later. At this juncture, it is sufficient to indicate that truth and falsity are not proper criteria for judging definitions; for definitions are by nature stipulations. One can stipulate a word to mean anything. Many such stipulations are very poor definitions, but they are not false.

What is probably meant when someone says a definition is true is that he thinks that it corresponds to the usual or lexical definition. "Propaedeutic means pertaining to or of the nature of preliminary instruction" is said to be a "true definition" because it corresponds to the usual way in which the term is used; or, specifically, it is the lexical definition of the word as recorded in *The Oxford Universal Dictionary*. This may be the case, but note carefully what "truth" means here. Specifically, "The definition 'propaedeutic means pertaining to or of the nature of preliminary instruction' corresponds to the common usage of the word as recorded in *The Oxford Universal Dictionary*" is a true statement. The definition of "propaedeutic" itself is not, however, "true" in this way. Contrary to present common usage, in some particular circumstances today or in the future, the word "propaedeutic" may be stipulated to mean something quite different.

When a definition is first advanced, formally or informally, it constitutes a proposal that a given symbol shall have a certain meaning. The proposal may be accepted or rejected for a variety of reasons. Aside from such matters as personal taste and temperament, the meaning stipulated in the definition may be too complex or confusing to be usable by the person or persons addressed. Some definitions are not as acceptable as others. One definition is superior to another if it is clearer, briefer, more adequate, more useful, and so on. Circumstances often determine what a satisfactory or adequate definition is. All the criteria for adequate or satisfactory definitions cannot be listed, but we can examine a few of the more important ones.

1. *A definition should specify certain of the essential properties or functions of the objects intended by the term being defined.* To define "unicorn" as a four-legged animal, "square" as a four-sided figure, or "politician" as a leader is to give definitions in which the essential properties or functions of the entity designated are omitted. To specify the essential nature or distinctive function is not always easy. In many instances, we must wait upon increased understanding and knowledge. A definition is useful to the extent that it clearly expresses the essential nature or functions of what is being defined.

2. *A definition should specify features by which instances of the set intended by the term can be easily identified.* In giving a connotative definition, it is often possible to include a great many properties of the entities denoted by the term being defined. Frequently, however, this is impractical. We select a few features for inclusion in the definition. Some properties, if selected, would not identify or delineate for many the objects intended. "A microphone is an instrument for changing sound waves into electrical variations" is a definition that does include an essential property of the objects called *microphones*, but it does not permit easy identification of these objects. If we say, "A 'microphone' means an instrument for converting sound waves into corresponding electrical variations for the purpose of transmission and reproduction of the sound through telephone, radio, and similar systems," we move further in the direction of the easy identification of the objects intended.

3. *A definition should be as brief as circumstances permit.* In defining "electricity," one could write a book; but such an expansive definition generally would not be usable. On the other hand, to define "man" as "an animal" is to give a definition that is so brief that the distinctive features of man are omitted. No arbitrary rules can be given for the length of a definition. A satisfactory definition strives for brevity. But we should never sacrifice adequacy, clarity, and precision in definition for the sake of brevity. Everything should be said that is necessary to make clear the meaning of the term in the context in which it is used.

4. *A definition, wherever possible, should be positive.* A definition should tell us what something *means* or *is*, not what it *does not mean* or *is not*. We can often be told what something is not, and yet not know what its distinctive properties are. For example, "dulse" may be defined as "a non-poisonous, non-animal organism not found in a natural habitat apart from the sea." Such negative specifications leave us without a positive understanding of what "dulse" is. Furthermore, we would find it difficult to identify objects that fall in the class intended by the term. Through auxiliary knowledge or by certain inferences, one can perhaps arrive at a better definition for "dulse." But one purpose of a definition is to eliminate the necessity for such inferences, with the errors that may

accompany them. A definition should lead us affirmatively toward an understanding of what a given symbol means.

5. *A definition should not employ the term being defined.* A symbol or term should not be explained by itself. The sentence "God means the almighty, supreme, and creative God" fails as a definition because we still do not have an explanation of what "God" means. The attributes of almighty, supreme, and creative have been specified for God; but they have been attributed to other entities as well. The definition does not help us to discover the meaning of the term "God."

6. *A definition should not be given in language that is obscure, ambiguous, or figurative.* The purpose of a definition is to make clear or precise the meaning of a given symbol. Obviously, if obscure language is employed, a definition fails to fulfill its purpose. In many contexts, highly technical definitions are necessary and they are not in any degree obscure. But to use technical or obscure language when the situation does not demand it or the people hearing or reading the definition do not understand it is to fail properly to define the term in question.

When an ambiguous term appears in a definition, the purpose of definition is also thwarted. Which meaning or use of the ambiguous term should be employed to understand the definition? The brevity of a definition does not provide an adequate enough context for a correct inference as to which meaning of the ambiguous term was intended. The use of non-ambiguous words is imperative.

The use of figurative language in definition is always a temptation. The power and vividness of figurative language are the very grounds of its misleading nature where definition is concerned. Although figurative language frequently points toward the meaning of the term, it does not tell us precisely what the term means. Einstein's humorous suggestion about relativity—when a man sits with a beautiful girl for an hour, it seems like a minute; but when he sits on a hot stove for a minute, it seems longer than an hour—should not be interpreted as a definition of the term "relativity," either at a popular or a scientific level.

3—4. DEFINITION AND EXISTENCE

Definitions are given for symbols. Although our discussion has centered on the definition of word-symbols, other symbols, such as musical, religious, and mathematical ones, also need definition. Words and musical notes are themselves physical objects, but they require definitions in their roles as symbols.

Definitions are not of things or entities, but of symbols. Symbols may stand for physically existing entities or other forms of being. "Lamp" is a symbol for a particular kind of physically existing entity. "Greater," "superego," and "unicorn" symbolize certain other forms of being.

Whether standing for a physically existing entity or some other form of being, the symbol itself is not to be confused with the thing that is symbolized. Thus, the word "man" is not the existing entity denoted; moreover, any definition of "man" represents only with partial success the object that it symbolizes. The understanding and successful manipulation of the word "man" should not be equated with or assumed to be the same as an adequate handling of the existential entity that "man" denotes.

Sometimes the symbol is a part of what is symbolized, or sometimes it partakes of the nature of the symbolized. One of the distinct and unique aspects of word-symbols, however, is their freely stipulated relation to the entities symbolized. Word-symbols are *not* a part of what is symbolized; they do *not* even partake of the nature of the entities they symbolize. This confers upon words and their usage an unusual freedom for change and development. Words neither have inherent or natural meanings, nor do they in themselves reflect anything about the symbolized. In the development of our language, "god" might have been stipulated to indicate *homo sapiens* and "Man" might have been stipulated to indicate the divine. A study of "god" and "Man" as words will reveal nothing about the natures of the entities they designate.

Definition neither establishes existence nor partakes of the nature of the entities intended. These contentions should be remembered, so that we do not confuse a definition of a symbol with the question of the existence of the things defined. To define the words "devil," "electron," and "time" does not establish the existence of a devil, an electron, and time. Their existence or non-existence is established on other grounds than definition. To be able to talk about something meaningfully does not establish its existence.

Definitions of symbols that do stand for existing things do not encompass the nature and character of those entities or existence. At best, such definitions can only point to states of existence that lie beyond the realm of symbols. Because definition and existence are two different realms or levels of being, definition cannot express the uniqueness, the concreteness, and the "brute surd" that are found among existing entities themselves.

The ease with which we can define and stipulate meanings for our symbols should not obscure for us the priority of the level of existing being, which definition can never adequately encompass. In their concreteness and dynamic character, existing entities provide the ground upon which symbolization and definition ultimately rest and build. Definition insures the existence of nothing, but no definition would be possible if there were not some existing entities to give us the material out of which symbols can be made and to provide us with referents for our symbols. "Unicorn" and "devil" can be defined only because there are at least some other existing entities.

Although existent being is prior to definition and although definition represents a form of being made and sustained by individual minds at work in the context of existing entities, definition can help man to influence, modify, and manipulate the various sorts of existing entities. The usefulness of definition as a tool for the manipulation of existent entities is evident in the record of civilized man's increasing control and manipulation of his environment. To stipulate in definition the meaning of "element 93" is a possible step in the discovery of such an element. More precise, additional definitions of "element 93" are useful in the manipulation of that element, if and when it is discovered to exist.

EXERCISE SET 3—4

1. Write out in your own words the difference between an ambiguous term and a vague term. Selecting a short editorial from a newspaper, point out, if you can, three terms of each type and write out reasons for your choices.

2. Use a dictionary to locate several synonymous definitions and connotative definitions based on cause, composition, construction, function, *genus* and *differentia*, purpose, origin, relation, and structure.

3. Produce definitions of the following terms by the use of the specified techniques:

   a. Demonstrative definitions of "chair," "book," "pen," and "shirt"

   b. Synonymous definitions of "job," "need," and "review"

   c. Denotative definition of "prime number"

   d. Connotative definition of "prime number"

   e. Denotative definitions of "mammal" and "plant"

   f. Transcriptional definition of "$2 \times 2 \times 2 \times 2$"

   g. Denotative definitions of "college," "plane," and "nation"

   h. Connotative definition by *genus* and *differentia* of "fountain pen"

   i. Connotative definition by *genus* and *differentia* of "unicorn"

   j. Transcriptional definition of "$3 + 3 + 3 + 3 + 3 + 3$"

   k. Connotative definition by structure or composition of "carbon" or "salt"

   l. Connotative definition by function or purpose of "pencil"

   m. Denotative definitions of "skyscraper" and "mountain"

   n. Connotative definition by function of "paperweight"

   o. Connotative definitions by origin of "silt" and "snow"

4. Write out your judgments about the adequacy of the following definitions:

   a. Spiritual being means a being that is not material.

   b. Apple means a fruit.

   c. Rational number means any number divisible by 2.

d. Fountain pen means a writing instrument.

e. Rabbit means a long-eared animal.

f. Time means the shadow of eternity.

g. Sulphuric acid means the chemical composed of hydrogen, sulphur, and oxygen.

h. Satan means the chief of the demonic beings.

i. Human means not being an animal.

j. Democracy means a way of life in which liberty, freedom, and justice are present.

5. What objections can be raised to arbitrarily stipulating new meanings for words already in common use?

6. What in general are the limitations of denotative definitions? Is there a difference between a denotative definition for "mammal" and one for "even prime number"? Are there any limitations to the latter?

7. What advantages are there to transcriptional definitions? Cite at least two with which you are acquainted.

RECOMMENDED FOR FURTHER STUDY

A detailed and extended treatment of the various sorts of definitions and the problems involved in giving adequate definitions can be found in H. S. Leonard's *An Introduction to Principles of Right Reason* (New York, 1957), Part IV, "The Theory of Definition."

Chapter 2, "Semantics," of W. H. Werkmeister's *The Basis and Structure of Knowledge* (New York, 1948) is a more sophisticated treatment than we have given of the problems involved in definitions.

In addition, the student may consult E. M. Adams, *The Fundamentals of General Logic* (New York, 1954), Chapter 4; John W. Blyth, *A Modern Introduction to Logic* (Boston, 1957), Chapter 8; R. Clark and P. Welsh, *Introduction to Logic* (Princeton, N.J., 1962), Chapter 4; A. M. Frye and A. W. Levi, *Rational Belief* (New York, 1941), Chapters 5 and 6; and Lionel Ruby, *Logic, An Introduction* (2d ed.; Chicago, 1960), Chapter 5.

No mention of Robinson

4

Fallacies

The manipulation of symbols or languages in the activities of imagining, recalling, analyzing, concluding, and so forth, is a common, yet very significant, feature of our experience. The misuse of these symbols and languages in these various mental operations is, of course, always possible. In a broad sense, any such misuse may be called a *fallacy*.

The types and kinds of fallacies are too varied to be classified satisfactorily. We shall discuss, in this chapter and subsequently, only a few of the very large number of fallacies treated in the literature of logic. Logicians usually have limited their examination to fallacies related to the reasoning processes in which conclusions are drawn or asserted. Intentionally or accidentally, we often manipulate symbols and languages in such a manner that they appear to be asserting one thing, when they are asserting something else or nothing at all. Improper manipulation of symbols and erroneous reasoning may appear in formal arguments or in the more informal reasoning or inferring that occurs in everyday communication. The mistakes and errors that occur in argument structure and form or in formal logical argument will be treated in Part II. In this chapter, however, we will be concerned with a few of the fallacies of another type. There are fallacies or errors in reasoning that result from emotion perverting reason, from carelessness in the use of words, from inattention to the subject matter under consideration, and from other similar factors or conditions.

Although fallacies are often the results of inattention, carelessness, and emotional bias, they frequently are employed deliberately as means of influencing, misleading, and deceiving others. As a few samples of the more common fallacies are examined in this chapter, we should be alert, not only to those instances in which we and others have fallen accidentally into such errors, but also to those cases in which such fallacies have been intentionally used as a means to some advantage.

4–1. IRRELEVANT CONCLUSION AND FALSE CAUSE

Whenever a conclusion is advanced that does not rest directly on the arguments or information presented, that conclusion is irrelevant. A fallacy of this kind would be committed if a particular action of our nation in relation to another country were declared fair and just on the grounds that the United States has had a long and memorable history of benevolence, that in times past the other nation had acknowledged our fair treatment of it, and that our current public mood was to treat the other country justly. Assuming all these assertions to be correct, they still do not say anything about the issue at hand, namely, whether the current action is fair and just. The conclusion does not follow from the evidence submitted; it is irrelevant.

Irrelevant conclusions are frequently the results of emotional involvement or of inattention stemming from weariness. Let us suppose a group of teachers and students has been confronted with a specific proposal for financial aid to education. They are acquainted in a personal way with the results of insufficient funds to implement educational objectives. Out of their concern for education and their enthusiasm, they may advance reasons to support the contention that aid is needed. From them, they conclude that the specific proposal advanced should be accepted. This is an irrelevant conclusion. The issue as to whether the specific proposal before these teachers and students is a satisfactory one for aid to education has not been resolved. The reasons and arguments they advance may well conclusively establish the urgent need for aid to education, but emotional involvement leads them irrelevantly to conclude that the particular proposal advanced should be accepted.

Frequently, fatigue and resulting inattention lead to the acceptance of an irrelevant conclusion. The span of attention of the human mind is short. In the course of a lengthy presentation or argument, attention is likely to wander, with the result that the mind accepts a conclusion that is somehow related to the evidence but that is irrelevant.

Clever politicians, advertisers, journalists, and others have frequently evoked and promoted emotional responses in order that they may introduce irrelevant conclusions. Shrewd lawyers, ministers, teachers, and others have frequently, by the use of lengthy briefs, extended speeches, or long lectures, induced fatigue and inattention so that they might introduce irrelevant conclusions.

A related fallacy is that of false cause. *Any attempt to establish as a cause something the evidence does not substantiate as such is an instance of false cause.* When we mistake what is not a cause for a cause, we are guilty of what has been traditionally called *non causa pro causa*. If we assert that the cause of a student's appendicitis was an evil demon or that the cause of an airplane crash was our failure to pray for a safe journey, we have committed the fallacy of false cause.

False cause appears in another common form, traditionally called *post hoc ergo propter hoc*. When something is termed the cause of a given event *solely* on the basis of priority in time, a false cause has been asserted. The simple fact that an event is *post hoc* does not establish that it is *propter hoc*. Those who saw bloodletting followed by the recovery of a patient and who concluded that bloodletting was the cause of the recovery established in society a set of false cause assertions that prevailed for some years in medicine. Magicians' successes in many of their tricks rest upon the acknowledged use of *post hoc ergo propter hoc*. The tricks of television advertisers frequently are based upon an unacknowledged use of the same type of false cause fallacy.

4–2. ARGUMENTUM AD HOMINEM

Whenever we endeavor to establish the correctness or incorrectness of a position or argument by lauding or attacking the person who advances the position or argument, instead of supporting or rejecting the issue itself by relevant evidence, we commit the fallacy of argumentum ad hominem. *Argumentum ad hominem* literally means "argument toward the man." It generally appears in an abusive, complimentary, or circumstantial form.

The abusive form of *argumentum ad hominem* is quite common. A typical instance is found in the high school girl's rejection of her father's reasons for her waiting longer before she marries by her assertion that her father is too old to understand how such things are today. A parent's rejection of his son's reasons for wanting to go abroad by contending that when his son is older he will understand why the trip is not a good idea is also a case of *argumentum ad hominem*. Attacks upon the character, personality, and intelligence of a person rather than upon the argument or issue at stake are common in political and social debates. Used in a rapier fashion, such attacks may be amusing and stimulating; but, whether cleverly or boldly done, they leave untouched the soundness or correctness of the issues or arguments under consideration.

The complimentary form of *argumentum ad hominem* often is flattering or appealing to the hearer or reader as well as being laudatory of the person who advances the position or argument. Perhaps, for these reasons, this form of *argumentum ad hominem* may not be as quickly detected. Two obvious examples, however, will suggest the nature of this fallacy. Whenever it is suggested that a particular campus program is desirable and that you no doubt will also find it desirable because all campus leaders are endorsing it, you are being subjected to a complimentary form of *argumentum ad hominem*. The acceptance is not asked on the evidence in relation to the program, but by lauding you and others who accept it as campus leaders. Again, to argue for the correctness of a belief in immortality on the basis that this belief was advocated by Kant, asserting that Kant was one of the most profound philosophers of all times, is to laud one of the advocates of the belief rather than to give evidence relating to the issue. The wrong basis is being employed for the establishment of the correctness of the belief.

The circumstantial form of *argumentum ad hominem* is equally unsatisfactory. It consists in suggesting that, due to the special or peculiar circumstances of the person presenting an argument or contention, his position cannot be correct. The son of a capitalist argues, for example, for government ownership and operation of a certain industry. His opponent quickly replies that, inasmuch as he is the son of a capitalist and therefore the product and continuing beneficiary of great wealth, he cannot with consistency argue for government ownership. Or again, a clergyman is asked how, in the light of his vows and affirmations, he can argue for capital punishment, war, or a racist policy.

To point out a seeming inconsistency between a person's circumstances and his argument or perspective does simply that. The task still remains to show whether or not the argument he is advancing is sound. The soundness or correctness of a contention is established quite apart from the circumstances of the man who advances it.

The seeming absurdity of the position advanced, a strong emotional bias against it, and a lack of information and understanding displayed in the presentation of it are some of the factors that often move us to respond with *argumentum ad hominem,* either abusive or circumstantial. While such a response is frequently emotionally satisfying, we have fallen into a fallacy that leads us away from the issues at hand. Our response should be a substantive one that deals with the argument or contention at hand, whether its spokesman be saint or sinner, fool or genius.

4–3. ARGUMENTUM AD IGNORANTIAM

Whenever we contend that a given idea or assertion is correct simply because nobody has ever proved it wrong, or wrong simply because nobody has ever proved it correct, we commit the fallacy of argumentum ad ignorantiam. Here we attempt to shift the burden of proof from an idea or assertion to its opposite. To contend for the presence of men on Mars, on the ground that nobody has proved there are not men there, is to argue a case in ignorance of the evidence necessary to establish it. Put in these terms, the argument clearly appears to be erroneous.

A religious person contends, for example, that there is a devil. He adds with conviction that the evidence that persuades him is that scientists, despite all their labors, have been unable to disprove the existence of the devil. Or, a science student denies that the human being has freedom simply on the ground that the truth of the statement that man has freedom has not been proved or established. The assertions or denials of the existence of a devil or the freedom of man should be based on some other grounds than the failures to disprove or prove their opposites. The *lack* of disproof of a statement does not itself constitute proof of its opposite, nor does the absence of the proof of a statement itself constitute disproof of its opposite.

4–4. EQUIVOCATION

Any perusal of lexical definitions reveals that most words have more than one meaning. Often we are not sure which of these meanings is intended in a given statement. On other occasions, a person, in a given discourse, may first utilize one meaning for a word and later employ a second meaning for it. In humor, this may be acceptable and enjoyable. But whenever such a shift of meaning occurs in an argument, either intentionally or through carelessness, the *fallacy of equivocation* occurs. Satisfactory progress in thought or argument cannot be made if a word means first one thing and then another, and no notice is given to indicate the shift in meaning.

If we were to assert that Pericles has been acclaimed one of Athen's most prominent politicians and as such must be viewed as one of Athen's most crafty and expedient politicians, we would be guilty of equivocation in the case of the word "politician." We first used the word "politician" to mean one versed in the theory and art of governing; but in the second usage, we meant one who engages in party politics in a crafty or expedient manner in order to advance his own interests or those of his friends.

Abstract words easily lend themselves to the fallacy of equivocation. "Democracy," "liberty," "mind," "spirit," and similar words are often deliberately or inadvertently used equivocally. In some instances, the equivocation is between a figurative and more literal meaning of the word. To affirm that, since the minds of many people cry out against injustice, the mind of man can be deemed a distinctive and separable segment of the human organism is to commit an equivocation between a figurative and a particular, more literal meaning of the word "mind."

The demand for careful definition of terms and symbols by ourselves and others is the best way to prevent the occurrence of such fallacies. Often in technical or scholarly discourses, the course of the analysis or argument demands a development or change in the meanings of key words. In such cases, the speaker or writer generally indicates that he is changing the meanings of his terms and provides us with definitions. In instances of this sort, the fallacy of equivocation is not present.

4–5. COMPOSITION AND DIVISION

The fallacy of composition occurs whenever properties properly ascribed to each member of a given group or body are improperly attributed to the group or body as a whole. Composition results in part from not recognizing that a group is a functional whole or organic unity, which exhibits properties that are its own. The failure to distinguish the relation and bearing that the properties of the parts have to the whole also contributes to the fallacy of composition.

To contend that, since each beam and rivet put into a bridge is strong and sturdy, therefore we have a strong and sturdy bridge is to commit the fallacy of composition. Whether these strong and sturdy pieces were organized by the engineer in such a manner as to produce a strong and sturdy bridge is still a question. When disaster calls attention to an error at this point, we are disposed to remark, "Never has so much strong material been used to produce such a weak structure."

The evidence that the parts of an airplane are each light in weight does not justify our asserting that the airplane as a whole is light in weight. Each singer in the chorus may have a beautiful and melodious voice, but the whole chorus is not necessarily melodious. The way in which the many voices are organized or integrated determines whether the chorus produces disharmony or not. Each campus building may be graceful and pleasing, but the campus may be an architectural monstrosity. To attribute to the whole a quality or property *simply* because each of the parts has that property is to commit the fallacy of composition. On the other hand, sometimes properties of members or parts of a group are properly ascribed to the group or whole. For example, "Since each part of this closet is made of wood, the closet as a whole is made of wood" does not commit the fallacy of composition.

Division is the reverse of composition. *The fallacy of division occurs whenever a property or character of a whole is improperly attributed to each of the parts or members.* Just as in the fallacy of composition, the organization of the whole, its organic character, or its functional unity is neglected in relation to the properties of the members or parts.

The judgment that this class is a good class in logic does not justify our concluding that each student is a good student in logic. The United States may be a prosperous country, but this does not justify our concluding that any given citizen is therefore prosperous. A good team in basketball may very well have a player on it who would not be called good. Sometimes a property of a whole or a group can properly be ascribed to its parts or members. For instance, "Inasmuch as this iron rod is magnetized, each segment of it is magnetized" does not commit the fallacy of division.

Since good teams regularly have good players and sturdy materials are regularly employed to build sturdy bridges, the temptation to commit the fallacies of composition and division is great. The relationship between a good team and good players or sturdy materials and a sturdy bridge is not accidental. But to recognize such relationships between certain properties of the parts and certain properties of the whole to the neglect of other organizational factors and relations and distinctive corporate attributes does an injustice to the whole as a whole. Thus, we open the door for either the fallacy of composition or of division.

4–6. BIFURCATION

To separate into two sections, sets, branches, or alternatives a domain that either should not be divided at all or rightly should have more divisions than two is to commit the fallacy of bifurcation.

Often there are more than two alternatives with respect to a given question or issue. Whenever these multiple alternatives are implicitly denied or ignored and are reduced to two alternatives, we have an instance of bifurcation. Bifurcation is often offered to us in an "either . . . or" sentence, in which the two alternatives are presented as being exclusive of each other. A speaker tells us we must either be a Democrat or a Republican in party affiliation in the United States, for this nation has a two-party system. To state or imply that there are no other alternatives for party affiliation oversimplifies the political situation. A person may become a member of the Constitution, Socialist, or Greenback party; or he may establish no party affiliation at all.

The "black or white" distinctions that are commonly affirmed are examples of bifurcation. To assert men are either good or bad is a "black or white" form of bifurcation. There are many "grays" between the extremes, many degrees of moral status between simply "good" and simply "bad"; and, of course, it may be that everybody can be classified under "gray." Classifying college men as either students or playboys, professors as either learned or incompetent, citizens as either patriotic or traitors, and nations as either democratic or communistic are all instances of the "black or white" type of bifurcation.

Sometimes a domain that is divided in two should not be divided at all, except at the level of analysis. Certain philosophers have suggested that one of the unfortunate bifurcations of this type is that which attempts to separate the universe and man into mind and matter. They should not and cannot be so split. Such terms or categories may have a value for purposes of analysis. But whenever they are pushed beyond this useful analytical function and are understood to mark out genuine divisions in man or the universe, we have an attempt to bifurcate what cannot be divided. Man is not encountered as mind or matter, but as a functional whole. To speak of mind and matter in any other manner than as helpful terms of analysis for dealing with certain phases and aspects of a functional whole results in erroneous divisions and distinctions.

Bifurcation often produces false problems and conflicts that are obstacles to knowledge and understanding. Frequently, bifurcation stems from a failure to sense or to face the complexities in situations, objects, or processes that confront us. Intense emotional bias or reaction often prompts us to commit the fallacy of bifurcation.

We must not generalize hastily and assume that all divisions into two sets, values, or alternatives are instances of the fallacy of bifurcation. There are cases where there are two divisions or alternatives and no more. For example, the integers are divisible into prime numbers and non-primes. But experience teaches us that, when we are confronted by an "either . . . or" assertion or a two-valued division of an issue or problem, we should at least examine it with care to see if the fallacy of bifurcation is present.

EXERCISE SET 4–6

1. What fallacy or fallacies are displayed in the following assertions or contentions?

    a. Good thoughts and prayers are causes of flourishing growth among plants, for my geranium plants became strong and healthy following my prayers on their behalf.

    b. You cannot trust Harry's testimony yesterday, for he was released only two months ago from a mental hospital.

    c. The university will have a good football team next season, because every man who qualified for the squad was a high school or junior college star.

    d. Inasmuch as no one can prove that a God exists, one does not.

    e. Since every student in the seminar is bashful and reticent, the seminar will not be one characterized by lively discussion.

    f. Every law is enforced by a power or authority; Kepler's descriptions of planetary motions are certainly laws; hence, they are enforced by a power or authority.

    g. Thomas T. Trumpie is a worthy candidate for the office of district attorney, for he has taught school for the last twenty-five years, has never been arrested, and has always treated his neighbors in a moral manner.

    h. Every sentence in Susan's essay is grammatically correct and elegantly expressed. As a result, her essay is well organized and inspiring.

    i. Since the Bible is a valuable and spiritually elevating book, the passage in Num. 1:46 must be inspiring.

    j. Since the U.S. Defense Department is a scene of confusion and anxiety these days, Sgt. Alexander A. Alexandroff at Fort Bragg must be tense and worried.

k. If we have peace, the United Nations is superfluous. If war, the United Nations is useless. Since there is either peace or war, the United Nations is useless or superfluous.

l. Either one joins the "Ban-the-Bomb Society" or he is a warmonger. Professor Jones has refused to join the group; hence, we all know he is a warmonger.

m. Man is a tool-maker. Tool-makers are a group of machinists. Hence, man is a group of machinists.

n. Since Gracie Lacie is licentious, a drunkard, and a rebel against customary morality, her poetry cannot have any real merit.

o. James is taking the course in logic. Consequently, he is a courteous person.

p. All students admitted to the University rank in the upper one-tenth of their high school classes. The University is, therefore, an academically excellent school.

q. The University has a great football team. It is, therefore, a great university.

r. You have faith in a life after death. I have faith in my wife. All men have faith.

s. The planets move in an orderly course about the sun. The progression of the seasons is orderly, as are processes of growth and decay in living creatures. Chemical compounds are found arranged in orderly patterns. And so it is throughout nature. Nature as a whole is, therefore, an orderly scheme.

t. To be useful is to be good. A shotgun is useful. Hence, a shotgun is good.

u. Universities are overrun with professors who are Communists. Well-known public figures have openly made this statement. No information to the contrary has come to my attention. Therefore, I am left with no alternative but to accept this as true.

v. Presidents turn out to be either politicians or statesmen. If they are politicians, they make promises and promote programs to get votes. If they are statesmen, they act for the best interest of the country.

w. You say that I'm going to hell. War is hell. I've already been in hell.

x. Since all Texans are loyal to their state, your claim that Houston is one of the fastest growing cities in the nation cannot be taken seriously.

y. I would never think of accepting a blind date with anyone but an English boy. Englishmen are well mannered and proper, so I have nothing to fear when I date an English boy.

2. Select a short editorial and mark by name all the fallacies that you can identify.

3. Listen to the conversations of your fellow students and list ten fallacies that you hear between now and the next class session.

RECOMMENDED FOR FURTHER STUDY

There are many presentations of fallacies in numerous texts. Among them we will mention A. Castell, *A College Logic* (New York, 1939), Topic 2; R. Clark and P. Welsh, *Introduction to Logic* (Princeton, N.J., 1962), Chapter 3; I. M. Copi, *Introduction to Logic* (2d ed.; New York, 1961), Chapter 3; W. W. Little, W. H. Wilson, and W. E. Moore, *Applied Logic* (Boston, 1955), Part I; E. W. Schipper and E. Schuh, *A First Course in Modern Logic* (New York, 1959), Chapters 5, 6, 7, 8, and 9; and W. H. Werkmeister, *An Introduction to Critical Thinking* (rev. ed.; Lincoln, Neb., 1957), Chapters 2 and 3.

The following books are suggested to the student who finds this subject of particular interest: A. Sidgwick, *Fallacies* (New York, 1884); Stuart Chase, *Guides to Straight Thinking* (New York, 1956); and L. S. Stebbing, *Thinking to Some Purpose* (New York, 1939).

5

Logic

5-1. WHAT IS LOGIC?

The words "logic" and "logical" are in common use. As they are usually employed, the precise meanings of these terms are not clear. They are used vaguely to mean "reasonable," "consistent," or "in accord with accepted patterns of thought." Their emotive and psychological aspects and overtones are often more in evidence than any technically precise meanings.

We can here only gradually establish, through our discussion, some technically adequate meanings for them. The scope and depth of their meanings will become clear after our whole course of study is completed. Initially, we may state that logic is the discipline that deals with forms of thinking. Although this specification may be preferable to one that equates logic with what is "reasonable," it is still too broad to be a satisfactory definition of logic. For one can deal with the various forms of thinking from a sociological or psychological perspective, but this is not the interest of logic. Logic is concerned with *inferences* among concepts. In simple terms, an inference is a matter of thinking on to new ideas on the basis of ideas already given or entertained. Logic does not deal with inference as a psychological or biological process. On the other hand, formal and informal inferences as correct and reliable rational processes are the object of study in logic. More exactly, *logic is concerned with rational patterns of inference based upon clear and meaningful symbols and upon some precise rules for moving from one thought (or symbol) to another thought (or symbol).* These symbols may be those of a word-language, those of mathematics, or some that have been especially devised for the task of laying bare the rational structures of thought processes. At this point, we can think of an argument as a chain of inferences, explicitly expressed. One chief function of logic is to distinguish correct arguments from incorrect arguments.

Inferences and arguments may proceed or be expressed in an informal or in a highly formal manner. In ordinary word-languages, inferences

44

and arguments usually appear in an informal manner. Inferences that are informally pursued and expressed can be just as correct as those that appear in more formal manners. The display of our inferences in formal terms and patterns, however, places us in a better position to spot and specify errors. We are also able thus to arrive at secure judgments about the correctness of our inferences and arguments.

Inferences and arguments are usually classified as *deductive* or *inductive* in nature. In a deductive argument, the relation between given statements and a conclusion drawn from them is supposed to be a rationally necessary one. One cannot escape the conclusion, if he grants the evidence given. In an inductive argument, the relation between given information and a conclusion drawn from this information is not a rationally necessary one. The conclusion is possible or probable, not certain. Correct deductive arguments conclusively demonstrate, within the framework of what is given, the conclusion that is inferred. Inductive arguments establish a degree of probability for the conclusions that are inferred. The nature of logic in deductive argument will be the subject we will discuss in Part II. Logic as it functions in inductive reasoning is in itself a very broad topic. It deserves a book in itself. Therefore, we cannot enter into inductive reasoning here, although certain materials that relate to it will be presented in Part III.

Although logic may be defined as the discipline that examines and judges rational patterns of inference based upon clear and meaningful symbols, it is more than a systematic study. It can also be justifiably viewed as a discipline that advances the art of making correct inferences. This art may be acquired apart from any systematic or rational study of inference. Moreover, a precise and thorough study of inference will not assure correct inferences in practice. Such a study, however, should provide a means for developing the facility for correct inference and argument. A knowledge of the kinds of fallacies, of incorrect argument forms, of ambiguities among symbol meanings, and of other such errors or occasions for errors should enable us better to avoid them. Similarly, the systematic study of correct argument forms and of certain techniques for making correct inferences should enable us to acquire with greater ease an ability to reason correctly, both formally and informally. The student of logic should approach this study with the intention of examining and understanding the various patterns of correct inference and with a desire to develop personally a greater skill in reasoning correctly.

5–2. STATEMENTS

One of the functions of word-languages that we examined was the informative function. Whenever we employ words to convey information, we do so by means of *statements*. In a statement, we make an assertion about some thing, state, condition, or relation. Whereas a definition stipulates the meaning of a word or another symbol, a statement employs words with already stipulated meanings to convey information about some situation or event. A simple example is the statement, "The dog is black."

Statements may be simple, such as "The room is cold," or lengthy and more complex, such as "If the heating unit is broken and the weather is cold outside, then the classroom will be cold and classes will be dismissed." In both simple and complex statements, the structure of the statement is important. A statement is not simply a series of words; it is a set of words arranged according to a certain structural pattern or according to certain rules of syntax. A series of words, each of which is meaningful in itself, is meaningless (is not a statement) unless some structural relation among the words performs the function of asserting. Thus, "Black dog full moon" or "The tall professor hastily" are expressions that are not statements. Each word in itself is meaningful, but in each instance there is no structural or syntactical pattern by means of which something is asserted. Only when we have a subject about which something is predicated, that is, only when we have a subject-predicate relation, do we have a simple statement.

The structure of a statement determines the nature of the assertion. "Mr. Jones bought a dog or a cat" has quite a different meaning from "A dog or a cat bought Mr. Jones," although the two statements contain the same words. "If I study, then I will pass the test" is a statement that asserts something different from "If I pass the test, then I will study." The natures of simple and complex statements become clear only when we understand the structures that relate the various words in them. In Part II, we shall undertake a careful examination of the various structures and forms of statements that we ordinarily encounter.

Obviously, we can say "the same thing" in different ways. Suppose I want to assert that each and every Freshman student takes a course in English grammar. This information can be communicated in the statement, "All Freshmen take the English grammar course." But the same assertion can be expressed in these statements: "Freshmen take the English grammar course," "No Freshman omits the English grammar course," and "No one is a Freshman and not in the English grammar course."

The introduction of this idea in another way may be helpful. The English statement "The dog is black" asserts that a particular dog is a member of a group or set of black things. But this same asserted relationship can be formulated in German, *Der Hund ist schwarz*, or in French, *Le chien est noir*. Here are two different statements, fashioned in languages with differing rules of grammar, but they make the same assertion.

A logician is concerned with statements that communicate information. Since the same information can be communicated by different words in various structural relationships, he directs his attention to the meanings involved. A large part of logic deals with statements, their meanings or assertions, and their relations to one another.

5–3. PREMISSES AND CONCLUSION

At a very simple level, we have seen that statements display different forms. *Not only do statements have forms or structure, but series of them, joined together to make an argument, exhibit forms or structure.* The logician is chiefly interested in the *forms of arguments*, that is, in the ways in which statements are related so that some of them are considered evidence for asserting others.

At this point, we want to call attention to only one aspect of the form of an argument. This can best be done by considering a specific example. Consider the following sequence of statements. "Either New York or Cincinnati won the series. Cincinnati did not win the series. Therefore, New York won." The conjunction "therefore" is used to indicate that *the first two statements are being used as a basis for asserting the third one. Statements used in this manner—as pieces of evidence—are termed* "premisses." *The statement that is asserted on the basis of them is called the* "conclusion." In a series of statements that constitutes an argument, one statement (the conclusion) is asserted on the basis of the meaning, structure, and relation of the others (the premisses). The transition from premisses to conclusion is usually indicated by some word such as "therefore," "hence," or "consequently."

Some arguments have only one premiss: "No non-courteous person is a Christian. Therefore, all Christians are courteous." The student should keep in mind that we are examining at this point premisses and conclusion in their relation to each other; we are not concerned with the truth or reality of the premisses or the correctness of the argument. Other arguments have two premisses: "Every liquid is non-metal. Iron is a metal. Therefore, iron is not a liquid." And others have three or more premisses: "If the United States invades Mexico, the United Nations will collapse or Russia invades Finland. If England does not form an alliance with France, then Russia does not invade Finland. Therefore, it cannot be that the United States invades Mexico and England does not form an alliance with France."

Many words are used to indicate where the conclusion is to be found in an argument. "Therefore" is a term that is followed by the conclusion and preceded by the premisses. But "for" is a word that is preceded by the conclusion and that introduces the premisses. Thus, "Lincoln is dead; for, if he is buried then he is dead, and he is buried." A list of some of the commonly used terms that serve to indicate the positions of conclusions and premises in arguments is as follows:

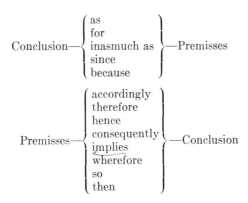

EXERCISE SET 5-3

In each of the following arguments, identify the conclusion and the premises:

a. Inasmuch as Dale is a pilot and all pilots are cautious, Dale is cautious.

b. Don is late for the meeting or he is ill. Consequently, he is not ill.

c. Since mammals are living beings and a fox is a mammal, a fox is a living being.

d. Linda is blue-eyed, for if she is blond she is blue-eyed.

e. 2 is a prime number, because it is divisible only by itself and by 1.

f. Mercury is a liquid, since some metals are liquids.

g. If Mars is inhabited, then it has an atmosphere. If it has an atmosphere, then it rains on Mars. Consequently, it rains on Mars.

h. Since Maggie is an artist, she is a philosopher, because all artists are philosophers.

i. $2 = \frac{4}{2}$ and $\frac{4}{2} = \frac{8}{4}$ implies $2 = \frac{8}{4}$.

j. Triangle ABC is scalene, for it is not equilateral and it is not isosceles.

k. $2^2 = 4$ implies that $4 = 2$.

l. If Dorothy is a statistician and a secretary, then Dorothy is a statistician.

m. Mark is a native of Germany. Consequently, he is a lover of mathematics, for all native Germans love mathematics.

n. The rain in Spain falls mainly in the plain. The rain in Spain does not fall mainly in the plain. Therefore, the Spanish people are vain.

o. Because the fox is a fur-bearer and fur-bearers are carnivorous, foxes are carnivorous.

p. $4 > 2$ and $2 > 1$ entails $4 > 1$.

q. If Pat marries, Louise is a bridesmaid. Either Louise is a bridesmaid or Louise is angry. Louise won't both be angry and courteous. Consequently, if Pat marries, Jack will be unhappy, inasmuch as Jack is unhappy if Louise is not courteous.

r. A triangle is equiangular if and only if it is equilateral. Thus, equiangular and equilateral triangles are equivalent classes.

s. Since an adequate definition must be unambiguous, an ambiguous definition is inadequate.

t. If the rain comes then I'll not go to the game, and if it doesn't rain I'll have a date; so, if it is nice weather, then I'll take my date to the game.

5–4. VALIDITY AND TRUTH

We have said that the logician studies the forms of arguments, that is, the patterns in which premises and conclusions are arranged. In an argument, the premises are offered as evidence for asserting the conclusion. The premises and the conclusion are statements, and each has the property of being true or false. We can say, then, that the logician wants to discover and analyze those forms of arguments in which the premises compel the conclusion, whether the premises be true or false.

While the logician is concerned with the *truth-status* (true or false) of statements, he is interested in it only in a particular way. He accepts *"true"* or *"false"* as qualities, values, or properties of a statement. *A true statement has the property or quality of accurately or satisfactorily symbolizing the relationships or subject matters described by the statement.* Consider the statement, "There is a book on the floor outside the door." If we open the door and discover that there is a book lying on the floor, this statement has the property or quality of being true. On the other hand, if we discover a grapefruit, a pencil, or nothing at all lying on the floor beyond the door, the statement is deemed false. Similarly, "Washington, D.C., is the capital of the United States" is considered to be true, but "All metals are liquid" is deemed false.

The logician is not particularly interested in *how* the truth of a statement is established. This is a matter for the philosopher or scientist to decide. Disagreements among such inquirers over the criterion for truth do not affect the logician's task and concern. As a logician, he is not really concerned whether a statement is *as a matter of fact* true. A typical question asked by a logician is: "Whether the premises are either true or false, does the conclusion necessarily follow from them?" In other words, he asks whether the *form* of the argument is such that the premises force the conclusion.

The truth or falsity of statements, as the logician considers this matter, may be called *proleptic truth or falsity,* that is, *a truth or falsity that is assumed or accepted in the attempt to discover the status of the conclusion in its connection with the premisses.* This point requires illustration. Consider, first, the argument

<blockquote>
All vegetables are plants.
All carrots are vegetables.
<hr>
Therefore, all carrots are plants.
</blockquote>

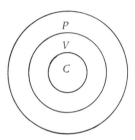

Figure 1

In this case, each of the statements would *ordinarily* be accepted as true. What is of particular concern to the logician is the form of the argument, especially the relations asserted among the sets or classes mentioned in the premisses. We can indicate the logician's concern with the argument's form by restating the argument this way: "Whether it is true or false that all vegetables are plants *and* whether it is true or false that all carrots are vegetables, *it must follow* that all carrots are plants, whether this conclusion is true or false." The diagram above will further suggest that, if set *V* is included in set *P*, and if set *C* is included in set *V*, then set *C* must be included in set *P*. At a later point in our study, we will provide more satisfactory methods for dealing with the form of an argument such as this. Here we can only suggest what is involved. *An argument is deemed valid if it has a form such that the premisses in their interrelations rationally substantiate or necessitate the conclusion.*

This point will become clearer if we compare another argument with the one considered above.

<blockquote>
All metals are liquids.
All basketballs are metal.
<hr>
Therefore, all basketballs are liquids.
</blockquote>

In this case each premiss would *ordinarily* be considered false. The form of the argument is the same as that in the previous case. Again, whether the premisses be accepted as true or false, we ask, "If _____ *and if* _____, does it necessarily follow that all basketballs are liquids?" We

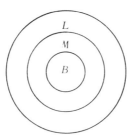

Figure 2

answer that the conclusion must be accepted, given the premisses. The *form of the argument* requires the answer just cited. At this point we have introduced a typical procedure of the logician. As he confronts an argument, he asks, "Whether we consider the premisses to be either true or false, what is the status of the conclusion in relation to the premisses? Is it validly inferred?"

Validity is a property or characteristic of the form of an *argument*. *Truth* is a property or quality of a *statement*. In the two examples given, the same validating form is present. Nonetheless, in the first case every statement would *ordinarily* be reckoned true, and in the second case every statement would *customarily* be considered false. We cannot emphasize too strongly that the terms "valid" and "invalid" are applied to forms of arguments, while the terms "true" and "false" are applied to statements. We do not speak of valid (invalid) statements or of true (false) arguments.

The two examples we have used suggest that the criteria of truth and validity are independent. (A valid argument can contain true statements or false statements.) This is a very important matter. It may be valuable, therefore, to consider a simple argument that exhibits an invalid form. Consider this argument:

No fox is a flying creature.
No flying creature is sentient.
Therefore, all foxes are sentient.

Now the first premiss is ordinarily considered true, the second is generally reckoned false, and the conclusion is ordinarily thought to be true. Our question as logicians is, however, whether the conclusion must follow if we accept the premisses in this form. *If we accept both premisses, then we grant that* foxes are excluded from flying creatures *and we grant that* sentient beings are excluded from flying creatures.

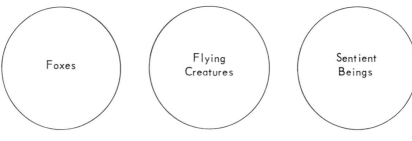

Figure 3

The fact that two groups, foxes and sentient beings, are excluded from a third group, flying creatures, does not make necessary any relationship between the first two groups. *The form of the argument* provides no basis for asserting a relation between the group of foxes and the group of sentient beings. Some other argument may provide such a basis, and our conventional knowledge of objects in the world may tell us that "All foxes are sentient" is considered true, but the form of this argument does not establish that conclusion. The argument form is invalid, whether the premisses be true or false.

The form of an argument and its validity or invalidity are independent of the specific content of the statements in it. Thus, the argument form

All Y is Z.
All X is Y.
_____
Therefore, all X is Z.

where X, Y, and Z are sets or classes is valid, no matter what specific type of things X, Y, and Z may be. They may represent real, imaginary, mathematical, or physically existent beings. The question of existence or non-existence of entities mentioned in arguments is settled by other means than by the forms of the arguments. The logician leaves this task, as he leaves the task of establishing *in fact* the truth or falsity of a statement, to other disciplines or to experience.

The form of the first and second arguments considered in this section may be displayed as follows:

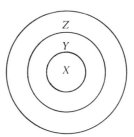

Figure 4

This is also the form of

> All elves are unicorns.
> All demons are elves.
> _____
> Therefore, all demons are unicorns.

and of innumerable other arguments that deal with all types and forms of being. A logician does not need to know *specifically what type of being he is talking about* in order to determine the validity of an argument form, so long as the *form* of the argument is clearly displayed.

The distinctions between validity and truth, and validity and existence, are extremely important in logic. The correct analysis and understanding of arguments depend upon these distinctions. The logician's primary concern is with the validity of arguments. He studies the *validating forms* for arguments.

In Part II, we will examine at length some valid argument forms and some techniques for judging the validity or invalidity of argument forms. The method of displaying the forms of the arguments used in Part I is perhaps satisfactory for introducing in an elementary way the notion of validity and for dealing with a few simple arguments. This technique, however, lacks the power, precision, and reliability of methods that we will present later in Part II.

The methods that we employ in Part I reflect something of the logical analysis that has been traditionally used. Since traditional or Aristotelian logic has been of such great importance historically, and since it was the source from which modern symbolic logic developed, we will present something of the skeletal structure of Aristotelian logic in Chapter 6 before we proceed to a detailed examination of the elements of modern symbolic logic.

5–5. SOUND, COGENT, AND CONVINCING

Now that it has been indicated that truth (or falsity) is a criterion for assessing statements in an argument, while validity is a category applicable to the form of an argument, we turn our attention to certain other characteristics of arguments. In ordinary argumentation and debate, we attempt to produce, not only a valid argument, but one that has true premisses. Thus, of the two valid arguments that follow, argument (I) is accepted in a manner in which argument (II) is not.

(I)

> Either New York or Washington is the capital city of the United States.
> New York is not the capital of the United States.
> _____
> Therefore, Washington is the capital of the United States.

(II)

Either Chicago or Detroit is the largest city in the United States.
Chicago is not the largest city in the United States.

Therefore, Detroit is the largest city in the United States.

The form of argument (II) is the same as that of argument (I). It is a valid form. Argument (I) has premisses that are, as a matter of fact, true. Its true premisses, along with its valid form, necessitate a true conclusion. In argument (II), or in any other valid argument, despite the valid form, a false premiss means that we cannot be certain *from the argument's valid form* whether the conclusion will be true or false. Argument (I) therefore possesses a feature not present in (II). We term it "soundness." *An argument is sound if the argument form is valid and the premisses are true.* In practical discussions, scientific discourse, and systematic investigations, sound arguments are the ideal toward which we strive.

Not all sound arguments are known to everyone to be sound. Let us examine arguments (III) and (IV), both of which are sound.

(III)

Mr. Smith was born in Oklahoma or Pennsylvania.
Mr. Smith was not born in Oklahoma.

Therefore, Mr. Smith was born in Pennsylvania.

(IV)

Lincoln was born in Indiana or Kentucky.
Lincoln was not born in Indiana.

Therefore, Lincoln was born in Kentucky.

We assume that all readers know that the two premisses of argument (IV) are, as a matter of fact, true and that the form is valid. Thus, we acknowledge argument (IV) to be a sound argument. By way of comparison, what about argument (III)? Both premisses of argument (III) are true, but this information will be limited to the few people who know Mr. Smith's place of birth. One may discover through investigation the information needed to assure himself that the premisses are true; but until he gains this knowledge he does not know argument (III) to be sound, even though it actually is. Argument (IV) *is sound, and it is known by you to be sound.* It differs from argument (III), *which is sound but is not known by you to be sound.* We speak of argument (IV) as being *cogent.* Argument (III) is not, however, cogent for you. In the discussion of any specific issue, sound arguments that are cogent are necessary if reasonable progress in thought or investigation is to be made.

Often we are told that a given argument is not convincing. Perhaps the person using the word "convincing" means cogent, valid, or something else. But, is there not some other significant sense for this term? Let us examine the following argument.

(V)

Washington lived at Mt. Vernon or Babe Ruth did not
   hit a home run.
Babe Ruth hit a home run.

Therefore, Washington lived at Mt. Vernon.

This argument is cogent. In addition to knowing this, we also know, quite apart from the argument itself, that the conclusion is true. The knowledge that "Washington lived at Mt. Vernon" is true is the basis for asserting the first premiss to be true. We really are not convinced by the argument that Washington lived at Mt. Vernon. In a sense, then, the argument to the conclusion is superfluous for us. It does not itself perform the function of convincing us concerning the truth of the conclusion. Where, however, we have a cogent argument in which the conclusion is not known to be true apart from the argument, the argument itself convinces us of the truth of the conclusion.

A convincing argument is a cogent argument in which we do not know the truth of the conclusion apart from the argument itself. Of course, what is a convincing argument for one person will not necessarily be so for another person; for people will differ as to the knowledge they possess of the truthfulness of the highly various statements that appear as conclusions in arguments.

RECOMMENDED FOR FURTHER STUDY

For additional elementary discussion of the basic ingredients of logical discourse, the student may consult Max Black, *Critical Thinking* (2d ed.; Englewood Cliffs, N.J., 1952), Chapter 3, "Validity and Form"; H. S. Leonard, *An Introduction to Principles of Right Reason* (New York, 1957), Units 36 and 37, "Inference and Proof" and "The Annotation of Proofs"; and Philip Wheelwright, *Valid Thinking* (New York, 1962), Chapter 1, "What Logic Is and Does."

Other works that will be of value in relation to the topics of this chapter are E. M. Adams, *The Fundamentals of General Logic* (New York, 1954); R. M. Eaton, *General Logic* (New York, 1931); H. W. B. Joseph, *An Introduction to Logic* (2d ed., rev.; Oxford, 1925); and A. P. Ushenko, *The Problems of Logic* (London, 1941).

6

The Syllogism

In the previous chapter, we described an argument as being composed of at least one premiss and a conclusion. Although arguments are encountered with a varied number of premisses and with premisses and conclusions arranged in different grammatical orders, nevertheless, they display particular forms or structures that are identifiable. As we discussed validity and truth in the last chapter, we made use of a particular argument form:

> All football players are men.
> All tackles are football players.
> ———————————————
> Therefore, all tackles are men.

This sort of argument is known as a *syllogism*. It has been one of the standard types of arguments for centuries, and a great deal of time has been invested in analyzing its various features.

In our discussion of sound, cogent, and convincing arguments, we employed a different type of argument, one commonly known as the Disjunctive Syllogism. It and many others will be discussed in detail in Part II. The role and significance of the standard syllogism, illustrated immediately above, has been so important that we must at least briefly examine it. The standard syllogism was the chief concern of classical or traditional logic.

Traditional or classical logic has been taught along lines formulated by Aristotle. In the Western world, logic has its roots in ancient Greece. The Sophists in their argumentative discussions, Socrates in his concern for definition, and Plato in his pursuit of classification are among those who gave logic its birth. Aristotle (384–322 B.C.) is usually regarded as the founder of logic as a discipline. He summarized what was known of logical principles in his day, formulated the theory of the syllogism, and probed various aspects of logical thought. His writings on these topics were brought together by his successors in the *Organon*. Aristotle's great influence on philosophy and particularly on logic continued through the

Middle Ages and into the early modern era. Traditional logicians have followed his teachings and have developed his ideas. Even today certain logicians represent the Aristotelian heritage.

Although the purpose of this text is to present logic in a modern idiom, students should recognize that the roots of modern logic reach back to the Aristotelian categories and structures. Aristotelian logic, as it has been refined and developed, is judged by some logicians to be the desirable approach even in this day to our subject. A brief discussion here of some of the features of the Aristotelian approach to logic will reveal much of value about language, abstract ideas, deductive reasoning, and the nature of inference. Moreover, the student who masters the more versatile and powerful techniques of modern symbolic logic should know something about the contributions and heritage of classical logic. Therefore, in this chapter, we will examine briefly a few of the basic features of Aristotelian logic, particularly as they find expression in the standard syllogism.

The syllogism is admirably suited for displaying clearly the nature of validity. Thus, as we discuss here the Aristotelian handling of the syllogism, we shall at the same time be illuminating, at least by way of examples, the important concept of validity that was introduced in Section 5–4. Further experience in dealing with validity and with validating forms of argument is desirable before we move into the treatment of symbolic logic in Part II.

6–1. CATEGORICAL STATEMENTS

Fundamental to Aristotelian logic and the standard syllogism are *categorical statements* with a subject-predicate form. We will briefly examine certain features of them. The categorical statement unconditionally affirms or denies a predicate for a given subject. Thus, in the statements "Professors are human" and "Girls are not males," we affirm without condition the predicate "human" for "professors" and categorically deny that the predicate "male" can be asserted for "girls."

Both of the categorical statements just cited are *general* in character. In each case, the subject does not refer to a specific person or an individual entity, but to whomsoever may rightly be called a "professor" or a "girl." "Plato is a Greek" and "Zeus is a god" are, on the other hand, called *singular statements*. They are categorical statements that assert a predicate for an individual or a single entity (a thing to which a proper name such as "Plato" and "Zeus" may be applied).

There are four essential elements in a categorical statement. They are the *quantifier*, the *subject*, the *copula*, and the *predicate*. The *subject*, as we have already indicated, is that individual or set of individuals about which something is affirmed or denied. We should observe that in the statement "Professors are human," the reference is implicitly to all professors. Similarly, in the statement "Girls are not males," the intent is to encompass all girls. Frequently, the "all" is explicitly stated, as in "All Spartans are brave" and "All Indians are stoical." The "all" expresses the *quantity* of the subject—the number of objects or individuals in the class or set designated by the subject about which an assertion is made. "All" in this context means *each and every one* of the individuals or objects in the set denoted by the subject. "Each and every Spartan is brave." "Each and every Indian is stoical." "All" is called a *quantifier*. Since it refers to each and every member of a given set and permits no exceptions with respect to the assertion made, it is called a *universal quantifier*.

The subject term can also be quantified by "some" or "no" (which includes the idea of exclusion). The "some" in "Some Romans are poets" means *at least one and perhaps all*. "At least one, and perhaps all, Romans are poets." "No slave is free" means that not a single slave is to be found among the free. Since "no" intends to exclude the subject set from the predicate set, it is also a *universal quantifier*. "Some" is called a *particular quantifier*, for it denotes at least one member of the subject set.

The *predicate* specifies the class or set in which the subject set or some of its members is included, or from which it is excluded. The statements we have been examining have, therefore, often been called *class-inclusion* or *class-exclusion* statements. Thus, the set designated by "professors" is included in the set designated by "humans," and the set designated by "girls" is excluded from the set designated by "males."

The *copula* joins the subject term and the predicate term. "Is," "is not," or other grammatical forms of "to be" (affirmed or denied) constitute the copula in categorical statements. The copula expresses the assertion of set inclusion or set exclusion. If the copula in conjunction with the quantifier affirms inclusion, then the statement is said to have an *affirmative quality*. If the copula in conjunction with the quantifier asserts exclusion, the statement is described as *negative in quality*.

The quantification ("all" or "some") and qualification ("is" or "is not") of categorical statements allow for four basic types of statements. They may be illustrated as follows:

	Quantifiers	Subject	Copula	Predicate
(I)	All	students	are	irritable.
(II)	No	players	are	injured.
(III)	Some	philosophers	are	optimists.
(IV)	Some	soldiers	are not	brave.

Since the quantifier in (I) is universal and the quality of the statement is affirmative, this set inclusion statement is a *universal affirmative*. The universal affirmative statement traditionally has been called **A**, from the first letter of the Latin *affirmo*. Since the quantifier in (II) is universal and the quality of the copula in conjunction with the quantifier is negative, this set exclusion statement is a *universal negative*. It is called *E*, from the first vowel of the Latin *nego*.

The third statement above is a *particular affirmative*, inasmuch as the quantifier is particular and the quality of the copula in conjunction with the quantification is affirmative. It is called *I*, from the second vowel of *affirmo*, and affirms set membership. The fourth statement, called *O*, from the second vowel of *nego*, is a *particular negative*. It differs from (III) in that the quality is negative. Set membership is denied by it. The *I* and *O* statements are general in character, referring to some individual in the subject set. *A* and *E*, in addition to their general forms, have singular forms, such as "Aristotle is a logician" and "Greece is not Persian." In these singular forms, we assume that we have references to sets of one member only.

Preserving the forms of the four categorical statements and designating the subject set by *S* and the predicate set by *P*, we can write them thus:

(I)	Type *A*	All *S* is *P*.
(II)	Type *E*	No *S* is *P*.
(III)	Type *I*	Some *S* is *P*.
(IV)	Type *O*	Some *S* is not *P*.

An examination of these basic categorical statements will reveal various logical relations prevailing among them. For example, *A* and *O* state completely opposed positions or advance contentions that *contradict* each other. *E* and *I* are also contradictories. In the case of contradictory statements, both cannot be true and both cannot be false. Let the student examine the meanings of *A* and *E* to determine if they are contradictory. ⋏ Suppose there are no S's? Cf r-65, where discussed

Employing one of these categorical statements, a person can, without using any other statement or any intermediary logical forms, infer another assertion. And from the latter, he can perhaps infer a third, and so on. Such steps of inference are called *immediate inferences*. One of the common immediate inferences is *conversion*, in which the subject and predicate terms are interchanged, while the quality remains unchanged and the meaning of the assertion is preserved. By conversion, one is able to make the following inferences:

		Original			*Converse*
From	*A*:	All *S* is *P*.	Infer	*I*:	Some *P* is *S*.
From	*E*:	No *S* is *P*.	Infer	*E*:	No *P* is *S*.
From	*I*:	Some *S* is *P*.	Infer	*I*:	Some *P* is *S*.
From	*O*:	Some *S* is not *P*.	Infer		(Conversion not possible.)

Presentations of Aristotelian logic usually invest a considerable amount of time to indicate the numerous relations that obtain among the *A*, *E*, *I*, and *O* statements and to display the numerous immediate inferences that may be made from any one of them.   Although some valuable insights are derived from such an investigation, many of these relations and immediate inferences can be handled more effectively by the devices of symbolic logic, which is the major concern of this text in Part II.   A further discussion of such matters, therefore, will be given at a later point.

In ordinary discourse, categorical statements frequently are not found in the "normal forms" in which we have given them.   Sometimes the statements are inverted, as in "Entranced is the traveler who first views the Taj Mahal."   For certain purposes, such a statement may have to be cast into a normal form; namely, "All travelers who first view the Taj Mahal are entranced."   Furthermore, the "is" or "are" of the normal forms must on occasions be regarded as present, even if it does not explicitly occur.   "All teams play for victory" is to be transformed into "All teams are in the set of those who play for victory."   In instances of these kinds, the student must be prepared to identify the essential elements of the categorical statements and to place them in their appointed positions.

6–2.   THE SYLLOGISTIC ARGUMENT

The syllogistic form of argument holds a central position in classical or traditional logic.   The emphasis upon it has been so great that some students are inclined to think that deductive reasoning is confined to the syllogism.   It is, however, only one form of deduction.   The great variety of forms of deductive reasoning will be displayed in our discussion in Part II.   Here we will briefly treat the structure of the syllogism and its use in making valid inferences.

The syllogism is distinguished, among other things, by being composed of categorical statements that affirm or deny set membership, or assert set inclusion or set exclusion.   The number of these statements in the standard syllogism is three.   Two of them constitute the premisses, and one of them is the conclusion.   Each statement contains, of course, two terms (a subject and a predicate).   The subjects and predicates in the three statements of the syllogism represent only three sets.   These characteristics are evident in this simple syllogism:

> All organisms are mortal.
> All men are organisms.
> _____
> Hence, all men are mortal.

"Men," "mortal (beings)," and "organisms" are the terms that designate the three sets involved in this syllogism.

Traditional logic uses a special vocabulary to designate the structural features of the syllogism. Following Aristotle, the subject of the con- *Check* clusion is called the *minor term.* The predicate of the conclusion is called the *major term.* The minor term appears in only one premiss, which is known as the *minor premiss.* Similarly, the one premiss in which the major term appears is known as the *major premiss.* The *standard form* of the syllogism is

Major Premiss
Minor Premiss

Conclusion: $\left\{\begin{matrix}\text{All}\\\text{No}\\\text{Some}\end{matrix}\right\}$ minor term $\left\{\begin{matrix}\text{is}\\\text{is not}\end{matrix}\right\}$ major term

As we have suggested earlier, in everyday discourse the conclusion may be stated before the premisses; or the major and minor premisses may be interchanged in their order. The order present in common usage should be recast into the standard form for the purpose of facilitating the analysis of the validity of syllogisms.

So far we have discussed only two of the three terms present in a syllogism. What of the third? The third term appears only in the premisses, once in each of them. Because it provides the connection between the major and minor premisses, it is called the *middle term.*

Let us examine this syllogism:

All metal is inanimate.
Iron is metal.
Therefore, iron is inanimate.

We note that "iron" is the subject of the conclusion and is, therefore, the minor term. "Inanimate" is the predicate in the conclusion; hence, it is the major term. "Metal" is the middle term that occurs once in the major premiss and once in the minor premiss. This syllogism, then, is in standard form. Preserving the structure of the syllogism but introducing S, P, and M to designate, respectively, the subject, predicate, and middle terms, we have

Major Premiss: All M is P.
Minor Premiss: All S is M.
Conclusion: Therefore, All S is P.

We indicated earlier that many syllogistic arguments have to be recast into standard form. Another variation in syllogisms present in ordinary discourse is the absence of one statement, which may be either one of the premisses or the conclusion. This premiss or conclusion is assumed or understood. In such instances, the premiss or conclusion must be explicitly stated in order to construct the standard form. Syllogisms in which one statement is omitted but understood are known as *enthymemes*. The argument "All professors are impractical, and Jones is a professor" can be recast into standard form to include the implied conclusion:

> All professors are impractical.
> Jones is a professor.
> _____
> *Hence, Jones is impractical.*

Although the syllogism has played an important role in traditional logic, a moment's reflection indicates that the syllogism, at least in its standard form, seldom appears in everday argumentation and discourse. Traditional logicians must, therefore, recast much of common argument or speech into syllogistic forms; and this often modifies the meanings involved. One of the motives at work in the development of modern symbolic logic was the desire to deal with many arguments in the forms in which they appear in everyday discussion, or at least to deal with them in such a way that the logical forms and patterns used for analysis preserve the authentic meanings in the original discourse.

EXERCISE SET 6–2

Wherever possible, put the following arguments into the standard form of the syllogism. Where enthymemes occur, add the premiss or conclusion that is implied.

a. Alexander is not a coward. In fact, no Greek is a coward. Hence, Alexander is a Greek.

b. All pointers are dogs, and we know dogs are mammals. Obviously, pointers are mammals.

c. Standingbear is an Indian, and all Indians are brave.

d. I contend that all congressmen are dishonest; for all who enlist support from diverse groups of people are dishonest, and all congressmen are supported by diverse groups of people.

e. All congressmen are dishonest; for all who enlist support from diverse groups of people are dishonest, and all congressmen enlist support from diverse groups of people.

f. All who are free are non-human. No student is free. Therefore, some non-human is not a student.

g. Some students of philosophy do not study logic. Therefore, some students of literature do not study logic, for some students of literature are students of philosophy.

h. No expensive place is in debt; for no hospital is in debt, and all hospitals are expensive.

i. All pilots are skilled men. No skilled man is unemployed; therefore, no pilot is unemployed.

j. Some laws are unfair to women. All rules of logic are unfair to women, for all rules of logic are laws.

k. Dr. Lawrence is a teacher; therefore, he is underpaid.

l. Some farms are electrified. Some farms are greater in area than 500 acres. Hence, some farm greater in area than 500 acres is electrified.

m. No book is written on Hittite linguistics. Something written on Hittite linguistics is not commercially published. Hence, some book is not commercially published.

n. Margaret is blue-eyed, for every blond is blue-eyed.

o. Fifty per cent of all automobiles have rear-view mirrors. Seventy per cent of all Fords have rear-view mirrors. Consequently, some Ford is an automobile.

p. Every Freshman enrolls in the course in orientation. Only those who enroll in orientation are enrolled in the course in logic. Therefore, every Freshman enrolls in the course in logic.

q. Some mechanic is not able to drive an automobile. Some mechanic is not able to pilot an airplane. Therefore, someone who is not able to pilot an airplane is not able to drive an automobile.

r. Only Spartans wrote lyric poetry. No one who wrote lyric poetry was a playwright. Thus, only Spartans were playwrights.

s. No Athenian was tried for heresy. Some astronomer was tried for heresy. Hence, some astronomer was not an Athenian.

t. Every ellipse is a conic section. Some conic sections are points. Therefore, some ellipse is a point.

6–3. FIGURE AND MOOD

The positions of the middle term in a syllogism indicate its *figure*. There are only four possible arrangements for the middle term and consequently four figures. They are

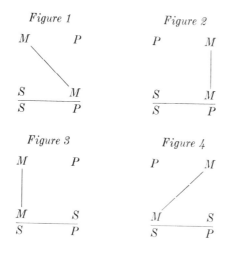

The syllogism may also be analyzed in terms of the quality and quantity of the categorical statements in the premisses and the conclusion. The argument

> All crime is destructive.
> Murder is a crime.
> _____
> Therefore, murder is destructive.

has type *A* statements in the major and minor premisses and in the conclusion. The designation of the quality and quantity of statements in a syllogism is called the *mood* of the syllogism. The mood of the syllogism just given is **AAA**. In order, the three letters designate the type of categorical statements in the major premiss, the minor premiss, and the conclusion. Since there are four possible categorical statements (*A, E, I, O*) for any statement position in the syllogism and there are three such positions, there are 4^3 (that is, 64) possible moods.

To describe both the figure and the mood of a syllogism is to specify the *frame*. The frame is denoted by writing the symbol for the figure, followed by the symbol for the mood; thus, *Frame: 1, AAA*. Since there are 64 moods and four figures, there are 256 possible frames. Of these 256 frames only a small number are valid. According to the traditional analysis of the syllogism, as many as 24 of the 256 possible frames can be reckoned as valid. Medieval logicians knew these valid frames by the mnemonic names that had been given to them. In *Figure 1*, they spoke of Barbara, **AAA** (and also the case with a weakened conclusion, **AAI**); Darii, **AII**; Celarent, **EAE** (and also the case with a weakened conclusion, **EAO**); and Ferio, **EIO**. In *Figure 2*, they spoke of Cesare, **EAE** (and also the case with a weakened conclusion, **EAO**); Camestres, **AEE** (and also the case with a weakened conclusion, **AEO**); Baroco, **AOO**; and Festino, **EIO**. In *Figure 3*, they referred to Darapti, **AAI**; Datisi, **AII**; Disamis, **IAI**; Felapton, **EAO**; Ferison, **EIO**; and Bocardo, **OAO**. In *Figure 4*, they referred to Bramantip, **AAI**; Camenes, **AEE** (and also the case with a weakened conclusion, **AEO**); Fesapo, **EAO**; Fresison, **EIO**; and Dimaris, **IAI**.

To determine the validity of any syllogism, diagram techniques have been developed. Some of them are simple to use, and they display visually the validity or invalidity of the syllogism. We shall present one of these diagram techniques in the next section.

Before we proceed to this task, a few remarks about the interpretations of the *A, E, I,* and *O* statements in the syllogism are in order. The student will recall that in Chapter 5 we indicated that logic is concerned with validity—that is, with that form or structure of an argument that compels a conclusion. The logician does not decide the question of the truth status of the premisses in an argument. The question of validity is answerable simply on the basis of the form of an argument, without regard to its specific content. In other words, it is possible to determine that

All Y is Z.
All X is Y.
_____
Therefore, all X is Z.

is valid, and that

Some Q is R.
Some S is R.
_____
Therefore, some Q is S.

is invalid, without having to know specifically what sorts of sets X, Y, Z, Q, R, and S are. Similarly, we can settle the question of validity, whether or not the sets X, Y, Z, Q, R, and S refer to physically existent objects, mythological entities, mathematical concepts, imaginary things, or whatnot. The existence or non-existence in some respect or other of the things named by the terms in the A, E, I, and O statements is independent of the question of validity. Thus, an I statement such as "Some elf is an even prime number greater than 2" can enter into an argument; and the validity of the argument can be determined apart from any position, affirmative or negative, one takes on some mode of being for elves and even prime numbers greater than 2.

Apart from this, however, one important thing can be said about the difference between A and E, on the one hand, and I and O, on the other. Categorical statements of types A and E are set inclusion statements and set exclusion statements. "X IS A SUBSET OF Y." "Set W IS EXCLUDED FROM set Z." These statements do not make any commitment about there being members in the sets. The sets referred to in the A and E statements may be empty or null sets. "All even prime numbers greater than 2 are round squares" is, _in terms of form_, just as acceptable an A statement as "All whales are mammals."

What about I and O? They are categorical and particular statements; that is, they make assertions about at least one, and perhaps all, _members_ of a set. "Some chair is wooden" and "Some ghost is not demonic" are particular statements. They mean "There is a member of the set chair that is also a member of the set of wooden things" and "There is a member of the set ghosts that is not a member of the set of demonic beings." These statements assert that the sets designated by their subject terms are not empty. The I and O statements either affirm or deny set membership. They assert that there is at least one member of some set. But, beyond this, there is no additional commitment about any other mode of existence or being.

[handwritten:] ?? Their solution is that I and O prop^{ns} affirm or deny set membership, but do not commit to any other sort of existence.

The meanings of the forms of *A* and *E* (set inclusion and set exclusion among sets that may be null) and the meanings of the forms of *I* and *O* (set membership, affirmed or denied) are crucial matters in determining the validity of arguments that involve them.   Our diagram technique will take account of this.   Over and above what is involved in the *forms* of these statements, we need not know anything else about them—for instance, about what kinds of things, existent or non-existent, their terms indicate.

EXERCISE SET 6–3

A

1. Arrange the following arguments in standard form.   Give the frame of each.

> a. All women are gracious, and the gracious are beautiful.   Hence, some who are beautiful are women.
>
> b. All Greeks loved art.   Sappho was a lover of art, and therefore Sappho was a Greek.
>
> c. Some romantics are Roman poets.   All romantics deprecate the role of reason in man's life.   Hence, some of those who deprecate the role of reason in man's life are Roman poets.
>
> d. Some students are on scholarship, while other students work their way through school.   Therefore, some who work their way through school are not on scholarship.
>
> e. Since some law enforcement officers are not city police and some government men are not law enforcement officers, then some government men are not city police.
>
> f. No sound economy has rising unemployment.   The United Isles has rising unemployment.   Therefore, the United Isles does not have a sound economy.
>
> g. No program of space exploration is inexpensive.   No extended research is inexpensive.   Therefore, a program of space exploration is extended research.
>
> h. No victory in war is worth the price in dead.   Many of the dead will not be males.   Hence, some of the males will not be victorious in war.
>
> i. Some bigots do not understand the nature of a democracy.   All dogmatists are in fact bigots; nevertheless, some dogmatists do understand the nature of a democracy.
>
> j. American education is disintegrating because its ideals have been discarded, and no educational system ever survived the discarding of its ideals.
>
> k. Since all radioactive elements emit gamma rays, something that emits gamma rays does not have an atomic weight over 150; for some radioactive element does not have an atomic weight over 150.

l. Every book published by the Alpha-Beta Press is in English, and everything in English is lucidly expressed; consequently, only things that are lucidly expressed are books published by Alpha-Beta Press.

m. Inasmuch as Aristotle was a botanist, he was an empiricist; for only empiricists are botanists.

n. Some sample of iron in this collection is magnetized. Hence, something that is magnetized is brass, because some sample of brass in this collection is magnetized.

o. Every kangaroo is a mammal. None but those that give birth to their offspring alive are kangaroos. Thus, some kangaroo gives birth to its offspring alive.

p. Some integer is even, but no integer has as its square an odd number. Hence, some even number does not have as its square an odd number.

q. No radio signal can be reflected from Jupiter. No laser emission can be reflected from Jupiter. Therefore, some laser emission is not a radio signal.

r. All unicorns are perfect beings. Every perfect being is a figment of the imagination. Thus, unicorns are figments of the imagination.

2. In the following exercises, a frame for a syllogism is specified. Construct the standard form in each case, using S, P, and M to denote the three classes of the syllogism.

a. *4, AEO.*	f. *4, AII.*
b. *1, AII.*	g. *4, AAI.*
c. *3, AOO.*	h. *2, EEO.*
d. *3, III.*	i. *1, EIO.*
e. *2, AAA.*	j. *2, OOO.*

B

3. "No epic poet is a religious person. Homer is an epic poet. All lyric poets are religious persons. Consequently, Homer is not a lyric poet." In this case, notice that there are three premises, instead of two. How can such a situation be handled so as to display the syllogistic character of the argument?

4. "Every book in the bookstore costs over $3.00. Every book written by Sappho is in the bookstore. *The Hymn to Aphrodite* is written by Sappho. *A book ?* Hence, *The Hymn to Aphrodite* costs over $3.00." Handle this case in a manner similar to that in Exercise 3.

6–4. TESTING SYLLOGISMS BY A DIAGRAM TECHNIQUE

Diagrams have been employed in logic since the days of Aristotle. Class relations, the structures of statements, interrelations among statements, and the syllogism have all been subject to interpretation by various schematic displays. Syllogisms may be tested for validity by the use of diagrams that are based on techniques devised by Leonhard Euler, an

eighteenth-century Swiss mathematician, brilliantly supplemented by
John Venn (1834–1923), an English logician. This method represents
the three terms or sets of the syllogism by three overlapping circles, as
the following diagram indicates.

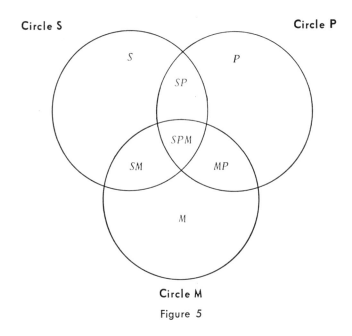

Figure 5

The circles *S*, *P*, and *M* in the diagram represent the subject, predicate,
and middle terms, respectively. By overlapping the circles, we are able
to display the possible set relations that the statements in the syllogism
affirm. The various conjunct sets that may be indicated in the argument
are represented by the segments in the diagram. Thus, in the diagram
above we have conjunct sets indicated by the segments *SP*, *SM*, *MP*,
and *SPM*. With this schema, we can analyze syllogisms for validity.

In displaying arguments in the schema, we mark out the major and
minor premisses. The result, if the argument is valid, will correspond to
the assertion of the conclusion. Particular categorical statements (*I*, *O*)
in the premisses are displayed by placing an **X** in any area or segment in
which the premisses assert there is at least one member. The universal
statements are displayed by shading those areas or segments of the specified circle that are asserted not to be included, or are asserted to be
excluded.

With these simple conventions we can proceed to the task of analyzing
the validity of syllogisms by the use of diagrams. Let us consider the

syllogism, *Frame 1*, **AAA** (Barbara). This syllogism is, of course,

	Mood	Figure
All M is P.	A	1
All S is M.	A	
Hence, all S is P.	A	

The first premiss asserts that all M is included in the set P. So, in the diagram that follows, we shade every segment of the circle M that is outside the circle P; that is, we shade the segments marked M and SM. The second premiss states that all S is included in the set M. Therefore, we shade every segment of the circle S that is outside the circle M; that is, we shade the segments marked S and SP. At this point we have plotted on the schema the "evidence" submitted by the premisses of the argument—we have recorded the meanings of the major and minor premisses.

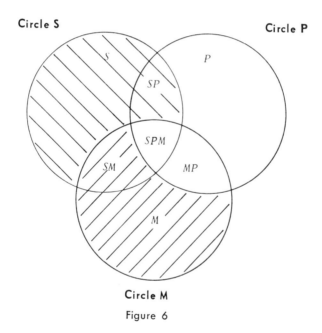

Figure 6

Now we compare the assertion made in the conclusion with the schema that shows the meanings of the premisses, taken together. The conclusion given asserts that all S is included in the set P. This is shown on the diagram; for the only unshaded portion of the original circle, S, is the segment SPM, and it is clearly included in the unshaded part of circle P. This display confirms that the premisses in their relation to each other compel the conclusion offered by the argument.   The argument is judged valid.

Let us now consider the syllogism, *Frame 1*, **AII** (Darii).   Its standard form is

	Mood	*Figure*
All *M* is *P*.	*A*	*1*
Some *S* is *M*.	*I*	
Therefore, some *S* is *P*.	*I*	

The first premiss indicates that all *M* is included in the set *P*.   We shade any part of circle *M* that is not within circle *P*.   Hence, the segments *SM* and *M* are shaded.   The second premiss states that at least one *S* is a member of set *M*.   So, we place an **X** in the segment of *S* encompassed by the circle *M* that is not shaded, that is, in segment *SPM*. The remaining segments of *S* are left unmarked.   The meanings of the premisses have now been plotted.

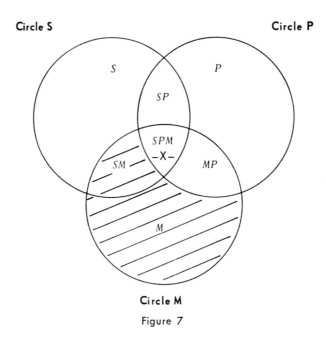

Figure 7

The conclusion asserts that at least one *S* is a member of set *P*.   We examine the circle *P* and find an **X** in segment *SPM*.   This indicates that there is at least one *S* having membership in set *P*.   The argument is valid.

Now let us consider the syllogism, *Frame 2, AII.* In standard form it is

	Mood	Figure
All *P* is *M*.	*A*	*2*
Some *S* is *M*.	*I*	
Therefore, some *S* is *P*.	*I*	

The major premiss asserts that all *P* is included in the set *M*. Therefore, on the schema, we shade the segments *SP* and *P*. The minor premiss asserts that there is at least one *S* that is in the set *M*. The premiss commits us *with certainty* to only one such member. Now on the schema, such a member might be in the segment *SM* or in the segment *SPM*. (We cannot be sure that there is a member in each of these segments. Why?) We place an **X** mark on the boundary line of segments *SM* and *SPM* to indicate that the member may be in the one segment or the other. We have now plotted the meanings of the premisses.

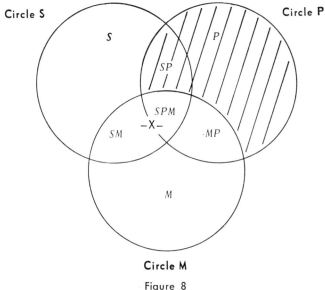

Figure 8

The conclusion of the syllogism "Some *S* is *P*" asserts with certainty that there is at least one *S* that is in the set *P*. Compare this assertion with the diagram. Since the **X**-mark could, in terms of the meanings of the premisses, lie in the segment *SM* (instead of in the segment *SPM*), the diagram does not indicate that the conclusion offered by the syllogism is compelled. The argument is invalid.

As a final example, let us analyze the syllogism

All teachers are wealthy.
No students are teachers.
_____
Therefore, no students are wealthy.

Examining its form, we discover *Frame 1*, **AEE**, which can be displayed symbolically in standard form in this way:

	Mood	*Figure*
All *M* is *P*.	**A**	*1*
No *S* is *M*.	**E**	
Therefore, no *S* is *P*.	**E**	

The first premiss indicates that all *M* is included in set *P*. Thus, any part of circle *M* that is not in circle *P* is shaded; segments *SM* and *M* are shaded. The second premiss indicates that set *S* is excluded from set *M*. One segment of circle *S* in the circle *M* remains unshaded at this point. It is the segment *SPM*. This is now shaded.

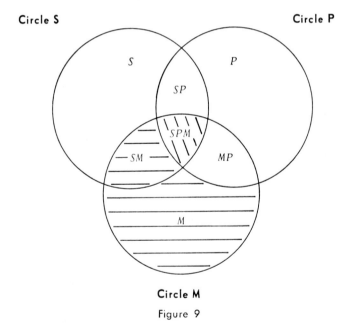

Circle M

Figure 9

The conclusion asserts that set *S* is excluded from set *P*. But on the diagram, we clearly have an unshaded segment, *SP*, which means that the sets *S* and *P* are not mutually exclusive as the conclusion asserts. The premisses do not compel the conclusion. The argument is invalid.

The application of this diagram technique will reveal which of the 256 possible syllogisms are valid. In Part II of our text, the symbolic apparatus we develop will permit us to analyze the syllogism as well as many other kinds of arguments.

As a result of a detailed analysis of syllogistic arguments, traditional logic formulated certain rules for the syllogism. These rules can be used in constructing valid syllogisms and in determining the validity of a given syllogism. Since in Chapter 13 we will be analyzing categorical statements and syllogistic arguments more thoroughly than is possible within the framework of traditional logic, we will not enter into a discussion of those rules.

EXERCISE SET 6–4

A

1. By the use of the diagram technique, determine the validity of the arguments given in Exercise Set 6–2.

2. Use the diagram technique to determine the validity of the arguments given in Exercise Set 6–3.

3. By the use of the diagram technique, ascertain the validity or invalidity of the following arguments.

a. All armed nations have sooner or later gone to war. Our country is well armed; and we can, therefore, expect to go to war.

b. The Greeks of Athens are noted for their appreciation of artistic work. The Greeks were admired by the Romans. Thus, those admired by the Romans appreciated artistic work.

c. Truth is never free from limitations. Some limitations destroy the worth of anything. Hence, some truth is not worth anything.

d. Any statement is to be interpreted in its context. No interpretation is complete. Hence, all statements are really incomplete.

e. Some Greeks colonized a part of Italy. All who colonized a part of Italy became at a later date a part of the Roman Empire, so some who were a part of the Roman Empire were Greeks.

f. All justice is dispensed by the deities, and no justice is to be found among men. Therefore, nothing found among men is dispensed by the deities.

g. All suffering destroys the pleasure of life, and some suffering is not just. Hence, some justice does not destroy the pleasure of life.

h. Whoever is careless is thoughtless in his actions, but some adults are not thoughtless in their actions. Hence, some adults are not careless.

i. No human is free from suffering, but some animals are free from suffering. Therefore, some animals are not human.

j. Some cities in this country are controlled by political bosses. All political bosses in control use force or power in some form. Thus, some persons using force or power control cities.

B

4. Use the diagram technique to decide what conclusions, if any, can be validly inferred from these given premises.

a. Whoever is a good dancer has a good sense of rhythm. Louise surely has a good sense of rhythm. Therefore, . . .

b. Some students are very good bridge players. Pat is a very good bridge player. Hence, . . .

c. Governments that have a single legislative assembly enact legislation efficiently. The enactment of legislation efficiently curtails free debate. So, . . .

d. The objective of a college is to produce trained men. The objective of industry is to produce trained men. Therefore, . . .

e. No baseball team can win the pennant without good pitching. Some teams never have good pitching, so . . .

f. Pat is a native of the United States. Natives of the United States are eligible to be President. Hence, . . .

g. Man is the measure of all things. No animal is the measure of all things. Therefore, . . .

h. All truth is based on fact. No myth is truth. Thus, . . .

i. Recreation lifts one above the mundane problems of life. Some businessmen who engage in recreation are trapped in the mundane problems of life. Hence, . . .

j. Some of the truths of science are eternal. Some eternal truths are revealed. Hence, . . .

6–5. EVERYDAY LANGUAGE AND THE SYLLOGISM

Many beginning students in logic who have been introduced to the syllogism want to know where in everyday language we encounter it. The syllogism is present in common discourse, but frequently does not appear in standard form. A person often either confronts or uses the syllogism unknowingly. One reason for this is that he does not possess the ability to "translate" certain modes and forms of everyday language into the standard form of the syllogism. It may, therefore, be advisable briefly to elucidate this problem of "translation." These comments will also be helpful as background for certain tasks we will undertake in Part II.

The first step in casting an assertion into one of the standard forms for the categorical statement is to identify the subject and predicate terms in it. Thus, "No student who has failed to take logic achieves a liberal education" has as its subject term "student who has failed to take logic" and as its predicate term "achieves a liberal education." Once the subject and predicate terms, no matter how long or involved they may be, are identified, they are joined by the copula. The student should think in terms of a subject set being included in a predicate set, of a subject set being excluded from a predicate set, or of a member of a subject set being or not being a member of a predicate set.

Suggestions with respect to a few of the more common problems in translating assertions into standard forms are expressed in the following examples.

1. "Unless a man works, he is not paid" can be translated into "All men who do not work are included in the set of the non-paid."
2. "Only young people are foolish" becomes "All foolish are included in the set of young people."
3. "If you are rich, you pay high income tax" translates into "All the rich are included in the set of those who pay high income tax."
4. "National League players are all professionals" means "All National League players are professionals."
5. "No one but lawyers receive a fair trial" means "All who receive a fair trial are lawyers."
6. "A student can enroll only if he has graduated from high school" is expressed as a categorical statement in "All who do not graduate from high school are students who cannot enroll."
7. "No one is free, but not responsible" translates into "All who are free are responsible."
8. "Dogs are always barking" means "All dogs are included in the set of creatures that are always barking."
9. "Teachers are never fair" becomes "All teachers are in the set of the unfair" or "No teacher is fair."
10. "Being a capitalist implies being an exploiter of labor" translates into "All capitalists are exploiters of labor."

Following the hints given in the examples just cited, one can translate other sorts of common expressions into standard forms. In some cases these "translations" modify the meanings. This is one of the limitations of treating deduction exclusively in terms of the Aristotelian patterns. In Part II, we shall be able to deal more directly and clearly with the many different kinds of assertions men make.

The task of casting assertions into standard categorical forms is only the first step in expressing the argument of everyday speech in the patterns of the syllogism. As we said earlier, we often encounter arguments in which a premiss or a conclusion is omitted, or in which the order and arrangement of statements and their parts are quite different from the structures of the standard form of the syllogism. In such cases, one helpful step is to identify the conclusion. Remember that if you have an enthymeme, one of the statements, possibly the conclusion, will be implied but not explicitly stated. Upon locating the conclusion and translating it into standard categorical form, the predicate and subject terms can be readily identified. Once they are identified, the major and minor premisses can easily be discovered.

Much more can be said about translating arguments from everyday speech into the patterns of the syllogism. But we must move on to our major task in this book: the presentation of logic in symbolic form. In Chapter 13, we will be returning to the analysis of the syllogism and will there be able to handle the task in a more precise and effective manner.

RECOMMENDED FOR FURTHER STUDY

An excellent treatment of traditional logic can be found in H. W. B. Joseph's *An Introduction to Logic* (2d ed., rev.; Oxford, 1925). Numerous satisfactory discussions of the various aspects of traditional logic are available for those who are disposed to pursue classical logic in a more thorough manner than we have adopted in this chapter. One may consult such books as E. A. Burtt, *Right Thinking* (3d ed.; New York, 1946); Lionel Ruby, *Logic, An Introduction* (2d ed.; Chicago, 1960); W. A. Sinclair, *Traditional Formal Logic* (London, 1945); and Daniel J. Sullivan, *Fundamentals of Logic* (New York, 1963), which is written within the Aristotelian framework. Students may find the treatment of the topics of this chapter helpfully handled in M. C. Beardsley, *Practical Logic* (New York, 1950); M. H. Hepp, *Thinking Things Through* (New York, 1956); J. N. Keynes, *Formal Logic* (4th ed.; London, 1906); and D. S. Robinson, *The Principles of Reasoning* (3d ed.; New York, 1947).

A good history of logic that treats the development from early Greek times is William and Martha Kneale's *The Development of Logic* (Oxford, 1962). Students may also be interested in I. M. Bochénski's *A History of Formal Logic* (Notre Dame, Ind., 1961).

Part II
LOGIC IN ARGUMENT

7

Symbolic Form

7–1. FORM OR STRUCTURE

Man has always relied primarily upon his mother tongue as the vehicle of argumentation and reasoning. For many centuries, Aristotelian logic was the discipline that studied arguments expressed in the various word-languages. The presentation of logic in these chapters of Part II advances for the analysis of arguments some modern tools that are more powerful, more precise, and of greater scope of application than those provided by the traditional logic of Aristotle.

Earlier we suggested that a statement is to be distinguished from its meaning and that a statement exhibits a *structure* or *form*. This form is generally displayed grammatically by a subject-predicate relation. Thus, "Susan went to the dance," "Gerry is a pilot," and "All whales are vegetables" are elementary statements. Whether they are expressed in French, English, or another word-language, the *meanings* and *forms* of such statements are two of the primary objects of study in logic.

The meaning of the statement "Susan went to the dance" would be changed if we said "John went to the dance," "Susan went to New York," or "David went to the show"; but a certain form is preserved in all four statements. This form can be schematically expressed thus: "_____ went to_____." Similarly, the meanings of the statements "Gerry is a pilot" and "All whales are vegetables" are changed if we replace each, respectively, by "Gerry is a lawyer" and "All whales are mammals." However, certain structural features again are preserved; namely, "Gerry is a_____," and "All whales are_____." This feature of a statement, which we call its *form*, is important, not only for expressing the meaning of the statement, but for the purpose of relating the statement to others in an argument. The forms of statements are crucial considerations for ascertaining whether given arguments are valid or not. As we proceed in our study, we shall repeatedly return to an examination of the forms or structural features of various kinds of statements.

In general, the statements in any argument are related to one another in some specific pattern. Sometimes the words used do not emphasize or accent the form of the argument or the forms of the statements in the argument. Nevertheless, some forms or structures are always present, whether the argument is set forth in a word-language, in mathematical symbols, or in some other devices of communication. Since the validity of an argument rests upon its form or structure, one of the major tasks in logic is to determine and display this form.

Statements and arguments can be expressed in other mediums than words. Mathematics provides many examples of arguments presented in non-word mediums. Here the various symbols stand for concepts, statements, functions, and relations. The meaning of the expression $C = \pi d$ in which C stands for the circumference of a circle, d stands for the diameter of a circle, and π stands for the ratio of the circumference to the diameter can be expressed in a longer word-language statement. The mathematical symbols are, however, much more economical; and they say the same thing.

Mathematics is a language that uses many special symbols. Every student is familiar with this language to some extent, even if only in the form of elementary arithmetic. The symbols of this mathematical language are related or joined to one another in precise ways. As a result, the forms or structures of any piece of reasoning are clearly displayed. For example, we can say, "If $C = \pi d$, then $\pi = C/d$," for in mathematics the formula $C = \pi d$ expresses a precise *relation among* the symbols as well as precise meanings *for* the symbols. The movement in thought to $\pi = C/d$ is not just an acceptable happenstance. It involves a logical inference from $C = \pi d$, based on a precise relation among the symbols; furthermore, it communicates clearly the nature of the transformation made. The inference itself—expressed in the "if-then" statement—is a topic we shall shortly be examining.

The special symbols of mathematics permit us to argue in this language with great accuracy and assurance. If we know the diameter of a circle (let us say, 3), we can infer or calculate with great confidence and precision the size of its circumference ($3\pi = 9.42478$). Using other mathematical formulas, we can go on to infer or compute a variety of properties of the circle. In brief, the use of symbols in mathematics results in economy, exactness, and confidence about the preservation of meaning.

Although a highly symbolic language such as mathematics is not adapted to perform some of the functions of word-languages, such as the expression of feeling, it is admirably suited for displaying the forms and structures of arguments. In some measure, then, we want to take some clues from mathematics as we develop tools for logical analysis. To do this will be beneficial for analyzing arguments and for making correct inferences. Thus, we will proceed to adopt some special symbols for the study of logic.

7–2. THE ROLE AND VALUES OF SPECIAL SYMBOLS IN LOGIC

In ordinary word-languages, the terms carry with them many psychological or emotive dimensions, because they are so frequently used to express feeling, to voice hopes and wishes, to utter fancies, and to give directions. Such psychological dimensions often obscure both the forms of statements or arguments and the meanings to be communicated. Emotive words frequently invade an argument and mislead us. As we remarked earlier, mathematics appears to be a discipline in which argument and inference have been largely liberated from such psychological factors. Can we devise special logical symbols for expressing the meanings and forms of statements and arguments, thus evading the confusions and complications introduced by ordinary words that serve other, nonlogical functions? The answer is "Yes." In modern logic, such special symbols have been invented; and they have been used with great success. Our study of statements and arguments will utilize them.

The use of special symbols results in a number of significant advantages. As we indicated, the stipulation of special symbols for statements (and other things as well) insulates logical analysis from emotional bias. If statements are symbolized by p, q, r, and so on, we can manipulate the p's, q's, and r's without being influenced by the feelings present in relation to the words or things mentioned in the statements designated by the letters.

Another benefit is related to the difficulty of remembering all that is involved in a long and complex argument. The number of statements, their recurrences, their negations, the complex relations affirmed among them, and so on, can outreach our competence to remember everything that is involved. But lengthy statements can often be briefly denoted by a p or a q. Once an argument has in this manner been properly symbolized, a heavy burden is removed from the memory and the eye. The argument's form can be briefly and economically expressed.

When statements and arguments are recast in shorter and simpler special symbols, the manipulation of them becomes much easier. Arguments that are otherwise unwieldy become manageable. Thus, the use of special symbols extends the scope of our rational powers in constructing and analyzing arguments beyond what is possible when we use ordinary words. ∠ ease of metatheory

The use of brief, precise special symbols also makes it easier to discern the form of an argument and to ascertain its validity. When the flesh of ordinary words is cut from the skeleton of an argument, we can see more clearly its fundamental structure. Since form is the basis on which we determine the validity of an argument, a set of devices that displays the form of an argument is clearly of very great value.

Furthermore, special symbols that display clearly and briefly the form of an argument often make it possible to see relations among the terms or parts of arguments that might otherwise go unnoticed. As a result, long and complex arguments become more meaningful and manageable for us.

Finally, the savings in time and energy that result from the use of special symbols are of great value. In days in which increasingly complex arguments are offered to us or are demanded from us—in science, religion, politics, economics, and other domains—economy in time and energy is a crucial consideration.

The reduction of statements to special symbols would not be legitimate or justified if our interest is to appreciate poetic and literary values and insights. But, such special notations, barren of emotional or psychological overtones, are accurate representations of the logical meaning, structure, and forms of arguments. In fact, special symbols not only are legitimate, but are ideal for meeting the logician's interest in dealing primarily with logical meaning and form.

7–3. PRINCIPLES FOR SYMBOLIZATION

As we begin to employ special symbols for logical analysis, the student may find it helpful to use single letters that are the initial letters of key words in the terms or statements to be symbolized. Such initial letters used in this manner are, of course, *symbols;* they are not *abbreviations*. Although this technique of symbolizing may be helpful in the preliminary stages of our study, because the symbols will then suggest the meanings and relations in the full statements, later we will abandon this practice in order to make logical analysis as mechanical as possible. Some students may find it helpful from the very beginning to employ purely arbitrary symbols such as p, q, and r for statements.

Let us start with the statement "James went to the play." This statement can be symbolized, without concern for its internal structure, by p, where the p reminds us of the meaning of the statement through the selection of the initial letter of a key word in it. If in our discourse or argument, we proceed to affirm "James went to the bank," we can symbolize this statement by b. We could have stipulated, however, that the first statement be symbolized by p and the second one by q. Additional statements could be symbolized by r, s, and t, and other letters. However, when in a given argument a statement is once represented by a specific symbol, *that symbol must regularly represent the same statement throughout the argument*. When one proceeds to another argument, the symbols may then be used to represent or symbolize other statements.

Often, the natures of the statements and the arguments in which they appear demand that the forms of the statements themselves be displayed. A statement may be a compound statement—for example, "John is a lawyer and John is a pilot"—and it may be necessary to express the relation between the elements in the statement. Chapters 8 and 9 will discuss the ways of symbolizing such compound statements. Sometimes it is necessary to symbolize the internal structure of non-compound statements, such as "John is a pilot." Chapter 13 will provide the symbolization techniques appropriate for this task. We will avoid until Chapter 13 those arguments and contexts that demand an expression of the internal structures of non-compound statements.

The student will shortly be given ample opportunity to practice symbolizing statements and arguments. As a preface to this practice, a list of some simple principles or rules to be observed will be valuable.

1. Different kinds of symbols should be used for different sorts of things. For example, we should not use the symbols "2," "3," and so on, to denote both numbers and also operations among numbers, such as addition and multiplication. Operations and relations $(\times, +)$ should have strikingly different sorts of symbols from statements (p, q, r). As the number of different kinds of things to be symbolized increases, we may have to resort to the use of other kinds of symbols besides the letters of the English alphabet.

2. The symbol we adopt for a given kind of entity should not strongly suggest things or relationships that are not intended. For example, it will only lead to confusion if we use $\uparrow$ to symbolize the meaning of "below." While it is not often possible, we should use symbols that in some way suggest what they represent. Thus, it might be advantageous in some domain to use $\leftarrow$ and $\rightarrow$ to designate "to the left of" and "to the right of."

3. Symbols should be compact and easy to write. Thus, ϵ is a better symbol for "is a member of" than $\text{O}\!\!\!\prec$.

4. A given symbol should not be easily confused with another symbol employed. For instance, it would not be wise to use C and C in the same context.

5. Be consistent in the matter of assigning meanings to symbols. If the University of Colorado is to be denoted by c, and University of Missouri by m, and the University of Texas by t, do not designate the University of Southern California by sc. If ϵ is stipulated to designate "is a member of," it should not later be used to symbolize "entails." Similarly, if a bar over a letter $(\bar{c})$ is one time adopted to indicate negation, it should not at another point be employed with the meaning "successor of," so as to indicate 3, the successor of 2, by $\bar{2}$.

In the adoption and use of symbols, we should be brief, consistent, and economical, always remembering, however, that the object in view is clarity and exactness in displaying the forms of statements and arguments.

7–4. STATEMENTS AND TRUTH-VALUES

Some statements are called *elementary statements.* Any statement such as "Xenophon lives in Athens" is an elementary statement. In an elementary statement, a predicate asserts one thing, state, or condition about a single thing or subject. If not even one thing is asserted about a single subject, then we are left with fragments rather than a statement. Thus, if we have merely "Xenophon" or "lives in Athens," we have two fragments. Neither one nor the other alone is a meaningful statement, for nothing has been asserted. One subject about which one thing has been predicated is a necessary condition for an elementary statement. Other examples of elementary statements are "All whales are mammals," "Kant is a philosopher," "John and Jesus are a pair," and "Chicago is between New York and San Francisco."

In contrast, "Phillip is a pilot and Dan is a mechanic" contains two subjects and two assertions or predications. The one subject, "Phillip," is asserted to be "a pilot"; and the other subject, "Dan," is asserted to be "a mechanic." This statement can be divided into two elementary statements (casting aside the conjunction "and"): "Phillip is a pilot" and "Dan is a mechanic." A statement composed of two or more elementary statements is called a *compound statement.* Likewise, "If Tim takes the train, then he misses the meeting" is a compound statement; for the "if-then" connective ties together two distinct assertions or elementary statements. Although the subject of each assertion in this instance is the same, two different predicates are advanced in relation to this single subject. The elementary statements are "Tim takes the train" and "He (Tim) misses the meeting." The nature and importance of the connective between them is a matter we will discuss later. "Bill and Jane are at the dance," "Mr. Jones is a professor and a lawyer," and "Susan or Ann will type the paper" are other instances of compound statements.

We stipulate that an elementary statement shall have one of two possible values, "true" or "false." These are called the *truth-values* of the statement. The truth-value "true" can be represented by the symbol "T" or by the symbol "1." The truth-value "false" can be designated by the symbol "F" or by the symbol "0." For reasons that relate to certain applications of logic, we adopt the symbols "1" and "0." When speaking of these symbols, they may, if desired, be vocalized as "true" and "false."

If we let any statement, such as "Sappho lives in Lesbos," be denoted by the letter p, then the possible truth-values for p can be displayed thus:

(p)

Case 1:	1	(True)
Case 2:	0	(False)

Notice carefully, we have said above that we *stipulate* that a statement p shall have one of two possible truth-values. We emphasize again that the logician is not concerned with determining whether or not a statement is, *as a matter of fact*, true or false. That is a task for someone else, perhaps for an empirical scientist. A logician is concerned only with the *possible* values a statement may have and what they, considered along with the possible values of other statements, permit him to infer.

One of the major tasks of logic is to determine what can justifiably be inferred about the *truth-status* of some statements on the basis of the possible truth-values of other given statements. For example, the logician wants to know what can justifiably be concluded *if* "No metal is liquid" has the truth-value 1 and "Some acid is liquid" has the truth-value 1. What can be inferred about the truth-status of "My dog is black or my dog is lame," *if* we assume that "My dog is black" has the truth-value 1?

EXERCISE SET 7–4

1. Formulate three elementary statements and three compound statements.

2. Indicate which of the following are elementary and which are compound statements. If the statement is a compound statement, give the elementary statements that compose it.

 a. Peter is a ball player and a banker.

 b. Linda sings in the chorus.

 c. The radio and television are new and belong to James.

 d. If Betty is a blond, then she is not a competent person.

 e. Susan loves to dance, but she never has the opportunity.

 f. The electronic computer broke down because an electrician had failed to follow installation instructions.

 g. The Army was aided in the attack by the Marines.

 h. Students who take advanced logic should first take introductory logic.

 i. All those who teach should be well prepared in the subject being taught.

 j. Either men are born equal or they are not free.

3. Formulate an imperative statement and then express some logical statements it may *presuppose*.

4. Formulate an interrogative sentence. Indicate some logical statements it may *presuppose*. Express the statements that may be asserted in answering the question.

5. Given the two-position array, ⬜⬜, in how many different ways can you insert 1 or 0 in the array? Given the four-position array, ⬜⬜⬜⬜, in how many ways can you insert 1 or 0 in it?

7-5. THE NATURE AND USE OF THE TRUTH-TABLE

An array that lists the possible *truth-values* under any given statement or set of statements is called a *truth-table*. In a *truth-table*, all the possible *truth-values* of given statements, considered together or as standing in relation to one another, are schematically displayed. The display given in Section 7–4 is a truth-table for a single statement, p.

Let us proceed to the construction of such a truth-table for two statements, which we will designate by p and q. Both p and q could be true. Both could be false. Furthermore, one could be true, while the other is false, and vice versa. Thus, there are only four possible cases. These cases are displayed in a truth-table in the following manner:

	(p)	(q)
Case 1:	1	1
Case 2:	1	0
Case 3:	0	1
Case 4:	0	0

Suppose p and q are symbols for the two elementary statements, "I own a car" and "I own an airplane." In terms of this interpretation, the four cases just referred to in the truth-table are

		I own—
Case 1:	a car	an airplane
Case 2:	a car	no airplane
Case 3:	no car	an airplane
Case 4:	no car	no airplane

There are no additional possibilities, since all the meanings and truth-values are enunciated.

Truth-tables can be constructed for any number of statements, considered together or as standing in relation to one another. As the number of statements increases, the construction of such an array becomes an increasingly larger task. The basic character of the truth-table and the method of its construction remain, however, the same.

Let us construct a truth-table for three different statements, p, q, and r. Given three statements, the following possibilities exist. Each may be true (Case 1). Each may be false (Case 8). Further, two of the statements may be true, while one is false (Cases 2, 3, and 5). In addition, two statements may be false, while one is true (Cases 4, 6, and 7). No other possible combinations of truth-values can be conceived. The truth-table array expressing these cases is as follows:

	(p)	(q)	(r)
Case 1:	1	1	1
Case 2:	1	1	0
Case 3:	1	0	1
Case 4:	1	0	0
Case 5:	0	1	1
Case 6:	0	1	0
Case 7:	0	0	1
Case 8:	0	0	0

For two statements, there are four possible cases of truth-values; and for three statements, there are eight possible cases of truth-values. The addition of another statement to those already under consideration doubles the number of possible cases of truth-values. A quick mathematical way to determine the number of possible cases for any array is to compute 2^n, where n is the number of statements under consideration. For two statements, we have $2^2 = 4$; for four statements, we have $2^4 = 16$; and for six statements, we have $2^6 = 64$ cases.

An examination of the two truth-tables displayed above reveals an interesting pattern, which, once the nature of the truth-table is understood, becomes the basis for adopting a mechanical method for constructing other truth-tables. Let us re-examine the truth-table for three statements. Since there are three statements, $2^3 = 8$ is the number of possible cases of truth-values. Half of the truth-values in the first column will be true (1) and half will be false (0). Under p, therefore, we place four 1's, followed by four 0's, for a total of eight cases. Under q, we list two 1's, followed by two 0's; and then we repeat the pattern once more, for a total of eight cases. Under r, we write a single 1, followed by a single 0; and we repeat this pattern until we have a total of eight cases. Thus, we produce the complete truth-table.

If one considers two statements, in the first column he places two 1's, followed by two 0's. Reducing the pattern by one-half for the second statement, a single 1 is followed by a single 0, until the four cases are completed.

In the sixteen cases for four statements, the array is constructed by placing in the first column eight 1's, followed by eight 0's; and then one halves the pattern for each succeeding column, until the table is completed. The mastery of this simple mechanical procedure makes the construction of truth-tables a routine matter.

Thus far we have considered statements collectively in constructing truth-tables. We have not yet examined the use of truth-tables for compound statements or for the relations statements may have to one another in an argument. What truth-values statements have as they stand in such relations will be one of the objects of study in the chapters that follow. As we introduce and discuss logical negation, conjunction, disjunction, and the hypothetical or conditional as they are used in statements, truth-tables will be employed as devices for definition and analysis.

While the truth-table display of truth-values becomes rather large in many instances, it is a "tried and true" method of examining all the logical possibilities in a given argument context. At later stages in our study, when the student finds himself confused or in doubt in the face of certain logical relations, he can generally clarify matters for himself or test his judgment by constructing the appropriate truth-table.

EXERCISE SET 7–5

A

1. Given the three statements "I go to Springfield," "I go to Pittsburgh," and "I go to Atlanta," write out in brief form, referring to the cities, all the logical possibilities for truth-values in this situation.

2. Write the truth-table for the five statements p, q, r, s, and t, considered collectively.

B

3. Given the following array

(p)	(q)	$*$
1	1	
1	0	
0	1	
0	0	

can you determine the number of ways in which 1 or 0 can be put in the four rows in the truth-table column marked by $*$? How many distinct truth-table columns under $*$ can be constructed for this case of two statements? Produce a conjecture as to a formula that will yield the number of such assignments for n symbols. Does your conjecture stand up for $n = 1$? What does it yield for $n = 3$?

RECOMMENDED FOR FURTHER STUDY

A more philosophical discussion of logical form than we have offered can be found in R. M. Eaton's *Symbolism and Truth* (Cambridge, Mass., 1925), Chapter 2, "Logical Form."

The student who desires to acquaint himself with one of the first historical contributions to symbolic logic may consult *Leibniz: Selections* (New York, 1951), edited by P. P. Wiener, Part I, "On Method." With respect to the topics in our Chapters 5 and 7, he may also read George Boole's *An Investigation of the Laws of Thought* (London, 1854), Chapters 1, 2, and 3, and proceed as far beyond that as his preparation now permits.

Susanne K. Langer's *An Introduction to Symbolic Logic* (2d ed.; New York, 1953), Chapters 1, 2, and 3, gives a sound, more detailed presentation of the forms of statements in relation to abstraction, interpretation, universe of discourse, and the connection between elements and relations in statements.

A somewhat more advanced discussion than ours, offered from the perspective of general philosophy rather than logic, can be found in Arthur Pap's *Elements of Analytic Philosophy* (New York, 1949), Chapter 6, "The Nature of Formal Discourse."

8

Not, And, Or

8-1. NEGATION

There are a very few fundamental concepts, operations, and relations out of which the superstructure of formal logic is built. One of the *primitive terms* of logic is expressed by the word "not." It designates the *operation of negation.*

If we consider the collection of positive integers (1, 2, 3, . . .), we discover that certain of them have the property of being divisible by 2, while others lack this property. We pick a name to designate this characteristic—we say that certain of the integers are "even." The recognition of this property and the application of a name to it mean that we divide the domain of positive integers into two sets, the "even" and the "not-even" (or "odd"). The word "not" generally performs the function of maintaining the distinctions among the names of different things or collections of things. If such distinctions are not maintained, communication is virtually impossible. Within the *domain* of a clearly conceived set of things about which we are going to talk, the word "mammal," let us say, is applied to a subset of these things that share one or more properties. Other things in this domain are to be known by other names; that is, they are denoted collectively by the name "not-mammal." Every use of the operation of negation, signified by the word "not" divides the domain under consideration into two subsets: the subset of things that are denoted by a given name and the subset of things that are denoted by other names.

By an extension of this idea, we understand that, as regards the realm of truth-values for statements (1, 0), the word "not" maintains the mutual exclusion between truth and falsity. Thus, "not-true" designates the same value as "false," and "true" designates the same value as "not-false."

The negation of the statement "Pete is a pilot" is *"It is not the case that* Pete is a pilot," or "Pete is *not* a pilot." Using the operation of negation on "Henry went to the game," we get *"It is not the case that*

Henry went to the game," or "Henry did *not* go to the game." Negation will be represented by the symbol " ′ " (the prime mark). Such a symbol is called an *incomplete symbol*; for, standing by itself (apart from a statement that is negated), it is meaningless. Thus, if p is a statement, p' is its negation. The composite symbol (p') is properly formed and complete, but $(')$ by itself is not.

The sense of the operation of negation is specified in this way: if a statement, p, is true, then p' is false; if p is false, then p' is true. This situation can be simply displayed in a truth-table.

	(p)	(p')	*(Definition)*
Case 1:	1	0	
2:	0	1	

The truth-table for p' gives the *logical definition of the operation of negation.*

The student should proceed to the analysis of $(p')'$, showing that p and $(p')'$ have the same truth-values in all possible cases. He should also produce some sample sentences in English that conform to the pattern of truth-values described.

Since the value of p' depends on the values assigned to p, we say that p' is a *truth-function*. This idea will be discussed in more detail later.

EXERCISE SET 8–1

1. We have presented one logical operation: negation. Make a list of what you conjecture to be some other logical operations.

2. In terms of truth-values, what are the meanings of $(p')'$; $[(p')']'$; and $\{[(p')']'\}'$? Can you formulate a rule for reducing expressions of this type to either p or p'?

3. Suppose that p is "All men are bipeds." How would you express in English p'? Can it be expressed in different ways? Can p' be "No men are bipeds"? Why? If this question gives you trouble, our later discussions will clarify the issues involved.

8–2. CONJUNCTION

Statements such as "Bill went home," "My dog is black," "A circle is a plane figure," and "Xenophon lives in Athens" are *elementary statements*. They are given this name because they do not have as parts of themselves other statements.

The statement "My dog is black and your cat is white" is a *compound statement*, for it contains as parts of itself the elementary statements "My dog is black," and "Your cat is white." In this compound statement, the elementary statements, which are its parts, are joined by another of the basic logical operations, denoted by "and." The word "and" names the operation of *conjunction* (also sometimes called the logical product), and it is symbolized by the dot-mark, " · ".   If we designate "My dog is black" by *p* and "Your cat is white" by *q*, then the compound statement cited above is represented by the form $(p \cdot q)$. $(p \cdot q)$ is the form of a *conjunctive statement*.

When no confusion or ambiguity results, the dot-mark (·) between *p* and *q* in $(p \cdot q)$ is often omitted.   Thus, the form of the conjunctive statement can often be written (pq).   Similarly, one can often omit the parentheses, writing simply *pq*.

The sense attached to conjunction (·) in logic is very much like that associated with the use of the term "and" in ordinary conversation.   Consequently, no unusual problems or great difficulties appear here.   Along with negation ('), conjunction (·) can be considered as a primitive term in our logic.   We generally understand "and" to function so as to assert *both* of the two elementary statements conjoined by it.   Thus, in logic a conjunction $(p \cdot q)$ *is deemed true only if* p *and* q *are each true*.   If *p* is false, or *q* is false, or both are false, then the conjunction $(p \cdot q)$ is reckoned false.   Let *p* be "Mexico invades the United States" and *q* be "The United States concludes a treaty with Guatemala."   The compound statement "Mexico invades the United States and the United States concludes a treaty with Guatemala" is true only if "Mexico invades the United States" separately is true and "The United States concludes a treaty with Guatemala" separately is true; otherwise, the compound statement is false.

Now we add to the truth-table array introduced in Sections 7–4 and 7–5 an additional column for $(p \cdot q)$ in order to express precisely the meaning of (·).   For each case, we specify the value of $(p \cdot q)$.

	(p)	(q)	$(p \cdot q)$	*(Definition)*
Case 1:	1	1	1	
2:	1	0	0	
3:	0	1	0	
4:	0	0	0	

Only in Case 1 is the conjunction $(p \cdot q)$, deemed true; that is, it has the value 1, only when *p* has the value 1 and *q* also has the value 1. The truth-table for $(p \cdot q)$—the sequence of truth-values, 1, 0, 0, 0—gives the logical definition for conjunction.   The form $(p \cdot q)$ is another simple truth-function.   Its values are determined by the assignment of values to its parts, *p* and *q*.

By the employment of the procedures adopted above, we can extend our understanding of conjunction to forms and formulas that contain more than two elementary statements.   Consider the statement, "Harry is a lawyer, and Alice is Harry's wife, and James is their son." Here two appearances of "and" join three elementary statements to one another. Inasmuch as there are three elementary statements (let them be, respectively, q, r, and s), we have 8 (that is, 2^3) different cases of truth-value assignments for the three statements. The compound statement has the form $(q \cdot r \cdot s)$ or (qrs). The truth-table for this compound statement is as follows:

	(q)	(r)	(s)	(qrs)
Case 1:	1	1	1	1
2:	1	1	0	0
3:	1	0	1	0
4:	1	0	0	0
5:	0	1	1	0
6:	0	1	0	0
7:	0	0	1	0
8:	0	0	0	0

In every row of the truth-table columns for q, r, and s except the first, at least one 0 appears. Thus, the conjunction (qrs) has the truth-value 1 only in Case 1.

As a final example, let us consider the statement, "The United States is a republic, and Poland is not a socialist state." Let "The United States is a republic" be r and "Poland is a socialist state" be s. Then the right-hand side of the conjunction is s'. The form of the conjunction is (rs'). The student should complete the following truth-table for the truth-function (rs').

	(r)	(s)	(s')	(rs')
Case 1:	1	1	0	0
2:	1	0		
3:	0	1		
4:	0	0		

EXERCISE SET 8–2

1. Employing p and q and their negations p' and q', form all the possible conjunctions composed of two elements. Produce English sentences that represent these possible cases.

2. Produce the truth-table for $(p'q')$. Produce the truth-table for $(pq)'$. As a result of your work, make a statement concerning the relationship between these two formulas.

3. If you know that three statements, p, q, and r, have, respectively, the values 0, 1, 0, what conjunction of these elements will have the value 1?

4. Given: "Robert is a college student" is false, "Robert is not a Sophomore" is false, and "Robert takes a course in calculus" is true, what conjunctive statement of three elements is true? Give two examples of conjunctive statements of three elements each that are false.

5. Determine what the meaning is of an assertion with this form: "Harry is neither a Republican nor a Democrat." After studying this problem, arrive at a general formula, such as "Neither p nor q" means the same as "_____." What does "means the same as" seem to signify here?

8–3. PROPERLY FORMED EXPRESSIONS AND PUNCTUATION

In English grammar, certain rules (syntactical) are used to distinguish between sentences that are properly formed and those that are not. "The boy threw the ball into the basket" is a properly formed sentence, but "Threw the into ball the basket boy the" is not properly formed. In logic, we also need certain criteria for *properly formed formulas* or *properly formed statement forms*.

Since we are introducing this idea very early in our study, we presently have little logical material with which to compose logical expressions. This should, however, simplify matters. We have introduced symbols for elementary statements (p, q, r, s, . . .), a symbol for negation ($'$), and a symbol for conjunction ($\cdot$). We also have available parenthesis marks, ( ), brackets, [ ], and braces, { }. We will use them in this order {[( )]} to indicate the *scope* or *extent* of logical expressions.

In terms of the logical material now available, we can give the following rules for a properly formed formula:

Rule 1: Any symbol, (p), is properly formed.

Rule 2: If (p) is properly formed, then (p') is properly formed.

Rule 3: If (p) and (q) are properly formed, then $[(p) \cdot (q)]$ is properly formed.

Any expression that conforms to these rules, however long it be, is a properly formed formula; that is, it is a genuine formula in the realm of logic. The nature of these rules is such that, by a finite number of steps, a decision can be made as to whether or not any given logical expression is a properly formed formula. The following are examples of expressions that are *not* properly formed:

(a)　$\cdot (p))$

(b)　$(p) \cdot)q$

(c)　$(p)' \cdot '$

(d)　$(p) \cdot (q)) \cdot ($

These, in contrast, are properly formed formulas:

(a) $\{[(p') \cdot (q)] \cdot [r']\}$

(b) $\{[(p')'] \cdot [q']\}$

(c) $(\{[(p')']'\} \cdot \{q\})$

Where no confusion can arise, it is customary to write (p') as p', or $(p) \cdot (q)'$ as pq', or $(p) \cdot (q)$ as pq, etc.

After we have introduced and defined other logical symbols and operations, it will be possible to give additional rules for properly formed formulas that reflect the precedence that certain operations take over others. The reason for introducing now the idea of a properly formed formula is to alert the student, lest he be trapped into expending time and energy trying to logically analyze expressions that are not genuine logical forms in the first place. Logic is not concerned with non-sensical strings of symbols, but with properly structured formulas that express statements and arguments. This topic of properly formed formulas is, of course, discussed in more detail and more technically in advanced texts. For our purposes in this elementary course, we can be content with the simple ideas advanced above.

EXERCISE SET 8–3

1. Illustrate four different kinds of grammatical errors in English that could be called instances of grammatical expressions that are not properly formed.

2. Are these sentences properly formed? Why?

a. James threw the pliers into the box.

b. Chicago falls into between Los Angeles and New York City.

c. The man quickly into the elevator.

d. Loosely wrapped in a paper, she carried the box across the street.

e. He and I and entered the room.

3. Are the following logical formulas properly formed? Why?

a. $\{[p'] \cdot [(q) \cdot (r)]\}$

b. $(\cdot \ p)$

c. $(q) \cdot \{(r) \cdot [s')']\}$

d. $(p) \cdot \cdot (q)$

e. $(\{[p') \cdot (q)] \cdot (r)\} \cdot (s'))$

4. Assuming p and q each to be true (1) and r and s each to be false (0), indicate the values of the following:

a. $[(pq) \cdot (r')]$

b. $[(pr)' \cdot (qs')' \cdot (p)]$

   c. $[(pqrs)' \cdot (p'q'r's')']$

   d. $\{[(pq)' \cdot (rs)']' \cdot [(p'rs') \cdot (q'rs)']\}$

   e. $[(pq) \cdot (p') \cdot (s'q'r)' \cdot (s'r')']'$

8–4. DISJUNCTION

Another fundamental connective that appears frequently in ordinary discourse and that yields, after proper definition, a logical operation is "or."

The word "or" is sometimes used ambiguously in ordinary speech. A statement such as "George is a pilot or a lawyer" permits three possibilities: George is a pilot but not a lawyer; George is a lawyer but not a pilot; George is both a pilot and a lawyer. This is the *inclusive* meaning of "or." But, "An integer is even or odd" means the one alternative (even), or the other alternative (odd), but *not both* of them. This is the *exclusive* "or." A decision is required at this point so that this ambiguity is not carried over into logical discourse and analysis. In conformity with the general practice among logicians, we adopt the inclusive meaning of "or." This sense of "or" is represented by the symbol "$+$." The exclusive "or" will be dealt with in another way later.

Sometimes people contend that they use simply "or" when they mean the inclusive "or" and that they use "either . . . or" when they intend the exclusive "or." Thus, they maintain that they say "John is a father or John is a lawyer," but "Harry is *either* a Freshman *or* a Sophomore." An examination of customary usage does not really bear out the contention that there is a widespread care and consistency in the use of "or" and "either . . . or." Consequently, we find it necessary to establish a clear-cut distinction between the inclusive "or" and the exclusive "or." The inclusive "or," which permits three possibilities—one, the other, both—will uniformly be expressed in logical formulas by "$+$." "Or" and "either . . . or" as they appear in ordinary word-language statements should be symbolized by "$+$." Exception to this method of symbolizing should be made only in those instances where the context and meaning of the terms conclusively indicate that the exclusive meaning of "or" must be employed. The exclusive "or," which permits only two alternatives, will be expressed in another way—for example, by saying "p or q, and not both p and q." The student will be asked to give a logical formula for the exclusive "or" in Exercise 1 in Exercise Set 8–4.

A compound statement such as "Alexander is red-haired or Alexander is blue-eyed" exhibits the logical form $(p + q)$. A formal definition for $(p + q)$ can be given by stipulating that it shall have the same truth-value in each case as $(p'q')'$, which may be read "not both not-p and not-q." That is, the *disjunction* $(p + q)$ precludes only the case in which p is false and q is false. Of the two elementary statements, one, or the

other, or both are true. The truth-table expressing the definition of
$(p + q)$ is this:

	(p)	(q)	(p')	(q')	$(p'q')$	$(p'q')'$	$(p + q)$ (*Definition*)
Case 1:	1	1	0	0	0	1	1
2:	1	0	0	1	0	1	1
3:	0	1	1	0	0	1	1
4:	0	0	1	1	1	0	0

↑equivalent↑

The formula $(p + q)$ is another simple truth-function.

As another example, let us consider the statement, "The man is not a
mathematician or his attention is distracted." This compound statement may be symbolized by $(m' + a)$. The truth-table for it is as
follows:

	(m)	(a)	(m')	$(m' + a)$
Case 1:	1	1	0	1
2:	1	0	0	0
3:	0	1	1	1
4:	0	0	1	1

We note that in Case 2 the disjunction is false. In all other cases, it is
true.

If we assume that m is true and a is true, we can assert as disjunctions
$(m' + a)$, $(m + a)$, and $(m + a')$. We cannot assert as a true disjunction $(m' + a')$. Thus, we can assert "The man is not a mathematician
or his attention is distracted," "The man is a mathematician or his attention is distracted," and "The man is a mathematician or his attention is
not distracted." Under the assumption cited, we cannot assert as true
"The man is not a mathematician or his attention was not distracted."

In Exercise 5 in the Exercise Set 8-4 that follows, the student is asked
to formulate the meaning of the formula $[(p + q) + (r)]$, where three
elementary statements are joined by the operation of disjunction.

[handwritten marginalia: No discussion of 'intensional' "or" (e.g. 'Either we catch this bus or we shall have to walk')]

EXERCISE SET 8–4

1. How would you express the meaning of the exclusive "or," using the
symbols for negation, conjunction, and disjunction?

2. Construct a truth-table for the formula you produced in Exercise 1.

3. Since $(p + q)$ is defined to have the same truth-values in all cases as $(p'q')'$,
how would you deny (contradict) a disjunctive statement? Suppose James says,
"The United States withdraws from the United Nations or the federal debt
increases by 15 per cent." Contradict James's statement.

4. Suppose the Dean of your college asserts, "A student takes the course in logic or he does not graduate." What three possibilities does the assertion allow? What state of affairs is precluded?

5. Formulate the meaning of $[(p + q) + (r)]$ by use of the truth-table technique. How many possibilities does it allow? What does it preclude? Give an example in English of this statement form. Give an English sentence that expresses what the original assertion prohibits.

6. What is the relation between "Jane is a statistician or a pilot" and "Jane is neither a statistician nor a pilot"?

7. Which of the following statements are true and which false? Assume that truth or falsity for the elementary statements is established on the basis of conventional knowledge about the entities mentioned in those statements.

   a. Lincoln was a president of the United States or he was a congressman.
   b. The Hudson River flows through Pennsylvania or the Ohio River flows through New York.
   c. It is not the case that Texas is larger than Alaska or that Cleveland is in Michigan.
   d. H_2O is the formula for water or H_2O_2 is hydrogen peroxide.
   e. It is not the case that Cuba is not south of the United States and that Washington is not the capital of Mexico.
   f. Plato was an ancient Roman or Aristotle did not live in ancient Rome.
   g. Homer was a famous poet, or it is not the case that Athens is in Greece or that Rome is in Italy.
   h. Lincoln was shot in New York, or it is not the case that Lincoln was not buried in Washington.
   i. Children born in the United States are citizens, or the earth rotates about the sun.
   j. Plato taught in Athens or Aristotle taught in London, or George Washington lived at Mount Vernon or at Los Angeles.
   k. Mr. Smith is a resident of New York or Mr. Jones is a resident of Chicago, or George Washington lived at Mount Vernon or John Arnold lived at Mount Wilson.

8. If p, q, and r are each true and s, t, and u are each false, indicate which of the following are true and which are false:

   a. $[(p + s) + (t)]$
   b. $[(s + t) + (u + s) + (p' + r') + (s' + u)]$
   c. $[(p' + q')' + (s + t)']$
   d. $\{[p + s + r]' + [(s') + (p + u' + q')']'\}$
   e. $(\{[s + t] + [(p') + (q + t)'] + [t + u]\} + \{p\})$
   f. $(\{[t' + q] + [(r') + (p + r)']' + [s + u]\} + \{u\})$
   g. $(p + s + q + t + r + u)'$
   h. $[(p + q + u)' + (r')']'$

   i. $\{[p'] + [(q' + s) + (t' + u)]\}$

   j. $[(p + q)' + (p' + q')' + (s + t) + (s' + t')']$

9. If p, q, and r are each true and s, t, and u are each false, indicate which of the following are true and which are false:

   a. $[(pqsu) + (r)]$

   b. $[(st) \cdot (p + r)]$

   c. $\{[pu] + [(q + u)' \cdot (p + u)]\}$

   d. $\{[(t + u + q) \cdot (p)] + [(stp) + (p' + t + u')]\}$

   e. $(\{[p] + [(t'u')' + (p + r)]\} \cdot \{[(t) \cdot (p + q)] \cdot [(t') + (pu)']\}')$

8–5. INTERCHANGE FORMS

Thus far we have presented a few of the basic statements with which logic deals. These statements, whether they are elementary or compound, have a truth-value of true (1), or false (0). If any two such statements have, in all possible cases, the same truth-values, we say that they are *equivalent in truth-values*.

One can speak of equivalence in meaning, in language, among argument forms, and so forth. But "equivalence" as we use the term here refers to an agreement in truth-values in all possible cases. When the various cases for statements or formulas are compared and they are found in all cases to be both true (1) or both false (0), we say there is an equivalence of truth-values. When, however, in some case we have a value of true (1) for a formula and in a similar case a value of false (0) for another formula, or vice versa, we say that the two formulas are not equivalent. In other words, two statements or formulas are equivalent in value if they have in all possible cases the same truth-values.

The nature of equivalence in truth-values can be displayed in the following examples. "Allen is a boy" and "Cynthia is a girl" are not equivalent in truth-values. Let us display the values of the statements in a truth-table, where the first statement is expressed by p and the second by q.

	(p)	(q)
Case 1:	1	1
2:	1	0
3:	0	1
4:	0	0

The truth-table indicates that p and q agree in truth values in Cases 1 and 4, but do not agree in Cases 2 and 3. The two statements are not equivalent.

"James is a pilot" and "It is not the case that James is not a pilot" are equivalent in truth-values. The first statement may be expressed by *p*. The second will then be expressed by $[(p')']$. Writing the truth-table, we have

	(p)	(p')	(p')'
Case 1:	1	0	1
2:	0	1	0

↑   equivalent   ↑

This relation expresses the familiar *law of double negation*.

Whenever, as in the instance of the *law of double negation, two statements or formulas have in all cases of the truth-table the same truth-values, the formulas are called interchange forms.*

We recall that $(p + q)$ was defined to mean the same as $(p'q')'$. The truth-table

	(p)	(q)	(p')	(q')	(p'q')'	(p + q)
Case 1:	1	1	0	0	1	1
2:	1	0	0	1	1	1
3:	0	1	1	0	1	1
4:	0	0	1	1	0	0

↑ equivalent ↑

indicates that these are interchange forms, for they have in all cases the same truth-values. Additional interchange forms will be presented in the next section and in succeeding chapters.

Since interchange forms are statements or formulas that have the same truth-values in all cases, we can stipulate a Rule of Interchange: *Given two interchange forms, the one can be replaced by the other in any logical formula in which it occurs.* Such a replacement or interchange obviously does not modify the truth-values of the logical formula in which the interchange occurs. Thus, the formula $(p')'$ can be replaced by its interchange form (p), and $(p'q')'$ can be replaced by its interchange form $(p + q)$, and vice versa. The fact that we have forms that are interchangeable is symbolized by " _____ ." The interchange forms above are written:

$$(p) \text{\_\_\_\_} (p')'$$

and

$$(p + q) \text{\_\_\_\_} (p'q')'$$

Two simple interchange expressions that, like the laws of double negation, are well known in everyday language are the *laws of tautology*, expressed by the interchange symbol thus: $(p) \text{\_\_\_\_} (p + p)$, and $(p) \text{\_\_\_\_} (pp)$. The laws of tautology assert that the meaning and significance of "The sun has set" is not changed when we say either "The sun has set or the sun has set," or "The sun has set and the sun has set."

EXERCISE SET 8–5

A

1. Construct statements in English equivalent in meaning to the following assertions:

    a. Susan and Don went to the dance.

    b. Norman was not undressed.

    c. It is not the case that Oscar is not a basketball player and Roger is not a baseball player.

    d. Ann received her Master's degree or Ann was married.

    e. Merry was married and Miss Smith was married, or Merry was not married and Miss Smith was not married.

2. Express the above statements in symbols. Express in symbols the statements equivalent in meaning that you produced. By means of truth-tables display the equivalences of truth-values among the statements.

3. If p, q, and r are each true (1) and s, t, and u are each false (0), which of the following statements are equivalent in truth-values?

    a. $[(p + t) + (s)]$ $[(ps) + (r)]$

    b. $[(p')' + (u')']$ $[(s')' \cdot (p')']$

    c. $[(sp)' + (tu)']$ $[(p + r)' \cdot (s' + q')']$

    d. $[(p + q)' + (tu)']$ $[p + u]$

    e. $[(p + r) \cdot (s + u)]$ $[(p + u) \cdot (t + q)]$

4. With respect to which of the following can the Rule of Interchange be used?

    a. $(p + q)'$ (pq')

    b. $(p' + q)$ $(q + p')$

    c. $[(p) \cdot (q + r)]$ $[(pq) + (pr)]$

    d. $[(p + q) \cdot (r)]$ $[(p) + (qr)]$

    e. $(p'q')$ $(p + q)$

    f. $[(p + q)' + (r)]$ $[(pr) + (q + r)]$

    g. $[(p) + (qr)]$ $[(p + q) \cdot (p + r)]$

B

5. The Rule of Interchange reads, "Given two interchange forms the one can be replaced by the other in any logical formula in which it occurs." Let the interchange forms be (pq) and $(p' + q')'$. Let the formula in which we are going to use the Rule of Interchange be $[(pq) + (r') + (p' + q')' + (st) + (pq)]$. Now show that, if the Rule is used for both occurrences of (pq), the truth-value of the formula remains unchanged. Does it remain unchanged if the Rule is used for only one occurrence of (pq)? Apply the Rule at every point in the formula where it is possible to use it.

8–6. DEMORGAN'S RULES

Two interchange expressions are of great importance in logic. They are

$$(pq)' \overline{\quad\quad} (p' + q')$$

and

$$(p + q)' \overline{\quad\quad} (p'q')$$

These interchange expressions are known as *DeMorgan's Rules,* after Augustus DeMorgan (1806–1871), an English mathematician and logician, who was among the first to state them. By the use of them, any formula joining two statements by $+$ may be changed into a conjunctive form. Similarly, any formula containing $\cdot$ may be transformed into one that uses $+$. These rules state that the denial of a disjunction is the conjunction of the denials of the sides of the disjunction, and the denial of a conjunction is the disjunction of the denials of the sides of the conjunction.

The rules may be generalized, giving:

$$(pqr \ . \ . \ .)' \overline{\quad\quad} (p' + q' + r' + \ . \ . \ .)$$

and

$$(p + q + r + \ . \ . \ .)' \overline{\quad\quad} (p'q'r' \ . \ . \ .)$$

Example 1. "It is not the case that Albert is a lawyer and a Presbyterian and an author." By DeMorgan's Rule, the interchange form for this statement is, "Albert is not a lawyer, or not a Presbyterian, or not an author." The student should determine how many possibilities the assertion of the statement permits. Let him also construct the truth-table that shows that the interchange holds.

Example 2. "John smokes or his wife drinks." DeMorgan's Rule $(p + q)' \overline{\quad\quad} (p'q')$ may also be written $(p + q) \overline{\quad\quad} (p'q')'$. An interchange form for the statement is, then, "It is not the case that John doesn't smoke and that his wife doesn't drink."

Example 3. "The man lost his hat, or he doesn't own one, or he is inconsiderate." An interchange form for the statement would be, "It is not the case that the man didn't lose his hat and that he owns one and that he is not inconsiderate."

Example 4. Verify that $(pq'r's) \overline{\quad/\quad} (p + q' + r' + s)'$. The slash mark through the interchange sign, $\overline{\quad\quad}$, indicates "not interchangeable."

(p)	(q)	(r)	(s)	(q')	(r')	(pq'r's)	(p + q' + r' + s)	(p + q' + r' + s)'
1	1	1	1	0	0	0		
1	1	1	0	0	0	0		
1	1	0	1	0	1	0		
1	1	0	0	0	1			
1	0	1	1	1	0			
1	0	1	0	1	0			
1	0	0	1	1	1			
1	0	0	0	1	1			
0	1	1	1	0	0			
0	1	1	0	0	0			
0	1	0	1	0	1			
0	1	0	0	0	1			
0	0	1	1	1	0			
0	0	1	0	1	0			
0	0	0	1	1	1			
0	0	0	0	1	1			

The student should complete this truth-table. Is there another way to establish that these are not interchange forms? Considering $(pq'r's)$ and $(p + q' + r' + s)'$, try a set of values for p, q, r, and s. If, for the assigned values, the two formulas have the same truth-value, is the interchange established? (Why?) If, for the assignment of certain values, the two have different truth-values, is the non-interchange character of the formulas established? (Why?)

Suppose we want to form the negation of such a formula as $\{[(p) \cdot (q + r)'] + [s]\}$. By using successive applications of DeMorgan's Rules, we can proceed in the following way:

$$\{[(p) \cdot (q + r)'] + [s]\}' = $$

$$[(pq'r') + (s)]' = $$

$$[(pq'r')' \cdot (s')] = $$

$$[(p' + q + r) \cdot (s')]$$

As another example, let us negate $\{[(p' + q) \cdot (r')] \cdot [s]\}$. The successive applications of DeMorgan's Rules produce the following:

$$\{[(p' + q) \cdot (r')] \cdot [s]\}' = $$

$$\{[(p' + q) \cdot (r')]' + [s']\} = $$

$$\{[(p' + q)' + (r)] + [s']\} = $$

$$\{[(pq') + (r)] + [s']\}$$

The application of DeMorgan's Rules, under the Rule of Interchange, makes possible the quick and easy transformation of statements from a disjunctive to a conjunctive form, or vice versa.

In summary, let us display DeMorgan's Rules for two statements, p and q, in the four forms in which we shall be making use of them.

$$(p + q) \underline{\quad\quad} (p'q')'$$
$$(pq) \underline{\quad\quad} (p' + q')'$$
$$(p + q)' \underline{\quad\quad} (p'q')$$
$$(pq)' \underline{\quad\quad} (p' + q')$$

Again, in the case of any one of these, the one side of the $\underline{\quad\quad}$ can be interchanged for the other side in any formula in which the latter occurs.

EXERCISE SET 8–6

1. Your chemistry teacher instructs, "You must not both heat this acid and permit it to react with zinc sulphate." By the use of DeMorgan's Rules, express his meaning in terms of "or."

2. Given the statement: "The French do not send armaments to the Spanish border or Britain places an embargo on French merchandise." Deny (contradict) this statement. Produce in English an interchange form for the original that uses the word "and."

3. A college catalogue states, "The student must take History 143, Social Studies 201, or Humanities 012; but he must not take both History 143 and Social Studies 201." Rephrase the last clause in terms of "or." Determine what possibilities are open to the student under this regulation. Use the truth-table technique.

4. A salesman makes a circuit of customers in Chicago, Elgin, Gary, Waukegan, Joliet, Evanston, Milwaukee, and Woodstock. He reports, "I visited neither Evanston, nor Milwaukee, nor Waukegan." Express in a disjunctive statement the interchange form for his statement. How many possible conditions does his statement allow?

5. Apply DeMorgan's Rules to the following:
   a. $[(p'q') + (p + q)']$
   b. $\{[p + q + s]' \cdot [(pq)' \cdot (s)]'\}$
   c. $[(pq)' + (p' + q')']'$
   d. $\{[(p) + (qrs)']' + [ps']'\}$
   e. $[(p' + q' + s' + t' + u')']'$

RECOMMENDED FOR FURTHER STUDY

Two books that discuss some of the problems related to equivalence and the Rule of Interchange and that adopt a more conventional position than ours are

A. Ambrose and M. Lazerowitz' *Fundamentals of Symbolic Logic* (rev. ed.; New York, 1962), pp. 152–55; and W. V. O. Quine's *Methods of Logic* (New York, 1953), pp. 46–52. In our discussion, we have deliberately avoided the category of material equivalence ($\equiv$) and have used either the biconditional ($\supset\subset$)—see Chapter 9—or an interchange expression (_____). One reason is that, in the conventional definition of material equivalence, namely, $[(p \equiv q) \equiv (pq + p'q')]$, it seems quite clear that the $\equiv$ is used in two different senses. This ambiguity is to be avoided.

The student who desires to become acquainted with DeMorgan's work in logic should examine *Formal Logic* (London, 1926), by Augustus DeMorgan.

L Strawson

(a) This is not the conventional definition, i.e. —

$A \equiv B \quad =_{Df} \quad (A \supset B) \cdot (B \supset A)$

$p \equiv q \quad =_{Df} \quad (p \supset q) \cdot (q \supset p)$

(b) If it were a definition, then the sign in the middle would be $=_{Df}$ anyway.
— Df

Whitehead & Russell *P.M. I.* p.115 :—

$* \, 4 \cdot 01 \quad p \equiv q \, . \, = \, . \, p \supset q \, . \, q \supset p \quad Df$

9

If-Then

9–1. THE HYPOTHETICAL STATEMENT

Up to this point, we have studied the meanings of four basic operations or relations in the language of logic (′, ·, +, ‾‾‾‾). Now we direct attention to another fundamental logical connective, the one denoted in English by "if-then." Our word-languages make extensive and varied use of "if-then" (hypothetical or conditional) sentences. The senses in which we use the "if-then," or what all is meant when we use it, is not always clear or precise. We may hypothesize, "If the train arrives on time, then we have dinner at six o'clock"; or we may state a condition for an event, "If one boils perchloric acid, then an explosion occurs." Frequently, the "if-then" statement is implicitly used to tie together the successive steps of a mathematical demonstration: "If $ax^2 + bx + c = 0$, then $ax^2 + bx = -c$." The "if-then" connective is also used widely in scientific discourse, for example, in order to express predictions made from hypotheses—"If hypothesis X is true, then we shall have results a, b, and c." Sometimes it is used to express a causal relation. Other senses and uses of the "if-then" connective can easily be recalled.

Throughout the history of logic, there has been disagreement on how to handle and to interpret the varied meanings of the common language "if-then" statements. Logicians have advanced differing views of the hypothetical or conditional statement in logic. The debates and discussions that were carried on among the ancient Megarians and Stoics on this subject have continued in various forms into modern logic. To raise and to attempt to solve the problems centering around the meanings of the hypothetical or conditional connective is not the task of an introductory work in logic. Even to report the diverse views on this subject would carry us beyond the scope of our present work. Nevertheless, the student should be warned that there are problems in this area, even if they are not at this juncture the proper subject for discussion.

Symbolic logic in its pure form, like mathematics, is composed of forms and categories that are applied to reality. We shall stipulate and set forth a definition and meaning for the hypothetical or conditional connective that we will then use to handle the wide variety of "if-then" statements. Although in our presentation of the hypothetical or conditional connective we identify ourselves with a view that has been advocated since the days of Philo of Megara, we recognize that its application to the "if-then" statements of ordinary language is not entirely satisfactory. Nonetheless, it ordinarily works very well in dealing with the wide variety of hypothetical or conditional statements, and it is probably the best definition for use in an introductory study of logic.

The symbol we adopt for designating the hypothetical or conditional connective is "$\supset$," and we employ it to symbolize the variety of "if-then" statements that appear in ordinary word-languages. Thus, we read $(p \supset q)$ as "If p, then q" or "p is a condition for q." The compound statement $(p \supset q)$ is called a *hypothetical statement* or a *conditional statement*. The "if" part of a hypothetical statement is called the *antecedent*. The "then" part is called the *consequent*.

What are the truth-values of a hypothetical statement? When the antecedent and consequent are connected by $\supset$, under what conditions is the connection reckoned as true and under what conditions is it reckoned as false? We stipulate that *the hypothetical statement is true except when the antecedent is true* (1) *and the consequent is false* (0). Displaying the possible cases in a truth table, we have

	(p)	(q)	$(p \supset q)$ "If p, then q" (*Definition*)
Case 1:	1	1	1
2:	1	0	0
3:	0	1	1
4:	0	0	1

Only in Case 2 is the hypothetical statement deemed false, for there the antecedent p is true (1) and the consequent q is false (0).

At first glance, the specification that the hypothetical statement is true in Cases 3 and 4 may seem strange. However, let us look at the matter in this way. The hypothetical statement goes beyond an *actual* state of affairs and asserts what *would happen*, were the conditions described in the antecedent fulfilled. Or, the consequent states what *will happen*, if the conditions specified by the antecedent *occur* or *are true*. Granting the conditions specified by the antecedent, if the event described in the consequent does *not* occur, then the hypothetical statement is *falsified*. Thus, falsification of a hypothetical statement occurs *only* when the truth of the antecedent is accepted and the consequent is false. The mere knowledge that the antecedent is false or that the conditions it describes are not fulfilled does not permit us to say that the hypothetical statement is false. This is reflected in Cases 3 and 4. Certainly, in Case 1 where the antecedent is true and the consequent is true, the hypothetical statement should not be deemed false. Thus, *only* when a true antecedent is followed by a false consequent is the hypothetical statement falsified.

In one sense, only Cases 1 and 2 are significant in relation to a hypothetical or conditional statement. We might be disposed, therefore, to ignore Cases 3 and 4 or not specify them as either true or false. If we were to adopt this suggestion, we would encounter all sorts of difficulties in developing a precise logical language. We are working in a two-valued logical system, and statements *must* be deemed either true or false. Since Cases 3 and 4 are not ones in which the hypothetical is falsified, we list them as true. For this reason among others, logicians customarily adopt the following procedure: the meaning of the formula $(p \supset q)$ is stipulated to be the same as the formula $(p' + q)$. This constitutes a definition of the meaning of the hypothetical or conditional connective. The truth-table for $(p' + q)$ and, therefore, for $(p \supset q)$ is this:

	(p)	(q)	(p')	$(p' + q)$	$(p \supset q)$	*(Definition)*
Case 1:	1	1	0	1	1	
2:	1	0	0	0	0	
3:	0	1	1	1	1	
4:	0	0	1	1	1	

This definition of $(p \supset q)$ says that the hypothetical or conditional statement is considered to have the value of 1, except in the case where the antecedent has the value 1 and the consequent has the value 0.

The student should recall that the operations of negation (′) and conjunction (·) were first described and then the truth-table definitions

(p)	(p')		(p)	(q)	(pq)
1	0	and	1	1	1
0	1		1	0	0
			0	1	0
			0	0	0

were specified for them. We pointed out that the disjunctive statement $(p + q)$ can be defined to mean the same as $(p'q')'$; that is, by definition $(p + q) \overline{\quad\quad} (p'q')'$. Now the hypothetical statement $(p \supset q)$ is defined to mean the same as $(p' + q)$; that is, by definition $(p \supset q) \overline{\quad\quad}$ $(p' + q) \overline{\quad\quad} (pq')'$. Notice that the last formula, $(pq')'$, directly expresses the idea that the hypothetical or conditional statement means that it cannot be the case that p has the value 1 and q has the value 0.

In terms of an example, "If John takes the train, then he is late for the meeting" expresses the idea that it cannot be the case that John takes the train and is not late for the meeting. "If your patient does not take the medicine, he dies" means that it cannot be the case that the patient fails to take the medicine and continues to live. "If the clouds disappear, then the ground is dry" means that it cannot be that the clouds disappear and that the ground is not dry.

One must remember that the horseshoe symbol ($\supset$) has been given a technical definition for logical purposes. It serves very well in handling the variety of "if-then" expressions we encounter. Even in other fields, such as science and mathematics, where different connecting words may serve in place of "if-then" ("p implies q," or "p causes q"), we will use the $\supset$ to symbolize the form or structure of the statements. We shall discover later that it also serves very well for the purpose of distinguishing between valid and invalid forms of argument. This is its justification, despite the fact that in some respects it seems peculiar. Furthermore, we should remember that a conditional statement in English is infrequently asserted when the consequent is already known to be true, and it is not often asserted when the antecedent is known to be false. The usual exception is a contrary-to-fact conditional sentence; for example, "If it were not snowing, I should go to the store."

What would have happened if he had not done what he did? *a qu. involved in asking for responsibility, blame, etc.*

EXERCISE SET 9–1

1. Symbolize the following statements using the $\supset$ and construct the truth-tables for the logical formulas expressed by them.

  a. If the senator retires, then the Democrats will not have a majority in the Senate.

  b. If Alaska elects a Republican and Hawaii elects a Democrat, then the balance of power remains the same in the Senate.

  c. Hydrogen is yielded if one permits sulphuric acid and zinc sulphate to react.

  d. If the school building burns or it is damaged by a tornado, then the school officials receive an insurance payment.

  e. If Harry graduated from college, he had a course in algebra or physics.

  f. If a number is a positive integer, it is a rational number.

2. Transform the following formulas so that they contain only $\cdot$ and $+$. You may have to use DeMorgan's Rules as well as the definition of the hypothetical or conditional, $(p \supset q) \underline{\quad\quad} (p' + q)$.

  a. $[(p \supset q) \supset (q)]$

  b. $[(p) \supset (p \supset q)]$

  c. $\{[(r) \cdot (p \supset q)] \supset [s + p]\}$

   d. $\{[p] \supset [(p \supset q) \supset (q)]\}$

   e. $\{[(p \supset q) \cdot (q')] \supset [p']\}$

   3. In the following formulas, introduce at some point the horseshoe, $\supset$.

   a. $[(p + q') + (r)]$

   b. $[(pq) + (r)]$

   c. $[(pq) \cdot (r)]$

   d. $\{[pq] + [(pq) \cdot (r)]\}$

   e. $(p + p')$

4. Express the following disjunctive or hypothetical statements as hypothetical or disjunctive statements.

   a. Alexander is idle, or his wife leaves him, or he doesn't write a book.

   b. If Argentina acquires a strong fleet, then, if the Chilean government falls, Argentina launches an invasion.

   c. The automobile is insured; or if we have an accident, then we pay the bills.

   d. If William studied his algebra, then he is stupid and careless or the examination was exceedingly difficult.

   5. Using $\supset$ as the interpretation of "if-then," determine (a) for what values of the elementary statements the statement in Exercise 4c is true, (b) for what values of the elementary statements the statement in Exercise 4d is false.

   6. Show that the statement of Exercise 4b is an interchange statement for "If Argentina acquires a strong fleet and the Chilean government falls, then Argentina launches an invasion."

   7. Show that the statement in Exercise 4d is an interchange statement for "If William studied his algebra and he is not stupid or not careless, then the examination was exceedingly difficult." Can you make this demonstration in two different ways?

   8. Produce the truth-tables for $[(p') \supset (p \supset q)]$ and $[(p) \supset (q \supset p)]$.

   9. Produce the truth-table for $[(xx') \supset (y)]$. State in English the meaning of this formula.

   10. Consider $[(x') \supset (x \supset y)]$. By the definition of the hypothetical or conditional connective, replace both horseshoes by $+$. How do you interpret the result?

9–2. THE CONTRAPOSITIVE

Consider the hypothetical statement, "If Harry drinks the milk, then he is ill." Intuitively, we sense that one can say the same thing by the statement, "If Harry is *not* ill, then he does *not* drink the milk." Similarly, "If $a = 2$, then $2a = 4$" may otherwise be expressed by "If $2a \neq 4$, then $a \neq 2$." (The slash-mark through $=$ gives a sign that means "not equal.")

The hypothetical statement $(p \supset q)$ is equivalent in truth-values in all cases to $(q' \supset p')$. The student should demonstrate this equivalence in truth-values by the use of a truth-table. They are interchange forms. This we indicate by writing $(p \supset q)$ ——— $(q' \supset p')$. The formula $(q' \supset p')$ is called the *contrapositive* of the formula $(p \supset q)$. Given any hypothetical statement, the contrapositive can be produced by interchanging and denying the antecedent and consequent. This operation is called *transposition*. This interchange expression, $(p \supset q)$ ——— $(q' \supset p')$, symbolizes the *law of transposition*.

The contrapositive of "If Norman is a lawyer, then he is a college graduate" is "If Norman is not a college graduate, then he is not a lawyer." For "If the professor is not ill, he meets his class," the contrapositive is "If the professor does not meet his class, then he is ill." The contrapositive of "If there is rain, then the river rises above flood stage" is "If the river does not rise above flood stage, then there has been no rain."

EXERCISE SET 9–2

1. Since the hypothetical statement $(p \supset q)$ is an interchange form for the disjunctive statement $(p' + q)$, what will be the hypothetical statement that is the interchange form for $(r + s)$? Prove or disprove your conjecture. Give an example in English of the relationship that you establish.

2. What is the contrapositive of "If a man does not eat, then he does not live"? What is the contrapositive of the contrapositive?

3. Produce the contrapositives of the following statements:
   a. If the police department adopts a civil service plan, then the city's budget will increase and there will be a more efficient control of traffic.
   b. The radio station goes off the air if the power fails or a piece of equipment breaks down.
   c. If the package weighs over 40 pounds, you send it by freight or by express or transport it in your car.
   d. If you study and pass the examination, then you graduate and receive the appointment.

4. Produce the contrapositives for the following:
   a. $(p' \supset q)$
   b. $[(p' + q) \supset (rs)]$
   c. $[(p \supset q) \supset (r + s)]$
   d. $[(p \supset q)' \supset (rs)]$
   e. $\{[(pq) + (r)] \supset [(s) \supset (t + q)]\}$

9–3. THE BICONDITIONAL

In Section 9–1, we discussed the hypothetical or conditional statement. $(p \supset q)$ asserts that p is a condition for the consequent q. Some-

Confuses use and mention ↑

times p is a condition for q, and q is a condition for p; thus, "If Bill passes his driver's test then he is happy, and if he is happy then he passes his driver's test." The passing of the driver's test is asserted as a condition for Bill's being happy, and his being happy is asserted as a condition for his passing his driver's test. This sort of statement is called a *biconditional*. We symbolize the biconditional by $(p \supset\subset q)$.

Logically, the biconditional is defined in terms of $[(p \supset q) \cdot (q \supset p)]$. The form $(q \supset p)$ is called the *converse* of $(p \supset q)$. The truth-values for $(p \supset\subset q)$ are stipulated to be the same as those for $[(p \supset q) \cdot (q \supset p)]$. We display this definition of $(p \supset\subset q)$ in the following truth-table:

(p)	(q)	$(p \supset q)$	$(q \supset p)$	$[(p \supset q) \cdot (q \supset p)]$	$(p \supset\subset q)$
1	1	1	1	1	1
1	0	0	1	0	0
0	1	1	0	0	0
0	0	1	1	1	1

$\uparrow$ equivalent $\uparrow$

In Section 9–1, we indicated that the definition of the conditional $(p \supset q)$ was expressed in the formula $(pq')'$ or $(p' + q)$. The biconditional can also be defined in terms of conjunction and disjunction. It asserts "p and q, or not-p and not-q." Symbolically, this is expressed by $[(pq) + (p'q')]$, which is an interchange form for the biconditional. Thus,

$$(p \supset\subset q) \text{=====} [(p \supset q) \cdot (q \supset p)] \text{=====} [(pq) + (p'q')]$$

The student should construct a truth-table for $[(pq) + (p'q')]$ to see that the values in all cases are the same as those for $(p \supset\subset q)$ and $[(p \supset q) \cdot (q \supset p)]$.

EXERCISE SET 9–3

1. Let p be "An object is an equilateral triangle" and let q be "An object is an equiangular triangle." State in English the relation between the two statements as a biconditional. Express the biconditional in two symbolic forms.

2. Express in English three biconditional statements. Symbolize each, using the biconditional form and its interchange forms.

3. Employing the Rule of Interchange, eliminate $(\supset \subset)$ and $(\supset)$ from the following:

    a. $(p \supset \subset p')$

    b. $[(p \supset \subset q) + (r \supset \subset s)]$

    c. $[(p \supset q) \supset \subset (r \supset s)]$

    d. $[(p + q) \supset \subset (rs)]$

    e. $\{[(p \supset q) \cdot (q \supset p)] + [r \supset \subset s]\}$

9–4. INTERCHANGE FORMS AND COMPOUND STATEMENTS

The following compound statements have fallen within the scope of our discussion (counting also the contrapositive of the hypothetical statement):

(p)	(q)	(pq)	$(p + q)$	$(p \supset q)$	$(q' \supset p')$
1	1	1	1	1	1
1	0	0	1	0	0
0	1	0	1	1	1
0	0	0	0	1	1

According to Section 8–6, $(p + q)$ and $(p'q')'$ are interchange forms involving disjunction and conjunction. In Section 9–1, we asserted $(p \supset q) \underline{\quad\quad} (p' + q)$. And in Section 9–2, we showed that $(p \supset q)$ $\underline{\quad\quad} (q' \supset p')$. By making the appropriate transformations, we can write the following interchange expressions.

Hypothetical	*Contrapositive*	*Disjunctive*	*Conjunctive*
$(p \supset q)$ $\underline{\quad\quad}$	$(q' \supset p')$ $\underline{\quad\quad}$	$(p' + q)$ $\underline{\quad\quad}$	$(pq')'$

By use of the truth-tables, the student should assure himself that these interchange expressions are correct. They indicate that a single statement can be expressed in different forms or by different formulas. For example, the meaning of the statement "If the glass of milk is knocked off the table, then the carpet is wet" can also be expressed by:

1. If the carpet is not wet, the milk has not been knocked off the table.
2. The milk is not knocked off the table or the carpet is wet.
3. It is not the case that the milk is knocked off the table and that the carpet is not wet.

It may be helpful to state explicitly how one can make the translations from one form to another.

1. From the hypothetical statement to its contrapositive: *Interchange and deny the antecedent and consequent.*
2. From a hypothetical statement to a disjunctive statement: *Deny the antecedent and place it on one side of the disjunction; place the consequent on the other side.*
3. From a disjunctive statement to a hypothetical statement: *Take one side of the disjunction, deny it, and place it in the antecedent; place the other side of the disjunction in the consequent.*
4. From a disjunctive statement to a conjunctive statement, or vice versa: *Make the transformation by the use of DeMorgan's Rules.*

The student must practice these transformations in a number of particular cases so that he can make them accurately and with confidence. The statement "Sam is a statistician or an insurance agent" becomes in the conjunctive form, "Sam is not both not a statistician and not an insurance agent." We can also say, "If Sam is not a statistician, then he is an insurance agent." Exercise Set 9–4 will give the student an opportunity to practice these operations. When we come to the problems of analyzing arguments, the ability to make such transformations with ease will be of great benefit.

EXERCISE SET 9–4

1. For each of the following statements, produce three others that are interchange statements for them.

a. Cal refuses to enter the gymnasium, or he is rebuked by the instructor.

b. If a man is an author and a lawyer, then he writes well.

c. It cannot be that a current flows in the wire and that there is no magnetic field about the wire.

d. Henry lives in Pennsylvania and drives a red Ford, or he was not involved in the accident.

e. If all animals are sentient beings, then if a fox is an animal it is a sentient being.

f. It cannot be that a number is a prime and that it is an even number greater than three.

g. If no man has twelve fingers, then it is not the case that some man has twelve fingers.

h. The planets move about the sun in circles, or they do not travel at a uniform velocity and do not sweep out equal areas in equal intervals of time.

2. For each of the following formulas, produce three others that are interchange forms for them.

a. $[(x \supset y) \supset (x)]$

b. $[(p + q) \cdot (q' + p')]$

c. $[(xy) \supset (x)]$

d. $[(p') + (pq)]$

e. $[(x + y) \supset (y + x)]$

f. $[(x + y + z) \supset (x)]$

g. $[(p \supset q) \supset (p \supset \subset q)]$

h. $\{[(p \supset q) \supset (p)] \supset [p]\}$

3. Show that $[(p \supset q) \cdot (q \supset p)]$ is an interchange form for $[(pq) + (p'q')]$. Produce three other formulas that are interchange forms for the disjunctive form $[(pq) + (p'q')]$.

9–5.   SOME STATEMENTS AND THEIR LOGICAL FORMS

The same meaning can be expressed in different ways. We give here a few statements along with the logical formulas that correspond to the statements. When in later chapters we turn to the problems of analyzing arguments, we shall discover that it is important to be able to recognize the logical form that is expressed in a given statement. If errors are made in interpreting the meanings and forms of statements, the attempt to analyze arguments is futile.

We call the student's attention to certain factors that should be taken into consideration as he proceeds to "translate" from word-languages to their logical forms. We have underlined elements of the statements as a means of emphasizing for the student the form and problems involved. This process should not be confused with abbreviation, which is quite a different thing.

1. The "then" that introduces the consequent of a hypothetical statement is frequently omitted. The sentence "If John fails his swimming test, he cannot go to camp" has the form $(f \supset c')$.

2. Very often the antecedent of a hypothetical statement is placed after the consequent. "The car can be used if the gas consumption is above 15 miles per gallon" has the form $(g \supset u)$.

3. "You will receive your degree on the condition that you pass the course in zoology" exhibits the form $(z \supset d)$. Not only does the consequent precede the antecedent, but "on the condition that" means "If you pass . . . , then you will receive . . ."

4. "The steel beam will expand only if it is heated" has the form $(h' \supset e')$. The consequent precedes the antecedent, but the use of "only if" makes $(h \supset e)$ an unsatisfactory symbolization of the statement. "Only if" means "If not p, then not q." *only if p v : only if p q. (has to be the 2nd, of course, but not much help to a student who is bothered by such things)*

5. "A number is even if and only if it is divisible by 2." The form in this case is $[(d \supset e) \cdot (d' \supset e')]$. "If and only if it is divisible by 2, then a number is even" places the antecedent in its proper place. What does "If and only if" signify? It introduces a compound hypothetical statement that states "If p, then q" and "If not p, then not q." In symbolic form, we have $[(p \supset q) \cdot (p' \supset q')]$.

6. "In the event that I go to Chicago, I shall call your grandmother" has the form $(g \supset c)$. "In the event that" expresses the hypothetical "if." The "then" that introduces the consequent is omitted.

7. The word "unless" is frequently used to introduce the antecedent of a hypothetical statement. In such cases, "Unless p, then q" means "If not p, then q." Thus, "Unless I eat dinner on the

road, I shall be there at seven o'clock" exhibits the form $(d' \supset t)$. "The city will pave Alabama Avenue, unless the bond issue is voted down" has the form $(b' \supset p)$.

8. The statement "Should it rain, we will meet in the lodge" expresses the form $(r \supset l)$. "Should" means "if," or is preceded by an implied "if" as in "If it should rain, then . . ."

9. The reader must also be sensitive to "or" sentences that intend the exclusive "or." Thus, "I shall be in class tomorrow or on the train to Chicago" may express the form, $[(c + t) \cdot (ct)']$. A sentence like this one can sometimes intend to say that at least one side is false. In this case, the form would be either $(ct)'$ or $(c' + t')$. A judgment as to whether the speaker or writer intends the exclusive "or" or the idea that at least one side is false must be made on the basis of the context.

10. Quite often, for purposes of brevity or style, the assertion that two statements or sets are biconditional is affirmed in a sentence like this: "If a triangle is equilateral, it is equiangular." A knowledge of the context within which such an assertion is made is required to determine that the intent is to affirm $[(l \supset a) \cdot (a \supset l)]$.

As other problems of translating English sentences into logical forms occur, we will call them to the student's attention.

RECOMMENDED FOR FURTHER STUDY

In Chapter 3 of William and Martha Kneale's *The Development of Logic* (Oxford, 1962), one can find a treatment of the hypothetical or conditional in early logic. This is a valuable book for tracing the discussion of this topic throughout the history of logic.

One may also profitably consult C. I. Lewis' *A Survey of Symbolic Logic* (Berkeley, 1918) and I. M. Bochénski's *A History of Formal Logic* (Notre Dame, Ind., 1961).

10

Interchange Expressions and Simple Arguments

10–1. COMMUTATION AND ASSOCIATION (COMM., ASSOC.)

We are now acquainted with the basic logical operations of negation, conjunction, and disjunction and with the meaning of the hypothetical statement. Certain interchange expressions among statements have been examined. There are other important interchange expressions involving the fundamental connectives of logic that require our attention. Two of these are the *laws of commutation and association.*

If a friend says, "I go to Paris or to Rome," and later asserts, "I go to Rome or to Paris," we judge that he said the same thing on both occasions. The interchanging of the statements around "or" is termed "commutation." In logical symbols, we have $(p + r)$ and $(r + p)$.

When we display in a truth-table the interchange expression $(p + r)$ $\overline{\quad\quad} (r + p)$, which expresses the law of commutation for $+$, we will modify the truth-table array in the interests of brevity. This modification consists in listing the columns of truth-values under the symbols to which they apply. Thus, in the new pattern, the truth-tables for (pq) and $[(p) \supset (q + r)]$ will be

$(p$	$\cdot$	$q)$
1	1	1
1	0	0
0	0	1
0	0	0

and

$[(p$	$\supset$	$(q$	$+$	$r)]$
1	1	1	1	1
1	1	1	1	0
1	1	0	1	1
1	0	0	0	0
0	1	1	1	1
0	1	1	1	0
0	1	0	1	1
0	1	0	0	0

We proceed in the same basic manner as before, except that the truth-values are listed in columns under the letters or operations to which they apply.   In the second illustration given, the sequence of values, 1, 1, 1, 0, 1, 1, 1, 1, under the $\supset$ is the set of values for the eight cases in the last column of the conventionally displayed truth-table.[1]

Returning to the law of commutation for $+$, the truth-table is then

$$(p \ + \ r) \underline{\quad\quad} (r \ + \ p)$$

1	1	1		1	1	1
1	1	0		0	1	1
0	1	1		1	1	0
0	0	0		0	0	0

$\uparrow$ equivalent $\uparrow$

The values in the two columns under the two $+$ signs are exactly the same.   There is an equivalence in values, and the forms are established as interchange forms.

The law of commutation also holds for conjunction $(\cdot)$: $(pq) \underline{\quad\quad} (qp)$. The demonstration of this is left as an exercise for the student.

These simple statements of the laws of commutation, $(p + q) \underline{\quad\quad}$ $(q + p)$ and $(pq) \underline{\quad\quad} (qp)$, are of great value when we are dealing with more complex formulas involving disjunction and conjunction.   The formula $\{[(pq) + (r \supset t)] \cdot [(r' + t) + (pt)]\}$ is, for example, an interchange form for $\{[(tp) + (t + r')] \cdot [(r \supset t) + (qp)]\}$.   A truth-table, of course, will demonstrate this to be the case; but an appeal to the laws of commutation as expressed in $(p + q) \underline{\quad\quad} (q + p)$ and $(pq) \underline{\quad\quad} (qp)$ is all that is needed to justify the assertion that the two complex formulas are interchange forms.   A student may wish to move from the first formula to the second by intermediate steps, in each of which one application of the laws of commutation is made; but, whether this procedure is followed or all the changes are made at once, the justification for the transformation is the laws of commutation.

The laws of association have been frequently employed by students in mathematics, if in no other domain.   In elementary arithmetic, a student is taught that, if he is asked to compute the sum of 10, 5, and 2, he can proceed in one of two ways: $(10 + 5) + 2 = 17$, or $10 + (5 + 2) = 17$. The different ways or orders in which the terms are associated or connected to one another in no way modify the final result.

In logic, the laws of association can be stated thus: $[(p) + (q + r)]$ $\underline{\quad\quad} [(p + q) + (r)]$ and $[(p) \cdot (qr)] \underline{\quad\quad} [(pq) \cdot (r)]$.   The use of truth-tables will show that the interchange expressions hold.   Just as in

---

[1] The display of the truth-table in this manner may at first appear to be confusing. If, however, the student will be careful to place the values under the proper symbols and proceed to become familiar with the method, he will quickly discover that much time can be saved through the use of this method.   The value of spacing a formula to produce a neat and easily read truth-table is apparent.

the case of commutation, the laws of association can be displayed in more complex statements.

Frequently in the manipulation of statements in arguments, we shall find it advantageous to employ both the laws of commutation and the laws of association. For example, starting with $\{[(p + q') + (r)] \cdot [s + p'] \cdot [q + r']\}$, by the laws of commutation we get $\{[q + r'] \cdot [(p + q') + (r)] \cdot [p' + s]\}$, and by the laws of association we can get $\{[q + r'] \cdot [(p) + (q' + r)] \cdot [p' + s]\}$.

Sometimes we deal with statements and expressions containing both conjunction and disjunction in which the punctuation, structure, or context does not make it clear in what order the operations should be performed or how the elementary statements should be associated; for example, "Robert is a professor and John is a teacher or the university is closed for the day" or "Plato lived in Athens or Aristotle lived in Athens and Philip lived in Macedonia." *In this situation and others involving both conjunction and disjunction where a contrary interpretation is not clearly specified, the conjunctive connection takes precedence (is performed before) the disjunctive one.* This we call a *Rule of Precedence.* The first statement, then, will be symbolized $[(pq) + (r)]$; and the second will have the form $[(p) + (qr)]$. Considering all the logical operations and connectives we have introduced $(', \cdot, +, \supset, \supset\subset)$, we formulate for ambiguously or imperfectly punctuated formulas a general *Rule of Precedence: In any ambiguously or imperfectly punctuated formula, the operations denoted by the connectives shall be performed in this order: $', \cdot, +, \supset, \supset\subset$, where any symbol to the left of another designates an operation that takes precedence over (is performed before) the operation designated by the latter.* Thus, under the Rule of Precedence, the expression $\{p + r \cdot s' \supset t\}$ will be fully punctuated in this way: $\{[(p) + (rs')] \supset [t]\}$.

When we encounter expressions in which there is a series of disjunctive (or conjunctive) connectives and the punctuation is imperfect, we invoke the *Rule of Association to the Left.* Consider the statements, "Barbara went to the game and Pat had an accident and Tom was arrested" or "Mr. Kant was the professor or the test was given yesterday or the administration building was burned." In terms of the way we have so far proceeded, the symbolic form of the first statement is (pqr). The second statement has the form $(p + q + r)$. *Whenever the punctuation, structure, or context of the statement or expression does not indicate the contrary, association is to the left.* Thus, (pqr) is punctuated $[(pq) \cdot (r)]$, and $(p + q + r)$ is punctuated $[(p + q) + (r)]$.

10–2. DISTRIBUTION AND EXPORTATION (DISTR., EXP.)

Two other interchange expressions of importance are the *laws of distribution* and the *law of exportation.* A law of distribution has been used by all students in arithmetic.   It is displayed when we write $2 \times (4 + 6) =$ $(2 \times 4) + (2 \times 6)$.   In logic, there are two laws of distribution.   One is $[(p) \cdot (q + r)] \rule{1cm}{0.4pt} [(pq) + (pr)]$.   The other is $[(p) + (qr)] \rule{1cm}{0.4pt}$ $[(p + q) \cdot (p + r)]$.

Certain English statements display the use of the laws of distribution. If someone says, "I will go to Paris, or stay in New York and write a book," this assertion can be restated through distribution by saying, "I will go to Paris or stay in New York, and I will go to Paris or write a book."   While such a restatement may not occur frequently, the interchange expression does hold.   The other form of distribution is perhaps clearer in English.   The statement "I will go to Paris, and attend the University or write a book" has the same meaning as "I will go to Paris and attend the University, or I will go to Paris and write a book."

If the two English statements in each set do not seem to be interchange forms, the student should write the truth-tables for the laws of distribution in order to assure himself that they are.

The laws of distribution have been stated in their simplest forms.   The student, however, should be alert to the fact that the principles frequently appear in more complex manners.

The law of exportation states that when a conjunction is a condition for a statement, $[(pq) \supset (r)]$, one of the conjuncts may be "exported" across the hypothetical connective and be joined as antecedent by $\supset$ to the consequent originally given, $[(p) \supset (q \supset r)]$.   According to the law, "If John is a pilot and a lawyer, then John is a writer" is an interchange statement for "If John is a pilot, then if John is a lawyer he is a writer." In symbolic form, the law is $[(pq) \supset (r)] \rule{1cm}{0.4pt} [(p) \supset (q \supset r)]$.

One can make the transformation indicated from one of the formulas to the other.   That is, "If Harry is a Sophomore, then if he is a Sigma Chi he owns a Buick" can be placed in the form "If Harry is a Sophomore and a Sigma Chi, then he owns a Buick."

The student should complete the following truth-table in order to familiarize himself with this interchange expression.

[(p	·	q)	⊃	(r)]	———	[(p)	⊃	(q	⊃	r)]
1	1	1	1	1		1	1	1	1	1
1	1	1	0	0		1		1	0	0
1	0	0	1	1		1		0	1	1
1	0	0	1	0		1		0	1	0
0	0	1	1	1		0		1		1
0	0	1	1	0		0		1		0
0	0	0	1	1		0		0		1
0	0	0	1	0		0		0		0

An important use will be made of this law when later we set forth one of the logical methods of proof.

The student who uses Exportation must be careful *not* to fashion $[(p \supset q) \supset (r)]$ as an interchange form for $[(pq) \supset (r)]$. The form $[(p \supset q) \supset (r)]$ is *not* an interchange form for $[(p) \supset (q \supset r)]$. The student should construct a truth-table to establish that the truth-values for these two formulas are not the same in all cases. $[(p \supset q) \supset (r)]$ is, of course, an interchange form for $[(p' + q) \supset (r)]$.

In dealing with statements involving more than one "if-then," care should be taken to see that the symbolic form properly represents the structure and meaning of the original statement. Attention to the punctuation and positions of the "then" or "implies" will usually care for this matter. "If I study then I'll know logic, implies I'll pass the course" is symbolized by $[(p \supset q) \supset (r)]$. "If I study, then if I know logic I'll pass the course" is expressed by $[(p) \supset (q \supset r)]$. If one encounters an English statement where the punctuation, structure, or context leaves the form obscure, or if he encounters a formula such as $(p \supset q \supset r)$, the Rule of Association to the Left should be used with respect to the $\supset$'s. Thus, $(p \supset q \supset r)$ becomes $[(p \supset q) \supset (r)]$.

10–3. ADDITION, SIMPLIFICATION, CONJUNCTION, AND ABSORPTION (ADD., SIMPL., CONJ., ABSORP.)

1. **Addition.** This principle asserts that, given a statement p, one is logically justified *in asserting a disjunctive statement in which one side is the given statement* p *and the other side is any statement whatsoever.* We can display it thus:

$$\text{Given: } (p). \qquad \text{Assert: } (p + q).$$

The student should carefully note that this is *not* an interchange expression; that is, $(p) \ne (p + q)$. He should show this.

We adopt the symbol "⊢" for "assert," which may be thought of as similar to "therefore," by which the conclusion of a line of argument is introduced. The principle of addition can, therefore, be expressed:

$$(p) \vdash (p + q)$$

We now need some method for justifying Addition in terms of the logical materials at hand. We shall stipulate that the transition in thought "Given p, assert $(p + q)$" be interpreted by the hypothetical or conditional connective. As a result, we express the principle of addition in an *associated logical formula* (**alf**), $[(p) \supset (p + q)]$. Writing the truth-table for this formula, we have

$$[(p) \supset (p + q)]$$

1	1	1	1	1
1	1	1	1	0
0	1	0	1	1
0	1	0	0	0

The associated logical formula for the principle of addition is true in all cases. It never occurs that p has the value of 1 and $(p + q)$ has the value 0. A formula that is true in all possible cases is called *tautological*. We will discover that all valid argument forms are tautological. On the basis of the tautological character of the **alf**, we deem the principle of addition to be justified. Since $+$ is commutative, $[(p) \supset (q + p)]$ is a tautology and the principle of addition can also be expressed:

[handwritten marginalia: is a valid argt form a formula then ?]

$$(p) \vdash (q + p)$$

Given "Aristotle was a student of Plato," Addition justifies our saying, "Aristotle was a student of Plato, or the moon was made of green cheese," or "The moon was made of green cheese, or Aristotle was a student of Plato."

2. Simplification. This principle affirms that, on the basis of a conjunction of two statements, one can assert either one of the statements separately.

Given: (pq).   Assert: (p).
                 Assert: (q).

This does not affirm an interchange expression, for $(pq) \neq (p)$.

Here again we write for the principle, $(pq) \vdash (p)$, the **alf** $[(pq) \supset (p)]$. The **alf** is tautological, as the student can easily show. Similarly, $[(pq) \supset (q)]$ is a tautology. We deem the principle to be warranted.

Considering the conjunction "Harry buys an insurance policy and he sells his house," the principle justifies asserting separately "Harry buys an insurance policy" or asserting separately "Harry sells his house."

3. Conjunction. This principle states that, given two statements, one is warranted in asserting the conjunction of the two.

Given: (p), (q).   Assert: (pq).

Suppose we have as given the statements "Alice is blue-eyed" and "Alice is irritable." The principle of conjunction says that one is justified in asserting the statement, "Alice is blue-eyed and irritable."

4. Absorption. Two other principles, which we call *Absorption*, will be helpful later in our analysis of arguments.   The first is given by the expression $[(p) + (pq)]$ ——— $[p]$.   That is, any statement joined by disjunction $(+)$ to the conjunction of itself with some other statement is an interchange form for itself.   "Peter is a machinist, or Peter is a machinist and a golfer" is an interchange statement for "Peter is a machinist." The truth-table that displays that these are interchange forms is

$$[(p) \quad + \quad (p \quad \cdot \quad q)] \text{———} [p]$$

1	1	1	1	1		1
1	1	1	0	0		1
0	0	0	0	1		0
0	0	0	0	0		0

↑_____ equivalent _____↑

The second form of the principle of absorption is $[(p) + (p'q)]$ ——— $[p + q]$.   "Mexico elects a new president, or Mexico does not elect a new president and expands its armed forces" is an interchange statement for "Mexico elects a new president or Mexico expands its armed forces." The student should justify this form of the principle of absorption by writing the truth-table.   Moreover, he should justify an alternative version, namely, $[(p') + (pq)]$ ——— $[p' + q]$.

EXERCISE SET 10–3

1. Demonstrate by truth-tables that these are interchange expressions:
   a. $[(pq) \supset (r)]$ ——— $[(p) \supset (q \supset r)]$
   b. $[(p) + (qr)]$ ——— $[(p + q) \cdot (p + r)]$
   c. $[(p) \cdot (q + r)]$ ——— $[(pq) + (pr)]$
   d. $[(p') + (pq)]$ ——— $[p' + q]$

2. Demonstrate by truth-tables that these formulas are tautologies:
   a. $\{[(pq) \cdot (r)] \supset [p]\}$
   b. $\{[p] \supset [(p + q) + (r)]\}$
   c. $[(pq) \supset (pq)]$
   d. $[(pp') \supset (q)]$

3. Demonstrate by truth-tables that these formulas are not tautologies:
   a. $[(p + q) \supset (p)]$
   b. $[(p) \supset (pq)]$
   c. $[(q) \supset (pp')]$
   d. $[(p \supset q) \cdot (q \supset p)]$

4. Produce in English interchange statements for 1a, 1b, 1c, and 1d.   State in English the formulas in 2a, 2b, 2c, and 2d.

10–4. DISJUNCTIVE SYLLOGISM (D.S.)

The word "syllogism" refers to an argument that has two premisses and a conclusion.   When we refer to a Disjunctive Syllogism, we therefore mean a simple argument form in which one premiss is a disjunctive state-ment.   More precisely, D.S. is exhibited by an argument form such as:

Given: John owns a restaurant or he owns a hotel.
John does not own a restaurant.

Assert: John owns a hotel.

In symbols, the *form of the argument* is

$$(p + q), (p') \vdash (q)$$

The **alf** for D.S. is, therefore,

$$\{[(p + q) \cdot (p')] \supset [q]\}$$

where we stipulate that the premisses $(p + q)$ and (p') shall be interpreted as joined by the operation of conjunction.

The **alf** for D.S. is tautological, as the following truth-table shows.

$$\{[(p \quad + \quad q) \quad \cdot \quad (p')] \quad \supset \quad [q]\}$$

p		q		p'	$\supset$	q
1	0	0		1	1	
1	0	0		1	0	
1	1	1		1	1	
0	0	1		1	0	

On this basis, we deem D.S. justified; that is, it is a valid argument form.

The student should show that another version of D.S. is valid, namely,

$$(p + q), (q') \vdash (p)$$

Given an argument with two premisses, in which one premiss is a disjunctive statement, the other premiss must deny one side of the dis-junction, if one is validly to infer the assertion of the other side.

Let us state here clearly the procedure that has been emerging in our discussion of certain of the simple arguments.

1. Given an argument, we symbolize it, using the symbols we have available (p, q, . . . , $+$, $\cdot$, etc.).   In this way, we display the *form of the argument*.

2. The question before us is, then, whether or not the premisses justify the assertion of the conclusion.

3. We adopt a device for making this decision.   It is to write an *associated logical formula*.   This **alf** is constructed by joining the premisses to one another by $\cdot$, and by joining the conjunction of

premisses to the conclusion by $\supset$. In general, for an argument with premisses $P_1, P_2, \ldots, P_n$, and the conclusion C, the **alf** is $[(P_1 \cdot P_2 \cdot \ldots \cdot P_n) \supset (C)]$.

4. We write the truth-table for the **alf**. If the **alf** is a tautology, the argument is judged valid; otherwise, it is invalid.

Up to this point, we have justified Addition, Simplification, and Disjunctive Syllogism in this way. In part, the rationale for this procedure is this: If the **alf** is not a tautology, there is at least one case in which the premiss conjunction has the value 1 (and, therefore, each premiss has the value 1) while the conclusion has the value 0. But validity means that if the premisses are true, the conclusion must be true. Consequently, under this condition the argument would be invalid. On the other hand, if the **alf** is a tautology, in every case in which the premisses have the value 1, the conclusion has the value 1; and thus we deem the argument valid.

10–5. MODUS PONENS AND MODUS TOLLENS (M.P., M.T.)

Modus ponens (the briefer form of *modus ponendo ponens* meaning the mood that by asserting, asserts) and *modus tollens* (the briefer form of *modus tollendo tollens* meaning the mood that by denying, denies) are two of the most frequently used forms of argument. The first is displayed by

> If the patient takes the medicine, then he does not die.
> The patient takes the medicine.
> _____
> Hence, the patient does not die.

The form of this argument is

$$\frac{\begin{array}{c}(p \supset q) \\ (p)\end{array}}{(q)}$$

The one premiss is a hypothetical statement, and the other premiss asserts the antecedent of the hypothetical statement. The **alf** for *modus ponens* is $\{[(p \supset q) \cdot (p)] \supset [q]\}$. It is a tautology, as this truth-table indicates:

$\{[(p$	$\supset$	$q)$	$\cdot$	$(p)]$	$\supset$	$[q]\}$
1		1	1	1	1	1
0		0	1	1	1	0
1		0	0	0	1	1
1		0	0	0	1	0

M.P. is, therefore, a valid argument form.

Modus tollens has for its **alf** $\{[(p \supset q) \cdot (q')] \supset [p']\}$. The student should produce the justification for the validity of M.T.

Given an argument with two premisses, in which one premiss is a hypothetical statement, valid argument forms are produced when the other premiss either asserts the antecedent or denies the consequent of the hypothetical statement.

10–6.   HYPOTHETICAL SYLLOGISM (H.S.)

A very familiar type of argument is illustrated by

$$\text{If } 2x = 4, \text{ then } x = 2.$$
$$\underline{\text{If } x = 2, \text{ then } x^2 = 4.}$$
$$\text{Hence, if } 2x = 4, \text{ then } x^2 = 4.$$

or by

If Harry takes the train, he misses the meeting.
If Harry misses the meeting, he is discharged.

Hence, if Harry takes the train, he is discharged.

In each case the argument form is

$$(p \supset q)$$
$$\underline{(q \supset r)}$$
$$(p \supset r)$$

The **alf** is $\{[(p \supset q) \cdot (q \supset r)] \supset [p \supset r]\}$. It is a tautology. The student should demonstrate this. Hypothetical Syllogism is a simple valid argument form.

10–7.   CONSTRUCTIVE AND DESTRUCTIVE DILEMMAS (C.D., D.D.)

The last of the simple argument forms that we will consider are the Constructive and Destructive Dilemmas.

In an English example, the first of these is

If I go to the library, then I study.
If I go to the movies, then I see Jane.
I go to the library or I go to the movies.

Hence, I study or I see Jane.

The student should observe that the disjunctive premiss asserts one or the other or both of the antecedents of the hypothetical statements. Constructive Dilemma appears, therefore, to be based on *modus ponens*. Its argument form is

$$(p \supset q)$$
$$(r \supset s)$$
$$\underline{(p + r)}$$
$$(q + s)$$

We can introduce the Destructive Dilemma by means of this simple argument:

> If I sleep late, then I miss class.
> If I do not hear the lecture, I am unprepared for the test.
> I did not miss class or I am not unprepared for the test.
> ——
> Hence, I did not sleep late or I heard the lecture.

It appears to be based on *modus tollens*. The argument form is

$$(p \supset q)$$
$$(r \supset s)$$
$$\underline{(q' + s')}$$
$$(p' + r')$$

The **alf** for C.D. is

$$\{[(p \supset q) \cdot (r \supset s) \cdot (p + r)] \supset [q + s]\}$$

and that for D.D. is

$$\{[(p \supset q) \cdot (r \supset s) \cdot (q' + s')] \supset [p' + r']\}$$

The truth-tables will show that these formulas are tautologies and that, therefore, C.D. and D.D. are valid argument forms. The student should construct the truth-table in order to make the demonstration in one of these cases. (How many rows will be required in the array?)

EXERCISE SET 10–7

A

1. Construct truth-tables for the associated logical formulas for M.T., H.S., C.D., and D.D.

2. How would you justify the argument form $(p \supset q)$, $(q \supset r)$, and $(r \supset s)$; hence, $(p \supset s)$? Do so.

3. From the study of H.S. and the result of Exercise 2, produce a generalization about argument forms of this type.

4. If in M.P., we replace $(p \supset q)$ by its contrapositive, what is the result?

5. If in D.S., we replace $(p + q)$ by its interchange form, $(p' \supset q)$, what is the result?

6. Symbolize the following simple arguments and identify the argument forms or relate them to previously known formulas.

    a. If John is a golfer and a writer, then he is happy. Therefore, if John is a golfer, then if he is a writer he is happy.

    b. If Harriet goes to the grocery store, then she misses Alice's visit. She does not miss Alice's visit. Hence, Harriet does not go to the grocery store.

c. All metals are carbon compounds or some metal is not radioactive. It is not the case that some metal is not radioactive. Consequently, all metals are carbon compounds.

d. If there is war, Joe becomes a combat pilot. If there is peace, Joe becomes a television repairman. Joe is not a combat pilot or not a television repairman. Hence, it is not the case that there is war or it is not the case that there is peace.

e. Alexander is a general or not an artist. Alexander is an artist. Therefore, he is a general.

f. 2 is an even number. 2 is a prime number. Hence, 2 is an even prime number.

g. All unicorns are mammals. Therefore, all unicorns are mammals, or Joe is insane.

h. If $1 = 0$, then $2 = 1$. If $2 = 1$, then Grace is a mathematician. Hence, if $1 = 0$, then Grace is a mathematician.

i. If Harry is a preacher, he is eloquent. If Harry is a lawyer, he is eloquent. Harry is a preacher or a lawyer. Thus, Harry is eloquent or he is eloquent.

j. The student in that room is a Sophomore and a fraternity member. Consequently, the student in that room is a Sophomore.

B

7. In the **alf** for M.P., replace the $\supset$ by the definition of the hypothetical or conditional. Now use DeMorgan's Rules to remove the signs of negation to single letters. On the result, use Absorp. What is the result? How do you interpret it?

8. Consider the formula $\{[(p \supset q) \cdot (q' + r) \cdot (rs')'] \supset [p \supset s]\}$ as an **alf** for an argument form. What is the argument form? Is it valid? Produce an argument in English that will exhibit this form.

9. Treat the formula $(\{[(p + q) + (r)] \cdot [q'] \cdot [r']\} \supset \{p\})$ as in Exercise 8.

10. Treat the formula $\{[(p \supset q) \cdot (q)] \supset [p]\}$ as in Exercise 8. Are your results here different from those in Exercises 8 and 9? Explain.

10–8.   REFERENCE LIST OF INTERCHANGE EXPRESSIONS AND SIMPLE ARGUMENT FORMS

Interchange Expressions   *Section*

1. $(p')' \underline{\quad\quad} (p)$ · Law of Double Negation   8–5
   (D.N.)

2. $(pq)' \underline{\quad\quad} (p' + q')$ · · · · · · · · · · · · · · DeMorgan's Rules (D.M.)   8–6
   $(p + q)' \underline{\quad\quad} (p'q')$

3. $(p \supset q) \underline{\quad\quad} (p' + q)$ · · · · · · · · · · · Definition of the Hypo-   9–1
   thetical or Conditional
   (D.C.)

4. $(p \supset q) \underline{\quad\quad} (q' \supset p')$ · · · · · · · · · Law of Transposition   9–2
   (Trans.)

5. $(p) \underline{\quad\quad} (p + p)$ · Laws of Tautology (Taut.)   8–5
   $(p) \underline{\quad\quad} (pp)$

6. $[p \supset \subset q] \underline{\quad\quad} [(p \supset q) \cdot (q \supset p)]$ · · Definition of the Bicondi-   9–3
   $[p \supset \subset q] \underline{\quad\quad} [(pq) + (p'q')]$ tional (D.B.)

7. $(p + q) \underline{\quad\quad} (q + p)$ · · · · · · · · · · · · · · · · Laws of Commutation   10–1
   $(pq) \underline{\quad\quad} (qp)$ (Comm.)

8. $[(p) + (q + r)] \underline{\quad\quad} [(p + q) + (r)]$ Laws of Association   10–1
   $[(p) \cdot (qr)] \underline{\quad\quad} [(pq) \cdot (r)]$ (Assoc.)

9. $[(p) \cdot (q + r)] \underline{\quad\quad} [(pq) + (pr)]$ Laws of Distribution   10–2
   $[(p) + (qr)] \underline{\quad\quad} [(p + q) \cdot (p + r)]$ (Distr.)

10. $[(pq) \supset (r)] \underline{\quad\quad} [(p) \supset (q \supset r)]$ Exportation (Exp.)   10–2

11. $[p] \underline{\quad\quad} [(p) + (pq)]$ · · · · · · · · · · · · · Absorption (Absorp.)   10–3
    $[p + q] \underline{\quad\quad} [(p) + (p'q)]$

Simple Argument Forms

12. $(pq) \vdash (p)$ · Simplification (Simpl.)   10–3
    $(pq) \vdash (q)$

	Simple Argument Forms		*Section*

13. $(p) \vdash (p + q)$ Addition (Add.)   10–3

     $(p) \vdash (q + p)$

14. $(p), (q) \vdash (pq)$ Conjunction (Conj.)   10–3

15. $(p + q), (p') \vdash (q)$ Disjunctive Syllogism   10–4

     $(p + q), (q') \vdash (p)$ (D.S.)

16. $(p \supset q), (p) \vdash (q)$ *Modus Ponens* (M.P.)   10–5

17. $(p \supset q), (q') \vdash (p')$ *Modus Tollens* (M.T.)   10–5

18. $(p \supset q), (q \supset r) \vdash (p \supset r)$ Hypothetical Syllogism   10–6

                               (H.S.)

19. $(p \supset q), (r \supset s), (p + r) \vdash (q + s)$ Constructive Dilemma   10–7

                               (C.D.)

20. $(p \supset q), (r \supset s), (q' + s') \vdash (p' + r')$ Destructive Dilemma   10–7

                               (D.D.)

RECOMMENDED FOR FURTHER STUDY

The student may be interested in Chapters 11 and 12 of Susanne K. Langer's *An Introduction to Symbolic Logic* (2d ed.; New York, 1953) as another approach to simple argument forms. We also recommend L. S. Stebbing's *A Modern Introduction to Logic* (6th ed.; London, 1948), Chapter 7, which presents a good discussion of simple argument forms.

For a different and more advanced study of these topics, see John M. Anderson and Henry W. Johnstone's *Natural Deduction* (Belmont, Calif., 1962).

11

Inference in Extended Arguments

11–1. COMPLEX AND EXTENDED ARGUMENTS AS EXTENSIONS OF BASIC FORMS

In the last three chapters, we have been concerned with the basic logical operations, interchange expressions, and simple argument forms. Additional simple argument forms and interchange expressions could be formulated and demonstrated. In general, however, they would be modifications and extensions of the basic operations, interchange forms, and arguments already presented.

The contention has been advanced that all logical thought and all logical forms, however the modes of symbolism vary, can be reduced to a few basic operators or postulates. Scholars in mathematics and logic who have accepted this contention have differed about the number of basic postulates or operators that would suffice. Some logicians have stressed the importance of the three traditional laws of thought. These traditional laws have been called the *law of identity*, the *law of contradiction*, and the *law of the excluded middle*. These laws or principles have been variously stated, and their areas of application and meanings have been a matter of debate. For our purposes, it will be sufficient and satisfactory to express them as follows:

Identity: If anything is A, it is A.

Contradiction: If anything is A, it cannot also be non-A.

Excluded Middle: Everything must either have the property A, or not have it.

Expressed in special symbols, we can state them thus:

Identity: $(p \supset p)$
Contradiction: $(pp')'$ or $[(p) \supset (p')']$
Excluded Middle: $(p + p')$

The student should show that the formula for each of these is a tautology. He should also demonstrate that $(p \supset p) \rule{2em}{0.4pt} (pp')' \rule{2em}{0.4pt} (p + p')$.

Whatever be the minimum number of basic postulates or operators for logic, it suffices for our purpose to observe that the interchange expressions and simple arguments that have so far been presented are based upon and have been developed from the operations of conjunction, disjunction, and negation. As we examine inference in extended arguments, we will observe that these more complex arguments rest upon the basic operations. They are applications of the simple interchange expressions and argument forms already introduced. All justifications of extended arguments should and will be given in terms of the fundamental principles already delineated. In Section 10–8 (and in the Appendix), we have listed for convenient reference twenty of these fundamental principles.

In the sections that follow in this chapter, we will utilize these basic principles and postulates to infer the conclusion or conclusions that legitimately may be drawn from a given set of premises. In brief, the question is, given a certain set of statements as evidence, what properly can be concluded from it? Logic books generally give major attention to the analysis of arguments given in full (premises and conclusion). This, of course, is important; and we shall treat the matter later. Only infrequently, however, do they treat the question of what conclusions can be validly inferred from a given set of premises. This is equally important.

11–2. INFERENCE BY TRUTH-TABLES

The truth-table has been used to display the possible truth-values of statements, establish interchange expressions, and demonstrate the validity of simple argument forms. It can also be employed as a means of making valid inferences.

Let us examine the case of a simple argument with whose structure we are already familiar. Given the premises $(p \supset q)$ and (p), what conclusion(s) can be validly inferred? Our understanding of *modus ponens* informs us, of course, that one conclusion is q. Let us assume, for the purposes of the discussion, that we do not know this.

The truth-table for $[(p \supset q) \cdot (p)]$—the associated logical formula for the premises alone—will be as follows:

$$[(p \quad \supset \quad q) \quad \cdot \quad (p)]$$

1	1	1	1	1
1	0	0	0	1
0	1	1	0	0
0	1	0	0	0

Interpreting the relation between the conjunction of the premises and the conclusion as hypothetical or conditional (as we have done in the **alf**), we know that in those cases in which the truth-value of the conjunction of the premisses is 1, the truth-value of the conclusion must be 1, if we are to have a tautological or valid formula.   If the truth-value of the conjunction of the premisses is 0, the truth-value of the conclusion may be 1 or 0 and the formula will still be tautological or valid.   In the hypothetical or conditional, 0 results only when the antecedent is 1 and the consequent is 0.   Thus, the crucial cases of truth-values in the column for the conjunction of the premisses are the cases that display 1.   Now let us examine again the truth-table for the **alf** of the argument form that connects $[(p \supset q) \cdot (p)]$ to some conclusion by $\supset$.

		I					II	[Conclusion]
	$[(p$	$\supset$	$q)$	$\cdot$	$(p)]$	$\supset$		
Case 1:	1	1	1	1	1	1		1
2:	1	0	0	0	1	1		
3:	0	1	1	0	0	1		
4:	0	1	0	0	0	1		

Only in Case 1 do we find 1 as the truth-value for the conjunction of the premisses.   The conclusion in Case 1 must also have the value 1 to produce 1 under the $\supset$, so that all values under $\supset$ will be 1 and the formula will be tautological or valid.   In Cases 2, 3, and 4, the conclusion may have the value 1 or the value 0.

Any conclusion that can be validly inferred from the given premisses must have the truth-value 1 in Case 1.   In the other cases, it makes no difference what its truth-value is.   Therefore, we now examine the premisses to find any statements, premiss, premisses, relations among statements, or negations of any of these that have in Case 1 the truth-value 1.

The formula $[(p \supset q) \cdot (p)]$ itself has the truth-value 1 in Case 1.   One can, therefore, assert $[(p \supset q) \cdot (p)]$ as a conclusion.   The **alf** for the argument with this conclusion is a tautology, and it has the form $(p \supset p)$. Are there other conclusions that can be asserted?   We observe that $(p \supset q)$ and (p) each have the truth value 1 in Case 1.   Both can be validly inferred from the given premisses.   If we have asserted $(p \supset q)$ and (p) as premisses, the assertion of either of them separately in a conclusion will be logically justified; but we do not thereby get conclusions that are drawn from the two premisses in their relation to each other.

The statement q also has a truth-value of 1 in Case 1.   It can, therefore, be validly inferred from the premisses; and it represents a conclusion not given as a premiss.   We assert q, then, as a conclusion drawn from the premisses advanced.

An examination of the statements, premisses, and conjunctions of premisses will reveal that no negation of any of these will have the truth-value 1 in Case 1; thus, none will qualify as a validly inferred conclusion.

Had we selected the premisses given in *modus tollens*, a negated statement would qualify as a validly inferred conclusion.

The student will recognize that, in the case under discussion, $(p' + q)$ and $(q + q')$ are also formulas that employ the elementary statements p and q and that have the truth-value 1 in Case 1. They can be validly inferred from the given premisses. The student should note, however, that $(p' + q)$ is an interchange form for $(p \supset q)$, and that $(q + q')$ is the result of the use of the principle of addition (Add.) on q. By this principle, any statement whatsoever may be joined to q by $+$, and the result will be a conclusion that can be validly inferred from the premisses.

The student should show that (pq) and $(p \supset\subset q)$ qualify as validly inferred conclusions for the premisses given above. He should also produce an argument that indicates that $(p + p')$ is a formula that is a validly inferred conclusion for any set of premisses whatsoever.

Now let us apply this technique for making valid inferences to a set of premisses whose conclusion(s) is not obvious. Assume that we are given the set of premisses $(p \supset q)$, $(q \supset r)$, $(r \supset p)$, and $(p \supset r')$. What conclusion(s) can be validly inferred? Making use of the **alf**, we construct the following truth-table:

	I	II	III	IV	Value of Premisses	
	$[(p \supset q)$	$\cdot (q \supset r)$	$\cdot (r \supset p)$	$\cdot (p \supset r')]$	Conjoined $\supset$	[Conclusion]
Case 1:	1 1 1	1 1 1	1 1 1	1 0 0	0	1
2:	1 1 1	1 0 0	0 1 1	1 1 1	0	1
3:	1 0 0	0 1 1	1 1 1	1 0 0	0	1
4:	1 0 0	0 1 0	0 1 1	1 1 1	0	1
5:	0 1 1	1 1 1	1 0 0	0 1 0	0	1
6:	0 1 1	1 0 0	0 1 0	0 1 1	0	1
7:	0 1 0	0 1 1	1 0 0	0 1 0	0	1
8:	0 1 0	0 1 0	0 1 0	0 1 1	1	1	1

The truth-table indicates that any validly inferred conclusion must satisfy the simple condition that it has the truth-value 1 in Case 8. In the other seven cases, the truth-value may be 1 or 0. What qualifies for a conclusion?

Bypassing the premisses $(p \supset q)$, $(q \supset r)$, $(r \supset p)$, $(p \supset r')$, and their conjunction, each of which can be validly inferred, we examine the truth-tables for the statements p, q, and r. None of these will qualify as a conclusion with a value 1 in Case 8. But, in each instance the negation will have the value 1 in Case 8. Thus, p', q', and r', individually or in any conjunction or disjunction, will be a validly inferred conclusion for the given set of premisses. From these, we can form any number of other validly inferred conclusions by the use of the principle of addition.

Is $(p \supset \subset r)$ a conclusion that also qualifies? Why? The student should formulate another conclusion and give an argument justifying his contention.

One limitation of inference by the use of the truth-table is the size of the truth-table required when the number of statements becomes large. The method enables one, however, to decide in a certain and easy manner what conclusions can be validly inferred from the premisses in an extended or complex argument.

EXERCISE SET 11–2

1. Given the following sets of formulas, each of which is considered a set of premisses, determine at least two conclusions other than the premisses that can be validly inferred.

 a. $(p \supset q)$, $(q' + r')$

 b. $[(p' + q) + (r)]$, $[q \supset r]$, $[r']$

 c. $[pq]$, $[(p) \supset (q \supset r)]$

 d. $[(p) \supset (qr)]$, $[q \supset r]$, $[r' + s]$

 e. $(p \supset \subset q)$, $(p + q)$

2. Given the following sets of statements in English, each of which is considered a set of premisses, determine at least two conclusions other than the premisses that can be validly inferred. State the conclusions in English.

 a. If Harry is a pilot, then he is a mechanic and a navigator. Harry is not a navigator. Therefore, . . .

 b. Peter is not a student or he passes algebra. If he passes algebra, then he does not join the football squad. Peter joins the football squad. Therefore, . . .

 c. Gregg goes to Paris, or he buys a car and a television set. If Gregg doesn't buy a car, then he is unpopular. Gregg is not unpopular or he is depressed. Therefore, . . .

 d. If Alice is conscientious, she is religious. If Alice is religious, she is conscientious. Alice is not conscientious. Therefore, . . .

 e. If the teacher is angry, he fails Joe or Alice or Peter or Linda. The teacher is courteous but angry. He neither fails Peter nor Linda. Therefore, . . .

11–3. INFERENCE BY COMPLEMENTARY ELIMINATION[1]

Disjunction $(+)$ is one of the basic connectives among statements. Our analysis to this point has clearly indicated its importance. The definition of the hypothetical or conditional statement (D.C.) and DeMorgan's

[1] The discussion in this section is an adaptation and development of the procedure advanced by B. K. Symonds and R. M. Chisholm, "Inference by Complementary Elimination," *Journal of Symbolic Logic*, Vol. 22, No. 3 (September, 1957), 233–36.

Rules (D.M.) make it possible to transform *modus ponens* (M.P.), *modus tollens* (M.T.), and Hypothetical Syllogism (H.S.), as well as many other formulas, into formulas involving disjunction.

For example, the **alf** for H.S., $\{[(p \supset q) \cdot (q \supset r)] \supset [p \supset r]\}$, can be changed in the following manner:

$$\{[(p \supset q) \cdot (q \supset r)] \supset [p \supset r]\} \qquad =\!=$$
$$\{[(p' + q) \cdot (q' + r)]' + [p' + r]\} \qquad =\!= \quad \text{D.C.}$$
$$\{[(p' + q)' + (q' + r)'] + [p' + r]\} \qquad =\!= \quad \text{D.M.}$$
$$\{[(pq') + (qr')] + [p' + r]\} \qquad \quad \text{D.M.}$$

Any formula involving $\supset$ or $\supset\subset$ can, by the use of D.C., D.B., and D.M., be changed so that it takes on a disjunctive form.

The student may have already observed that M.P. and M.T. can be reduced to D.S. For example, the **alf** for M.P., $\{[(p \supset q) \cdot (p)] \supset [q]\}$, becomes the **alf** for D.S. when D.C. is applied to $(p \supset q)$: $\{[(p' + q) \cdot (p)] \supset [q]\}$.

Let us examine D.S. We write its premisses thus:

1. $(p + q)$
2. (q')

Notice that if we adopt the device of striking out q and its negation (complement), q', we are left with p, the asserted conclusion of D.S.

1. $(p + q̸)$
2. $(q̸')$
   ———————
   Hence, (p)

We call this procedure *complementary elimination*. When developed and employed in such a manner as to preserve the structure of the argument, this procedure is a very useful method for validly inferring conclusions from a given set of premisses. It is superior to the technique of using the truth-table to make inferences, for one can handle complex premisses briefly and more efficiently.

To make inferences by complementary elimination, we must transform all premisses with hypothetical or conditional forms into premisses of disjunction. Thus, the premisses

1. $(p \supset q)$
2. $(q \supset r)$

become, through the definition of the hypothetical or conditional,

1. $(p' + q)$
2. $(q' + r)$

The premisses are then joined to one another by disjunction, each premiss being marked as a unit and each union of premisses being numbered. The above argument takes the form

$$(p' + q) +^1 (q' + r)$$

All in Symons & Chisholm [margin note]

Complementary elimination takes place *only between premisses*, and there can be *only as many instances of complementary elimination as there are instances of numbered disjunction signs*. In the argument under consideration, we have one numbered disjunction sign, indicating the union of two premisses by disjunction. Only one instance of complementary elimination can occur in this argument. The practice of marking the eliminations by numbers becomes highly desirable as we move to more complex arguments. Applying the stated operation to

$$(p' + q) +^1 (q' + r)$$

we have

$$(p' + q) +^1_1 (q' + r)_1 \quad Example \ (5)$$

There remain the p' and the r. These remaining elements, assuming there are no instances of conjunction present, are united in a single disjunctive expression. The disjunctive expression $(p' + r)$ constitutes a validly inferred conclusion for the premisses. By the application of D.C. and other interchange expressions, this conclusion, or others, can be changed into a form more in keeping with the forms in the original premisses. Thus, $(p' + r)$ may be changed into $(p \supset r)$.

Not in original [margin note]

Two more examples using familiar arguments will be of value. We express the premisses of the Destructive Dilemma as follows:

1. $(p \supset q)$
2. $(r \supset s)$
3. $(q' + s')$

Merging all the previously presented steps, we have

$$(p' + q) +^1_1 (r' + s)_2 +^2 (q'_1 + s'_2) \quad Example \ (6)$$

The elements not eliminated and that are set forth in disjunctive form, $(p' + r')$, constitute a validly inferred conclusion.

The premisses for the Constructive Dilemma, set forth in keeping with the above procedure, can be displayed as follows:

$$(p'_1 + q) +^1 (r'_2 + s) +^2 (p_1 + r_2) \quad Example \ (7)$$

The result is $(q + s)$.

Not all sets of premisses for arguments can be reduced to sets of premisses that contain only disjunction. Premisses containing conjunction ($\cdot$) will regularly appear. *If a premiss has* n *conjuncts, we may, if we desire, eliminate as many as* (n $-$ 1) *of these conjuncts.* The eliminations made will be based on our interests and purposes. In the premisses

Deo! I

1. $(p \supset q)$
2. $(q + r + s + t)'$

we encounter a formula that is denied. In such a case, the premiss should be transformed by the application of DeMorgan's Rules. The second premiss now becomes $(q' \cdot r' \cdot s' \cdot t')$. The application of the principle of eliminating $(n - 1)$ of the conjuncts permits one to eliminate all but one of the conjuncts in the second premiss. The nature of the first premiss (which does not contain r, s, and t) indicates that the r, s, and t may be dropped. We indicate this by a line through the statement. Thus,

$$(p' + q) +^1 (q' \cdot r' \cdot s' \cdot t')$$
$$\quad\; 1 \qquad\qquad 1$$

A validly inferred conclusion is p'. Now r', for example, need not have been marked out. $(p' + r')$ will be a validly inferred conclusion, as will be $[(p') + (r's't')]$. These forms can be secured as easily by applying the principle of addition to the conclusion p'.

Let us examine this technique in the case of a more complex set of premisses:

1. $[(p + q) \supset (rs)]$
2. $[(s + t) \supset (u)]$

Applying all the steps we have examined, we reach a validly inferred conclusion $(p' + u)$; thus,

$$(p'q' + rs) +^1 (s'u' + u)$$
$$\quad\; 1 \qquad\qquad 1$$

The formula $(p' + u)$ is not the only validly inferred conclusion possible. The formulas $(q' + u)$ and $[(p'q') + (u)]$ could just as easily have been concluded. The statement t' could also have been preserved as in the case of $(p' + t' + u)$, but this conclusion can just as easily be secured by applying the principles of addition and commutation to the conclusion $(p' + u)$.

The presence of a conjunction in the premisses presents us with an additional problem. For example, the premisses

1. $[(p + q) \supset (r)]$
2. $[(s) \supset (p + q)]$
3. $[s]$

when handled in accord with the steps previously described result in

$$(p'q' + r) +^1 (s' + p + q) +^2 (s)$$
$$\underset{1}{} \quad \underset{2}{} \underset{1}{} \quad \underset{2}{}$$

Note that q' was canceled out, but q in the second premiss was not. The student may be inclined to eliminate the complements q' and q, but to do so would violate the restriction on the number of complementary eliminations possible. However, by appeal to the principle of addition, one can legitimately add another statement to the disjunction. Ordinarily, this would make a new argument. But, if the statement added is a premiss already present, the premiss set remains logically the same. *(In org)* (Why?) Such an addition will permit an additional instance of complementary elimination. Therefore, we add in brackets the first premiss and proceed with the eliminations.

$$(p'q' + r) +^1 (s' + p + q) +^2 (s) +^3 [p'q' + r]$$

The result is $(r + r)$, or by the principle of tautology, r.

In those sets of premisses in which *a premiss is negated by a disjunct of another premiss, the disjunct may be eliminated in addition to any complementary elimination that has already been made.* *(In org)* Consider the argument

1. $(p \supset q)$
2. $(p \supset r)$
3. (p)

that, following the technique of complementary elimination, becomes

$$(p' + q) +^1 (p' + r) +^2 (p) \qquad \text{Example} \left(9\ \right)$$

Now the disjunct p' of the first premiss negates the third premiss. This disjunct may also be eliminated, and we indicate its elimination by a zero subscript. Thus, we have

$$(p' + q) +^1 (p' + r) +^2 (p)$$
$$\underset{0}{} \quad \underset{1}{} \quad \underset{1}{}$$

A validly inferred conclusion is $(q + r)$.

The same situation occurs in the following set of premisses.

1. $[p \supset r]$
2. $[(t) \supset (sp')]$
3. $[(t') \supset (r \supset q)]$
4. $[p]$

We infer q as a result of this group of eliminations:

$$(p' + r) +^1 (t' + sp') +^2 (t + r' + q) +^3 (p)$$
$$1 \qquad 2 \qquad\quad 3 \quad 0 \qquad 3 \quad 2 \qquad\quad 1$$

The use of complementary elimination makes possible the inference of validly inferred conclusions for complex sets of premises.

Several limitations should be noted before the student applies complementary elimination to certain premises. If there are unnecessary or spurious premises, these will appear in the conclusion as unnecessary elements. The following is an example. The premises are

1. $[(pq) \supset (r)]$
2. $[s \supset p]$
3. $[w \supset u]$
4. $[t \supset q]$
5. $[r']$

The complementary elimination

$$(p' + q' + r) +^1 (s' + p) +^2 (w' + u) +^3 (t' + q) +^4 (r')$$
$$1 \qquad 2 \quad 3 \qquad 1 \qquad\qquad\qquad\qquad 2 \qquad\quad 3$$

yields $(s' + w' + u + t')$. $(s' + w' + u + t')$ is a validly inferred conclusion. But, the simpler form $(s' + t')$ is not only a validly inferred conclusion, it does not contain $(w' + u)$, which is a spurious premiss. Any statement may, according to Addition, be a part of the conclusion. The unnecessary statement $(w' + u)$, which appears in the conclusion, or any other formula, such as $(v + l)$, may be added by disjunction to the conclusion $(s' + t')$, if desired.

Complementary elimination is limited in its usefulness as an instrument in dealing with premises that contain a biconditional. This is displayed in the following instance. The premises are

1. $[(r) \supset (p \supset q)]$
2. $[(pq) \supset (rs)]$
3. $[p]$

The elimination

$$(r' + p' + q) +^1 (p' + q' + rs) +^2 (p)$$
$$1 \qquad 2 \qquad\quad 0 \qquad\qquad 1 \qquad 2$$

yields $(q + q')$. $(q + q')$ is tautological and is a validly inferred conclusion. But, $[(r \supset q) \cdot (q \supset r)]$ is a validly inferred conclusion from these premises that is not tautological. As a matter of fact, $[(r \supset q) \cdot (q \supset r)]$ is the biconditional, $(r \supset\subset q)$, implicitly contained in the set of premises that limits the effectiveness of complementary elimination.

In dealing with a set of premisses that contains inconsistent statements, complementary elimination also has its limitations.   Consider the
premisses

1. $[(n) \supset (mg)']$
2. $[(p + d) \supset (w')]$
3. $[(w') \supset (k's')]$
4. $[g]$
5. $[d]$
6. $[k]$

We infer $(n' + m')$ from the elimination

$$(n' + m' + g') +^1 (p'd' + w') +^2 (w + k's') +^3 (g) +^4 (d) +^5 (k)$$
$$12334124$$

But, g', n', m', or any statement whatsoever can be validly inferred from
inconsistent premisses.   A discussion of inconsistent premisses will be
given in the last section of this chapter.

EXERCISE SET 11–3

Apply the technique of inference through complementary elimination to the
following:

A

a. $(p' \supset q)$, $(r \supset q')$, $(t' \supset p')$, (r)
b. $\{[p] \supset [(q) \supset (r \supset s)]\}$, $\{s \supset t\}$, $\{r \supset p\}$, $\{q\}$
c. $[p' \supset t]$, $[p \supset s]$, $[s']$, $[(r') \supset (q' \supset t')]$, $[r']$, $[q \supset p]$
d. $[(p') \supset (qr)]$, $[(s' + t') \supset (u)]$, $[u \supset t']$, $[p']$
e. $[(p + q) \supset (r)]$, $[(r + s) \supset (t)]$, $[(t + s) \supset (u)]$, $[(q + v) + (w)]'$
f. $[(p' + t') \supset (s)]$, $[(t') + (u \supset v)]$, $[(u' + v) \supset (t's)]$
g. $[(pq) \supset (r \supset t)]$, $[rst]'$, $[p']$, $[s]$
h. $[(p \supset q) + (su)']$, $[t \supset p]$, $[(us) \supset (pt)]$, $[t + s]$
i. $[(p \supset q') \supset (r)]$, $[ps'r']'$, $[r']$, $[st']'$
j. $[(p't') \supset (r)]$, $[(s' + t)' + (r)]$, $[(p'r) + (v)]$, $[(v + p') \supset (s')]$
k. Arnold wins the game, or I go to town and buy a coat.   I do not go to town,
   or I buy a coat and Arnold wins the game.   Therefore, . . .
l. If Sally goes to Detroit, then she will see her brother.   If Sally goes to
   California, then she will enjoy Hollywood.   If she does not go to Detroit
   and California, then she will be unhappy.   She will not be unhappy.
   Therefore, . . .
m. If it rains then the ground is wet implies if the grass does not grow then the
   soil is sandy.   If the ground is not wet then the soil is sandy.   Either it
   does not rain or the soil is not sandy.   Therefore, . . .

n. A man will not prepare for his old age, or he will invest his resources and be worried about their security. If he invests his resources, then he will be worried about their security. If he is worried about their security then he is unhappy. Therefore, . . .

o. John shot a deer, bear, and rabbit. John shot a deer and bear, and John shot a cow or a horse. John shot a deer implies if he shot a horse then he did not shoot a bear. It is not the case that John shot a man, bear, and cow. Therefore, . . .

B

p. $\{(p' + q) + (r)\}'$, $\{(t's') \supset (rw)\}$, $\{p' + u\}$, $\{(q' + r') \supset (t \supset u)\}$, $\{[p'] \supset [(s'w) + (q)]\}$, $\{(q + r) \supset (vs)\}$, $\{v \supset p\}$

q. $\{[p + q] \supset [(t + s) \cdot (w')]\}$, $\{(w) \supset (q \supset s')\}$, $\{(p + w') + (s')\}'$, $\{(p \supset q) + (p' \supset w)\}$

r. $[(pq) \supset (rs)]$, $[(t \supset p) \cdot (u \supset v)]$, $[(u \supset q) \cdot (s \supset g)]$, $[r']$

s. $[(p' + q') \supset (s + t)]$, $[(w') \supset (vp)]$, $[sq]'$, $[(p') \supset (q \supset s')]$, $[t + w]'$, $[(v + p) \supset (s')]$

t. $\{(p) \supset (q + r)\}$, $\{(st) \supset (qw)\}$, $\{rw\}'$, $\{[(s) \supset (p + q)] \supset [w]\}$, $\{w'\}$

11–4.   INFERENCES BY THE APPLICATION OF INTERCHANGE EXPRESSIONS AND SIMPLE ARGUMENT FORMS

In earlier chapters, the most common simple argument forms and interchange expressions were examined and listed. The complex arguments that occur are based on these simple arguments and interchange expressions. By the application of them, we are frequently able to deduce true conclusions or make valid inferences from complex sets of premises.

The success of this method depends upon the student's knowledge or his familiarity with the elementary valid argument forms and interchange expressions (Appendix and Section 10–8). It also depends upon his skill and ingenuity in applying them.

Given some premises, if we list along with them any statement that can be asserted on the basis of the forms listed in Section 10–8, we are often led to make additional inferences that lead to validly inferred conclusions.

Consider the set of premises

1. $(p \supset q)$
2. $(q \supset r)$
3. (r')

An examination of these statements shows that the consequent of the first premiss is the antecedent of the second one. Together they constitute H.S. and justify the assertion of $(p \supset r)$. We add $(p \supset r)$ to the list of the premisses, and we may thereafter use it in connection with the given premisses in order to make other inferences.   We now have

$$1.\ (p \supset q)$$
$$2.\ (q \supset r)$$
$$3.\ (r')$$
$$\overline{4.\ (p \supset r) \qquad \text{H.S., 1, 2}}$$

Now we observe that (r'), the third premiss, is the negation of the consequent of our first listed inference, $(p \supset r)$.   Together, these two (the statements in lines 3 and 4) permit, by M.T., the assertion of p'.   Consequently, we now list

$$5.\ (p') \qquad \text{M.T., 4, 3}$$

The formula p' is a validly inferred conclusion from the original premisses.   It may not have been obvious at first.   By the procedure described, however, it emerges as a warranted assertion.   (Any statement that results from a valid inference or a sequence of valid inferences from the premisses is, of course, a warranted conclusion.)

As a second example, consider the premisses

$$1.\ (p \supset q')$$
$$2.\ (r \supset s)$$
$$3.\ (p'r')'$$

An examination of the structures of the premisses indicates that the third premiss contains the statements p and r, which are the antecedents of the hypotheticals in the first and second premisses.   But, in its present form it does not, considered in connection with $(p \supset q')$ or $(r \supset s)$, model any one of the elementary valid argument forms.   The third premiss, $(p'r')'$, is ideal for an application of D.M.   We write, therefore,

$$4.\ (p + r) \qquad \text{D.M., 3}$$

Now $(p + r)$, along with $(p \supset q')$ and $(r \supset s)$, model C.D.   We can assert

$$5.\ (q' + s) \qquad \text{C.D., 1, 2, 4}$$

In the fifth line, we have a validly inferred conclusion.

Finally, we choose a more complicated case.   The premisses are

$$1.\ [p' + q]$$
$$2.\ [r' \supset q']$$
$$3.\ [(s) \supset (pr')]$$

None of the simple argument forms of Section 10–8 is directly applicable for making inferences.   Next, we ask about the applicability of interchange expressions listed in Section 10–8. We can, of course, use D.C. on premiss 1. This gives

4. $(p \supset q)$ D.C., 1

What interchange expression is usable in premiss 2?   D.C. yields $(r + q')$. Trans. gives $(q \supset r)$. The latter is the more promising; for, along with $(p \supset q)$, it constitutes H.S.   Thus, we write

5. $(q \supset r)$ Trans., 2
6. $(p \supset r)$ H.S., 4, 5

Can any simple argument form be applied to the formulas in the third and sixth lines? Not in their present form. The p and r of the sixth line are found in the consequent of the formula in the third line. Can M.T. be applied to the formula in the third line?   Only if we have the negation of the consequent (pr'), which would be $(pr')'$ or $(p' + r)$, can we do this.   The formula of the sixth line is now seen in a new light. The formula $(p \supset r)$ is an interchange form for $(p' + r)$, according to D.C.   The following steps now can be taken.

7. $(p' + r)$ D.C., 6
8. $(pr')'$ D.M., 7
9. (s') M.T., 3, 8

Line 9 thus gives a conclusion that can be validly inferred from the given premises.   (Lines 4, 5, 6, 7, and 8 each do also.)

At first one may not be skillful enough to move without wasted steps to a conclusion drawn from a process of inference involving all the premisses.   Repeated examination and operations on the premisses, using interchange expressions and the elementary valid argument forms, will produce valid inferences that result in "supplemental premisses."   These may be useful in moving to conclusions.   This situation is similar to the use of axioms in geometry in order to work out the proofs of theorems. Just as continuing use of the axioms in solving geometric problems develops the ability to move more easily to satisfactory solutions, so practice in using the interchange expressions and elementary valid argument forms enables one to move with increasing ease to valid inferences, drawn from the interrelation of the various premisses.

EXERCISE SET 11–4

1. Using the method of making inferences by the application of interchange expressions and simple valid argument forms, infer two conclusions in each case from the sets of premisses given.

a. $[(p + q) \supset (r)], [r']$
b. $(p \supset q), (q' + r'), (p)$

   c. $[(p) \supset (qr)], [q \supset r], [r' + s], [s']$

   d. $[(p \supset q) \supset (r \supset s)], [prs']$

   e. $[(pq) \supset (r' + s')], [p], [q], [r]$

2. Do the same for these sets of premises. In these cases, express the conclusion in English.

   a. Gregg goes to Paris, or he buys a car and is not depressed. If Gregg doesn't buy a car, then he is unpopular. Gregg is not unpopular or he is depressed. Therefore, . . .

   b. If the teacher is angry, he fails Joe or Alice or Peter or Gregg. The teacher is courteous but angry. He neither fails Peter nor Gregg. Therefore, . . .

   c. Harry visits Paris or Berlin. If he visits Paris, he goes by airplane. Harry visits Paris or he doesn't. Therefore, . . .

   d. If Paul wrote *Romans*, then if he was in Rome he saw some of those he addressed and baptized some of them. Paul wrote *Romans*, but he didn't baptize any of those he addressed. Therefore, . . .

   e. Plato was an artist, and he wrote *Phaedo* or *Euthyphro* or *Ion*. Plato was not an artist or was not the writer of *Ion*. Plato was not an artist or was not the writer of *Euthyphro*. Therefore, . . .

11–5.   ARGUMENTS WITH INCONSISTENT PREMISSES

Previously, we have mentioned the necessity of being alert to the possible presence of contradictory premises. A short excursion on this topic is worthwhile.

Let us suppose we have an argument that has the form

$$1.\ (p)$$
$$2.\ (p')$$
$$\overline{\text{Hence, } (r)}$$

The premises (p) and (p') are contradictory. The conclusion r is unrelated to the premises. The **alf** for this argument is $[(pp') \supset (r)]$. And the truth-table is

$[(p$	$\cdot$	$p')$	$\supset$	$(r)]$
	0		1	1
	0		1	0
	0		1	1
	0		1	0

The **alf** is a tautology. Since the conjunction of the premises has the truth-values 0, 0, 0, 0, then no matter what the conclusion is the **alf** is a tautology and the argument form is valid. Given contradictory premisses, one can validly infer any conclusion whatsoever.

Expressing the situation a bit differently but still considering contradictory premises

$$1. \ (p)$$
$$2. \ (p')$$

we may proceed in inference this way. Since (p) is asserted as a premiss, the principle of addition justifies the assertion of $(p + r)$, where r is any statement whatsoever. Now $(p + r)$ is asserted, as well as (p'), the second premiss. Consequently, from these two, by D.S. we can assert r. Thus, the original premises justify the assertion of any statement, r.

A contradiction in a set of premises is, of course, not usually obvious. Generally, it is fairly well hidden. Without appealing to a very complicated example, the premises of this argument contain a contradiction:

If Susan acts hastily, she is courageous.
Susan is not courageous or she is drastic.
Susan is not both drastic and not exhausted.
She acts hastily and is not exhausted.

Consequently, if Susan is exhausted, she does not act hastily.

The form of the argument is

$$1. \ (a \supset c)$$
$$2. \ (c' + d)$$
$$3. \ (de')'$$
$$4. \ (ae')$$

Hence, $(e \supset a')$

After examination, we perceive that $(c' + d)$ ____ $(c \supset d)$ and that $(de')'$ ____ $(d \supset e)$. (Why?) By two applications of H.S., we discover that the first three premises justify the assertion of $(a \supset e)$. But $(a \supset e)$ ____ $(ae')'$, and $(ae')'$ is the contradictory of the fourth premiss, (ae'). This argument has a contradiction among its premises, and it is valid. On the basis of the analysis above, we know this without examining the conclusion.

The student should write the **alf** for this argument form and construct its truth-table, giving particular attention to the column of the truth-table that displays the values of the conjunction of the premises.

12

Methods of Proof

12–1. THE TRUTH-TABLE METHOD OF PROOF

Chapter 11 deals with the problem of validly inferring conclusions when one is given a set of premises. Three simple procedures for doing this were described.

Very often we are confronted by a complete argument—premises and conclusion—and are asked to judge whether or not the conclusion given is warranted by the premises. Our question then is whether or not the argument form employed is valid.

Sometimes the arguments presented to us are very simple, modeling one of the elementary valid argument forms. This is the case with an argument such as

> If Alice is a tennis player or an acrobat, then she is dexterous.
> Alice is not dexterous.
> _____
>
> Hence, Alice is not a tennis player and not an acrobat.

The argument form is

$$[(t + a) \supset (d)]$$
$$[d']$$
$$\text{Hence, } [a't']$$

Noting that the conclusion, $(a't')$, is an interchange form for $(t + a)'$ by D.M., we recognize that, except for minor variations, the argument form is that of M.T. It has already been justified. The **alf** for M.T., $\{[(p \supset q) \cdot (q')] \supset [p']\}$, is a tautology.

In the list of elementary valid argument forms and interchange expressions in Section 10–8, we already have some simple argument forms that have been warranted. This chapter will, therefore, discuss techniques for proving the validity of arguments that are more extended or complex. In certain of these methods, we shall appeal to the elementary valid argument forms in Section 10–8.

The truth-table method of proof was used in the establishment of the elementary valid argument forms. It needs no extended discussion at this point.   While the method becomes cumbersome if we deal with arguments involving more than four statements, it is effective.

In order to recall the technique before we move on to other procedures, consider this argument:

> If the Democrats win a majority in the House, Congress passes measures providing for higher taxes.
> The Congress will not both provide for higher taxes and continue to subsidize educational projects.
> Educational projects are subsidized by Congress or the United States faces a shortage of competent scientists.
> ___
> Therefore, the Democrats do not win a majority in the House or the United States does not face a shortage of competent scientists.

First, we symbolize the argument, displaying its form:

$$(d \supset t)$$
$$(ts)'$$
$$\underline{(s + f)}$$
$$\text{Hence, } (d' + f')$$

Following our convention of relating the premisses to one another by · and joining the premiss conjunction to the conclusion by ⊃, we write the **alf** for the argument form:

$$\{[(d \supset t) \cdot (ts)' \cdot (s + f)] \supset [d' + f']\}$$

The argument involves four statements.   The truth-table has, therefore, $2^4 = 16$ cases.   Constructing the truth-table, we get this array:

	(d)	(t)	(s)	(f)	(d ⊃ t)	(ts)'	(s+f)	Premiss Conjunc.	(d'+f')	{[Premisses] ⊃ [d'+f']}
Case 1:	1	1	1	1	1	0	1	0	0	1
2:	1	1	1	0	1	0	1	0	1	1
3:	1	1	0	1	1	1	1	1	0	0
4:	1	1	0	0	1	1	0	0	1	1
5:	1	0	1	1	0	1	1	0	0	1
6:	1	0	1	0	0	1	1	0	1	1
7:	1	0	0	1	0	1	1	0	0	1
8:	1	0	0	0	0	1	0	0	1	1
9:	0	1	1	1	1	0	1	0	1	1
10:	0	1	1	0	1	0	1	0	1	1
11:	0	1	0	1	1	1	1	1	1	1
12:	0	1	0	0	1	1	0	0	1	1
13:	0	0	1	1	1	1	1	1	1	1
14:	0	0	1	0	1	1	1	1	1	1
15:	0	0	0	1	1	1	1	1	1	1
16:	0	0	0	0	1	1	0	0	1	1

In Case 3 (in which the truth-table values of d, t, s, and f are, respectively, 1, 1, 0, and 1), a value 0 appears in the final column. This means that in this case the premisses are all true and the conclusion is false. The argument is judged invalid.

Speaking of the logical formula that is the **alf** for this argument—$\{[(d \supset t) \cdot (ts)' \cdot (s + f)] \supset [d' + f']\}$—we call it a *contingent function;* that is, it sometimes has the value 1 and it sometimes has the value 0.

If a logical formula is always 0 (that is, if the final column of its truth-table shows 0 in every case), it is called *contradictory.* The simple formula (pp') is contradictory.

If the **alf** for an argument is a tautology, the argument is deemed valid. If the **alf** is not a tautology, the argument is judged invalid.

Very complex arguments can be analyzed by the truth-table method of proof, but they are generally so time-consuming and tedious as to be frustrating.

12–2. THE SHORTER TRUTH-TABLE METHOD OF PROOF

According to our prior contentions, a valid argument is one in which, if the premisses have the value 1, the conclusion must have the value 1. In such an argument, there is no case in which each premiss has the value 1 and the conclusion has the value 0. Now an argument is either valid or invalid. Consequently, if we can find one case in which the premisses have the value 1 and the conclusion has the value 0, the argument is invalid; otherwise, it is valid.

Let us examine the following argument, expressed in symbols. It is the form of the argument used in Section 12–1.

$$1.\ (d \supset t)$$
$$2.\ (ts)'$$
$$3.\ (s + f)$$
$$\overline{\text{Hence},\ (d' + f')}$$

We now try to make the conclusion, $(d' + f')$, false. This will be the case if we assign 1 for the value of d ($d = 1$) and 1 for the value of f ($f = 1$). With these assignments, the value of the conclusion is $(1' + 1') = (0 + 0) = 0$. For brevity, we adopt the procedure of substituting the truth-value of the statement for the statement; and we then compute, following the meanings of the logical connectives and operations, the truth-value that results. Now we want to see if we can make the premisses true, recalling that we now have the assignments $d = 1$ and $f = 1$. In the first premiss $(d \supset t)$, since $d = 1$, t must have the value 1 in order that the conditional form have the value 1. In the case of the second premiss, since now $t = 1$, s must have the value 0, in order to have

$(ts)' = 1$. Finally, with the assignments $s = 0$ and $f = 1$, the third premiss has the value 1: $(s + f) = (0 + 1) = 1$.

We have succeeded, therefore, in finding an assignment of truth-values
($d = 1$, $t = 1$, $s = 0$, $f = 1$) that makes each premiss true and the conclusion false. The argument is invalid. When we compare this result
with the complete truth-table of this argument form, given in Section
12–1, we see that the assignment of values is exactly the set of values for
the statements d, t, s, and f in Case 3 of the complete truth-table, the row
that displays 0 in the final column.

A convenient method of employing this shorter truth-table technique
in relation to an argument is to place the assigned values after or above
each elementary statement. Thus,

$$
\begin{array}{ccl}
1 \quad 1 & = 1 \text{ (True)} \\
1. \ (d \supset t) & \\
1 \ 0 & = 1 \text{ (True)} \\
2. \ (t \ s)' & \\
0 \quad 1 & = 1 \text{ (True)} \\
3. \ (s + f) & \\
\hline
0 \quad 0 & = 0 \text{ (False)} \\
\text{Hence, } (d' + f') &
\end{array}
$$

This method proves to be a much quicker and more efficient way of
analyzing the validity of an argument than the construction of the complete truth-table.

What happens if we have at hand an argument that is valid? When
we encounter a valid argument, we *cannot* assign values to the statements so that each premiss is true and the conclusion is false. Let us
examine the situation by means of an example.

> If John is an actor, he is eloquent.
> If John is eloquent, he is conceited.
> John is not conceited or he is a bore.
> _____
> Hence, John is not both an actor and not a bore.

Its symbolic form is

$$
\begin{array}{l}
1. \ (a \supset e) \\
2. \ (e \supset c) \\
3. \ (c' + b) \\
\hline
\text{Hence, } (ab')'
\end{array}
$$

We now apply the shorter truth-table technique to this form; that is,
we try to discover an assignment of values that makes $(ab')' = 0$, and
$[(a \supset e) \cdot (e \supset c) \cdot (c' + b)] = 1$. In order to make the conclusion false,

we must assign $a = 1$ and $b = 0$, for $(1 \cdot 0')' = (1 \cdot 1)' = (1)' = 0$. Since now $a = 1$, we must have $e = 1$ in order that the first premiss be true: $(a \supset e) = (1 \supset 1) = 1$. Inasmuch as $e = 1$, we must assign $c = 1$ in order for the second premiss to be true. Thus far, the conclusion has been made false and the first two premisses true, and we have been compelled to assign the particular values given to the statement symbols. We now proceed to the third premiss to see if it can be made true. Since we already have $b = 0$, in order to make the third premiss true we *must* have $c = 0$. But earlier we had to make $c = 1$. *The attempt authorized by this method leads to a contradiction, c = 1 and c = 0.* The endeavor to make the conclusion false and the premisses true fails. The argument is *not* invalid; it is valid.

The two examples that we have used are ones in which the nature of the arguments gave us no options in the assignment of truth-values as we carried out the shorter truth-table method. This is not always the case. With certain arguments we are confronted with a choice as to what values to assign. In such arguments, we should be prepared to exhaust all the possible truth-value assignments in the endeavor to secure the objective of all premisses with the value 1 and the conclusion with the value 0. Only when we know that *no possible assignment* of values will produce the desired objective can we conclude that we have not been able to prove the argument to be invalid, but have proved it to be valid. As an example, let us consider the following argument:

1. $(p \supset t)$
2. $(t \supset q)$
3. (tr)

Hence, (pq)

In this argument, the conclusion will be false if $p = 0$ and $q = 0$, if $p = 1$ and $q = 0$, or if $p = 0$ and $q = 1$. Which assignment of values should we make? Let us choose $p = 0$ and $q = 0$. We now turn to the first premiss. Since $p = 0$, t may be 1 or 0 and the first premiss be true. Looking at the second premiss, we observe that we have a false consequent ($q = 0$); thus, and to make this premiss true, t must equal 0. $(t = 0)$ not only establishes the second premiss as true, but the first as well. The third premiss is a conjunction of t and r. Both must be true, if this premiss is to be true; thus, $(tr) = (1 \cdot 1) = 1$. We now have $t = 0$ in the first and second premisses and $t = 1$ in the third premiss. A contradiction has resulted. Are we justified in calling the argument valid? We are *not*, for we have not exhausted all the options in our endeavor to establish true premisses and a false conclusion.

The conclusion may be made false, not only when $p = 0$ and $q = 0$, but when $p = 1$ and $q = 0$ or when $p = 0$ and $q = 1$. Let the student assign $p = 1$ and $q = 0$. What is the result? We will assign $p = 0$ and $q = 1$, and display the results:

$$\begin{array}{c}
0 \quad 1 \quad = 1 \\
\text{1. } (p \supset t) \\
1 \quad 1 \quad = 1 \\
\text{2. } (t \supset q) \\
1 \quad 1 \quad = 1 \\
\text{3. } (t \quad\quad r) \\
\hline
0 \; 1 = 0
\end{array}$$

Hence, $(p \; q)$

Thus, with the assignment $p = 0$, $t = 1$, $q = 1$, and $r = 1$, we have discovered that the premisses can be made true while the conclusion is false. The argument is invalid. Construction of the complete truth-table for the argument will indicate we have discovered the one case (Case 9) in sixteen cases in which the premisses are true and the conclusion is false.

A certain amount of trial and error will be present in the handling of certain arguments by this shorter truth-table method. Use of the technique will develop one's skill in its application and will suggest methods of proceeding that prove helpful (such as having as many true values in the false conclusion as is possible and working first with premisses displaying conjunction). Whenever the procedures authorized by the method *compel* us to assign contradictory values for any statement, the argument is valid.

EXERCISE SET 12–2

A

1. Use the truth-table method of proof to decide the validity of these argument forms:

　a. $[(p) \supset (q' + r)], [r'] \vdash [p']$
　b. $[(r' + q) + (s)], [r' \supset s] \vdash [r \supset q]$　*Invalid*
　c. $[(p) + (qr)], [q'] \vdash [r + s]$
　d. $[p], [q] \vdash [(p + q) + (r)]$　*reduces to* $q \lor \lor \lor (p . \bar p)$
　e. $[(p) \supset (p + q)], [(p + q) \supset (p + q + r)] \vdash [q + r]$

2. Use the truth-table method of proof to decide the validity of these arguments:

　a. If the document is clear and interesting, then it clarifies our problem. The document is interesting but fails to clarify our problem. Hence, it is unclear.

　b. If John's being a machinist implies that he is dexterous, then John has the capacity to be an able student. Consequently, if John is dexterous, he has the capacity to be an able student.

Invalid in ordinary sense?

c. Harry is not a poet or he is a scientist. Therefore, if Harry is a poet, then he is a poet and a scientist.

d. If Grace is not a secretary, she is well dressed. If Grace is a statistician, she is not well dressed. Consequently, Grace is a secretary or not a statistician.

e. The museum is understaffed, or its collection is limited and it is maladministered. It is not the case that its collection is limited or it is maladministered. If it is not maladministered, then it is not understaffed. The museum is, therefore, highly endowed.

3. Use the shorter truth-table method to decide the validity of the argument forms in 1a, 1b, 1c, 1d, and 1e.

4. Use the shorter truth-table method to decide the validity of the arguments in 2a, 2b, 2c, 2d, and 2e.

B

5. Use the shorter truth-table method on this argument form: (p), (p'), hence (r). What do you discover? Ignoring the conclusion, simply try to make the premises all true. What happens? Formulate a principle, then, about the use of this method in relation to argument forms of the type given.

6. Establish the invalidity, if possible, of the following arguments by using the shorter truth-table method:

a. $[(p \supset q) \supset (r)]$, $[(s \supset r) \cdot (p \supset t)]$, $[v + s]$, $[s'] \vdash [p \supset t]$

b. $\{[(pq) \supset (r \supset s)] \cdot [t]\}$, $\{(t \supset q) + (v \supset w)\}$, $\{(tw) + (pq)\}$, $\{[(tv) \supset (q)] \supset [r]\} \vdash \{st\}$

c. $\{p \supset \subset q\}$, $\{[(r \supset s) \supset (t)] \supset [p]\}$, $\{(v + w) \cdot (t + s)\}$, $\{(w + q) + (r)\}$, $\{[(uv) \supset (w)] \cdot [(ts) \supset (q)]\} \vdash \{(v + w) \cdot (t)\}$

d. $\{(p + q) + (r + s)\}$, $\{(t \supset \subset v) + (w)\}$, $\{[(p') \supset (r'w')] \supset [q']\}$, $\{(u'w') + (pv)\} \vdash \{qw\}$

e. $[(p \supset q) \cdot (r \supset s)]$, $[(q) \supset (v' \supset r)]$, $[vt]'$, $[(ut') + (ps)]$, $[(w \supset t) \cdot (u \supset q)]$, $[q' + v'] \vdash [(s \supset w') \cdot (v)]$

f. $\{[p \supset \subset s] + [r \supset \subset t]\}$, $\{[(w' + p) \supset (v)] \cdot [q + u]\}$, $\{w + q' + v\}'$, $\{[p \supset t] \cdot [r \supset s]\} \vdash \{r' + t\}$

g. $\{[wv] + [(s' + t) \cdot (w)]\}$, $\{[(q \supset t) \supset (w)] \supset [p + u]\}$, $\{q' + h + v\}'$, $\{[p \supset s] \cdot [v \supset h]\}$, $\{[h \supset t] \cdot [s \supset w]\}$, $\{h \supset u\} \vdash \{t'u'\}'$

12–3. THE ALGEBRAIC METHOD OF PROOF

The algebraic proof procedure depends, as does the truth-table method, on writing the **alf** for the form of the argument given. It also calls into use the interchange expressions in our reference list in Section 10–8.

Let us take as a first example the argument

> If Grant is captain, he is well paid.
> Grant is a captain and a pilot.
> ———————————————
> Hence, Grant is well paid.

The argument form is

$$(c \supset w)$$
$$(cp)$$

Hence, (w)

Its **alf** is $\{[(c \supset w) \cdot (cp)] \supset [w]\}$. If this formula is a tautology, the argument is valid. Formerly, we constructed the truth-table to decide if it were a tautology. The algebraic method is another way of determining whether or not the **alf** is tautological.

We begin with $\{[(c \supset w) \cdot (cp)] \supset [w]\}$. On the **alf** we perform two operations:

(I)   Remove all hypothetical or conditional signs ($\supset$) by D.C.

(II)   Use D.M. repeatedly until all prime or negation marks ($'$) stand only on single statements.

These operations are based on interchange expressions; therefore, the formulas derived are equivalent in truth-values to the **alf**. We implement these operations in the following manner. In this case and in similar procedures later, we will eliminate punctuation marks where no confusion results.

$$\{[(c \supset w) \cdot (cp)] \supset [w]\} \; =\!=$$

$$[(c' + w) \cdot (cp)]' + w \; =\!= \quad \text{D.C.}$$

$$(c' + w)' + (cp)' + w \; =\!= \quad \text{D.M.}$$

$$cw' + (c' + p') + w \quad\quad \text{D.M.}$$

We now proceed to three additional operations:

(III)   Distribute into disjunction (See 9a in Section 10–8), if the opportunity is present, any form derived from one of the premisses or the conclusion.

(IV)   Employ Commutation and Association in preparation for the use of the laws of absorption.

(V)   Employ the laws of absorption to eliminate superfluous terms.

In the formula under consideration, operation (III) is not possible; that is, there is no form derived from a premiss or the conclusion in which the law of distribution in the form of $[(p) \cdot (q + r)] =\!= [(pq) + (pr)]$ can be employed. We proceed to perform operations (IV) and (V).

$$(cw' + c') + p' + w \; =\!= \quad \text{Assoc.}$$

$$w' + c' + p' + w \quad\quad \text{Absorp.}$$

At this point we have a disjunction, and we are in a position to pursue the final operation:

$((p \cdot q) \vee r) \vee \sim r \sim (\sim (p \cdot q) \supset r) \supset \sim r$

$= \sim (\sim (p \cdot q) \supset r) \supset \sim r$

(VI) Inspect the resulting disjunction for a tautology of the form $(p + p')$, which in disjunction with any other statements is a tautology and indicates a valid argument.

In this instance, the disjunction contains $(w' + w)$. We know from our earlier analysis that $(w' + w)$ is a tautology (always has the value 1). Consequently, we write $(w' + w) = 1$ and substitute the value 1 for $(w' + w)$. As a result, we have

$$1 + (c' + p')$$

This is a disjunction with 1 on one side. A disjunction is true if one side is true. Therefore, we can write

$$1 + (c' + p') = 1$$

The **alf** reduces to 1. This testifies that it is a tautology, and that the argument is valid.

If the **alf** for an argument form reduces, under these rules of procedure, to 1, the argument is valid; if it does not, the argument is invalid.

Using these rules of procedure, let us examine an example of an invalid argument form. Consider the argument in Section 12–1. Its **alf** is $\{[(d \supset t) \cdot (ts)' \cdot (s + f)] \supset [d' + f']\}$. Applying the six steps of the algebraic method, we develop the following proof:

$\{[(d \supset t) \cdot (ts)' \cdot (s + f)] \supset [d' + f']\}$ ———

$[(d' + t) \cdot (ts)' \cdot (s + f)]' + d' + f'$ ——— D.C.

$(d' + t)' + (ts) + (s + f)' + d' + f'$ ——— D.M.

$dt' + ts + s'f' + d' + f'$ ——— D.M.

$(d' + dt') + ts + (f' + s'f')$ ——— Comm. and Assoc.

$d' + t' + ts + f'$ ——— Absorp.

$d' + (t' + ts) + f'$ ——— Assoc.

$d' + t' + s + f'$ ——— Absorp.

No further reductions are possible. Moreover, the result does not exhibit a tautology. The **alf** is a contingent function, not a tautology. The argument form has proved to be invalid.

In the two previous examples, it has not been possible to perform operation (III). This is frequently the case. However, for our last example let us employ a simple argument in which this operation is present.   Let us take the argument form

$$[(p) + (qr)]$$
$$\underline{[q']}$$
$$\text{Hence, } [r + s]$$

We proceed through operations (I) and (II).

$$(\{[(p) + (qr)] \cdot [q']\} \supset \{r + s\}) \; \overline{\underline{\qquad}}$$

$$\{[(p) + (qr)] \cdot [q']\}' + r + s \qquad \overline{\underline{\qquad}} \qquad \text{D.C.}$$

$$[(p) + (qr)]' + [q']' + r + s \qquad \overline{\underline{\qquad}} \qquad \text{D.M.}$$

$$[(p') \cdot (q' + r')] + q + r + s \qquad \overline{\underline{\qquad}} \qquad \text{D.M.,} \; \boxed{\text{D.N.}}$$

The formula now before us provides the opportunity for performing distribution into disjunction in the case of $[(p') \cdot (q' + r')]$, which is a form derived from the first premiss.   We perform operation (III) and proceed to complete the algebraic method of proof.

$$p'q' + p'r' + q + r + s \qquad \overline{\underline{\qquad}} \qquad \text{Distr.}$$

$$(p'q' + q) + (p'r' + r) + s \; \overline{\underline{\qquad}} \qquad \text{Comm. and Assoc.}$$

$$p' + q + p' + r + s \qquad\qquad \text{Absorp.}$$

There is no tautology of the form $(p + p')$.   The argument form has proved to be invalid.

EXERCISE SET 12–3

1. Use the algebraic method of proof for the following argument forms:

✓ a. $(p \supset q), (q \supset r) \vdash (p \supset r)$

✓ b. $(p), (p') \vdash (r)$

✓ c. $(p + q), (p') \vdash (q)$

✓ d. $(p \supset q), (r \supset s), (p + r) \vdash (q + s)$

✓ e. $(p \supset q), (p') \vdash (q')$ *Invalid*

✓ f. $(p) \vdash (pq)$ *Invalid*

2. Use the algebraic method of proof for the argument forms in Exercise Set 12–2, Exercises 1a, 1b, 1c, 1d, and 1e. *reduces to* $q \lor r \lor (p \cdot {\sim}p)$

3. Use the algebraic method of proof for the arguments in Exercise Set 12–2, Exercises 2a, 2b, 2c, 2d, and 2e.

12–4.   THE AXIOMATIC METHOD OF PROOF

The rudiments of the axiomatic method of proof were displayed in Section 11–4, where we discussed making inferences by the application of interchange expressions and simple argument forms.

In using this method, we consider the argument forms and interchange expressions of Section 10–8 to be warranted. They have, of course, been justified by the use of truth-tables. Proceeding as in Section 11–4, we list the premisses of the argument and employ our axioms to make warranted inferences. At each step, we list the principle, formula, or simple argument form that justifies the step taken. Since here we have a conclusion given for the argument, we want to show, if possible, that the given conclusion can be secured by a set of warranted steps from the premisses.

A comment made in Section 11–4 about making various inferences is applicable here also: it is through practice that one develops the "knack" of using this proof procedure. One should always keep in mind the end-in-view, namely, the arrival, if possible, by justified steps, at the conclusion given in the argument.

Consider this argument:

It cannot be that all of Dr. Gregg's rats are healthy and that his experimental results are not sound.

Rats show a capacity for anticipating situations or Dr. Gregg's experimental results are not sound.

If the study of rat-behavior is not fruitful for understanding human psychology, then rats do not show a capacity for anticipating situations.

All of Dr. Gregg's rats are healthy.

Hence, the study of rat-behavior is fruitful for understanding human psychology.

The argument form is

1. $(hs')'$
2. $(c + s')$
3. $(f' \supset c')$
4. (h) $/(f)$

We place the conclusion f to the right of the display of premisses as a reminder that we must, if possible, arrive at f by valid inferences from the four premisses. Those inferences must be made as in the discussion in Section 11–4. We proceed in this manner:

5. $(h' + s)$ D.M., 1
6. (s) D.S., 5, 4
7. (c) D.S., 2, 6
8. (f) M.T., 3, 7

We thus show that the conclusion f can be validly inferred from the premises; the argument is valid.

The student should prove the above argument to be valid by the algebraic method and by the shorter truth-table method.

As a second example, we choose

> James is a licensed pilot and an electrical engineer and a lawyer.
> If he is a licensed pilot and an electrical engineer, he qualifies for the government project in Iran.
> He is excused from military service or he does not qualify for the project.
> James cannot both be excused from military service and not be subject to a year's training in radar.
> _____
> Hence, James is subject to a year's training in radar.

The argument form is

> 1. $[pel]$
> 2. $[(pe) \supset (q)]$
> 3. $[m + q']$
> 4. $[mr']'$ $/[r]$

In this case, we list the steps in the proof, asking the student to supply the justification for each step.

> 5. (pe)
> 6. (q)
> 7. (m)
> 8. $(m' + r)$
> 9. (r)

In this sort of proof procedure, if the argument is valid, by a finite number of steps one can arrive at the conclusion. If the argument is invalid, he cannot. Thus, in the latter case, if after much trying one cannot arrive at the conclusion, he is not sure whether the argument is invalid or he simply has not been able to produce the right sequence of steps. Of course, this issue can be resolved by the procedure advanced in Section 12–2.

The student will recall that, in Section 11–5, we discussed arguments with inconsistent premises. Suppose we have such an argument at hand and desire to construct a formal proof of validity for its conclusion. If the premises contain a contradiction, we can deduce it from them, using the technique immediately above. To illustrate, let us use the example given in Section 11–5. The argument form is

1. $(a \supset c)$
2. $(c' + d)$
3. $(de')'$
4. (ae') $/(e \supset a')$

First, we deduce the contradiction contained in the premisses; thus,

  5. $(c \supset d)$ D.C., 2
  6. $(a \supset d)$ H.S., 1, 5
  7. $(d' + e)$ D.M., 3
  8. $(d \supset e)$ D.C., 7
  9. $(a \supset e)$ H.S., 6, 8
10. $(a' + e)$ D.C., 9
11. $(ae')'$ D.M., 10

At this point, we have shown that from the premisses (1–3) we can deduce $(ae')'$, which is the contradiction of (ae') in the fourth premiss. From this point, we proceed in this manner:

12. $(ae')' + (e \supset a')$ Add., 11

We join the conclusion, whatever it is, to one of the contradictory statements by disjunction.

13. $(e \supset a')$ D.S., 12, 4

The other of the contradictory statements, taken along with the disjunction produced by Add., yields the conclusion by D.S. Given a contradiction, p and p', this last set of steps in schematic form is

$p +$ (conclusion)   Add.
(conclusion)   D.S.

The student will now ask how we can know if the premisses are contradictory, especially if the contradiction is hidden. This can be decided by a slight adaption of the technique advanced in Section 12–2. If a set of premisses contains a contradiction, and if we attempt to make the *premisses true* by the assignment of truth-values to the premisses, *ignoring the conclusion*, we are forced to give contradictory values to a statement.

Taking the premisses in the example immediately above, we make the fourth premiss true by choosing the values $a = 1$ and $e = 0$. Since $e = 0$, we must have $d = 0$ in order that $(de')' = 1$. If $d = 0$, then we must make the assignment $c = 0$ to make the second premiss true. But if $c = 0$, then, in order for $(a \supset c)$ to be true, $a = 0$ must be assigned. The attempt to make the premisses true leads us to a contradiction: $a = 1$, and $a = 0$. The premisses cannot all be true; they are contradictory. In summary, by the shorter truth-table method, we can decide

1. Whether an argument is valid or invalid;
2. Whether or not the premisses of an argument are contradictory.

If the argument is valid (whether by reason of contradictory premisses or not), we can construct a formal proof of its validity.

EXERCISE SET 12–4

A

1. The following are argument forms, along with the steps of the axiomatic proof procedures that demonstrate the validity of the arguments. In each case, provide the justification for each step.

a. 1. $[h + k]$
  2. $[k'j]$
  3. $[(h) \supset (m + j')] \, /[m]$
  4. (j)
  5. (k')
  6. (h)
  7. $(m + j')$
  8. (m)

    5. $[a + c]$
    6. $[a' \supset b]$
    7. $[a' \supset c']$
    8. $[c + a]$
    9. $[c' \supset a]$
    10. $[a' \supset a]$
    11. $[a + a]$
    12. $[a]$

b. 1. $[(g) \supset (h \supset j)]$
  2. $[ghk] \qquad /[j]$
  3. (g)
  4. $(h \supset j)$
  5. (h)
  6. (j)

d. 1. $(a' + b)$
  2. $(b \supset c)$
  3. $(ac') \qquad /(c)$
  4. $(a \supset b)$
  5. $(a \supset c)$
  6. $(a' + c)$
  7. $(ac')'$
  8. $[(ac')' + (c)]$
  9. (c)

c. 1. $[(a) + (bc)]$
  2. $[b \supset c'] \qquad /[a]$
  3. $[(a + b) \cdot (a + c)]$
  4. $[a + b]$

2. Use the axiomatic method of proof to demonstrate the validity of these arguments:

  a. If the automobile exceeded the speed limit, then if the driver was careless he is guilty. If the automobile's exceeding the speed limit implies that the driver is guilty, then the driver is liable for the damages. It is not the case that the driver is liable for the damages or is wealthy. Hence, the automobile did exceed the speed limit.

  b. If Congress passes the bill, the national debt increases. If Congress does not pass the bill, a large segment of the populace will suffer. The bill passes or it does not. If the national debt increases, a large segment of the populace will suffer. The national debt increases or it does not. Hence, a large segment of the populace suffers.

c. If the laws are unfair, then Harry is innocent and George is guilty. If Harry is innocent, then the police officer was in error. If the police officer was in error, then he should be dismissed. If the laws are unfair, then the police officer should not be dismissed. Hence, the laws are not unfair.

d. If current flows in the circuit, then if the switch is not closed the motor fails to start. The switch is open or current flows in the circuit. The meter shows that current flows in the circuit. If the current flows in the circuit, the motor does not fail to start. Hence, the switch is not open.

e. A man becomes a good physicist if and only if he masters higher algebra. If a man becomes a good physicist, he engages in research. If a man teaches, he doesn't engage in research. A man doesn't master higher algebra or he teaches. Therefore, a man does not become a good physicist or he does not master higher algebra.

B

3. For the following arguments, give either a proof of invalidity or an axiomatic proof of validity.

a. Harry has not written two popular novels or he is a well-known writer. If Harry has written two popular novels and is a well-known writer, his next writing will be published. If Harry has written two popular novels, is a well-known writer, and his next writing will be published, then Harry will pay off his mortgage in a year's time. Hence, if Harry has written two popular novels, then he is a well-known writer and his next writing will be published and he will pay off his mortgage in a year's time.

b. If James runs the mile in less than five minutes, then he is in good health, is an able athlete, and he ran very swiftly or he was under the influence of a stimulant. If he ran very swiftly, then he was under the influence of a stimulant. James runs the mile in less than five minutes and he ran very swiftly. Therefore, he is in good health and he is an able athlete.

c. A creature is rational if and only if it has the power of articulate speech. Hence, if a creature does not have the power of articulate speech, it is rational or it has the power of articulate speech.

d. Rational creatures and creatures with the power of articulate speech are equivalent. Hence, if a creature has the power of articulate speech, then its not being rational implies that it has the power of articulate speech.

e. If the fish are biting, then John's being at the lake implies that he is resting and avoiding his work. John does not rest or not avoid work. If the fish are not biting, then John is not at the lake. If John is resting, then he is not at the lake.   Therefore, the fish are biting or John is not avoiding his work.

f. The object on the table is an expensive, unpolished jewel.   If it is unpolished, it is not attractive.   Not being attractive is the same as not being desired.   If the object is unpolished, then it is likely to be mistaken for a common stone.   If the object is not desired and is not attractive, it is likely to be mistaken for a common stone.   Hence, the object on the table is not attractive or it is likely to be mistaken for a common stone.

g. William enlists in the Army, and he is not mature or he will make a good officer.   If he will make a good officer, then he will make a good officer and also a fine business executive.   But, if he is not considerate of other's wishes, then he will not make a fine business executive and he enlists in the Army.   If William will give unreasonable orders, then he is not considerate of other's wishes.   He will give unreasonable orders or not become a captain.   Consequently, if William is mature, he does not become a captain.

h. If the metal is annealed and contains nickel and is not cracked, then it makes a satisfactory magnetic path.   The metal is not annealed or it is cracked.   If it contains nickel, then its not being a brass compound implies that it makes a satisfactory magnetic path.   Consequently, the metal is annealed.

i. A mathematical system is significant if and only if its postulates are consistent.   A mathematical system's postulates are consistent and independent or they are not consistent and not independent.   Hence, if a mathematical system is significant, then its postulates are independent.

12–5.   THE CONDITIONAL METHOD OF PROOF

This method adds just one additional feature to the axiomatic method of Section 12–4 in order to handle easily *arguments in which the conclusions are conditional.*

Suppose an argument displays this pattern:

$$\text{Premisses; hence, } (p \supset q)$$

The **alf** for this sort of argument would be

$$[(\text{Premisses}) \supset (p \supset q)]$$

Now by using Exportation (Section 10–8), we get

$$[(\text{Premisses}) \supset (p \supset q)] \equiv\!=\!= [(\text{Premisses} \cdot p) \supset q]$$

The right-hand member of the interchange expression is the **alf** of an argument form in which there is one premiss *in addition to* those of the original argument, namely, (p), and in which the conclusion is q.   In other words, given an argument with a conditional or hypothetical as its conclusion, we may take up among the premisses the antecedent of the conditional, leaving the consequent as the conclusion.

Form A		*Form B*
[Original Premisses]	becomes	[Original Premisses]
		[Additional Premiss (p)]
Hence, $[p \supset q]$		Hence, $[q]$

For example, the argument

John is not a good writer or was ill when he wrote this essay.
John was not ill when he wrote this essay or his efforts
on it were repeatedly interrupted.

Therefore, if John is a good writer, then his efforts on
this essay were repeatedly interrupted.

with the form

Form A
1. $(g' + i)$
2. $(i' + e)$

Hence, $(g \supset e)$

becomes an argument with the form

Form B
1. $(g' + i)$
2. $(i' + e)$
3. (g)

Hence, (e)

If we can produce a proof of validity for Form B, we take it to be a proof of validity for Form A.

Another way to express the procedure involved here is to say that, in addition to the original premisses, we make an extra assumption (which is the assertion of the antecedent of the conditional in the conclusion). Taking this assumption along with the premisses, we try to infer from it the consequent of the conditional in the conclusion. If we can do so, we have shown that the assumption (antecedent) implies the consequent, which is precisely what the conclusion asserts; that is, we have proved the conclusion.

Let us use as an example the argument

Robert is not an artist or he is an engineer.
Robert is not an engineer or he is a radiologist.
Hence, if Robert is an artist, he is a radiologist.

The form of the argument is

$$1.\ (a' + e)$$
$$2.\ (e' + r) \qquad\qquad /(a \supset r)$$

Following the procedure suggested immediately above, we now write

$$3.\ (a) \quad \text{Assumption} \quad /(r)$$

noting that (a) is taken as an assumption and that we now wish to try to deduce from it r. Proceeding as earlier, we get

$$4.\ (e) \qquad\qquad \text{D.S., 1, 3}$$
$$5.\ (r) \qquad\qquad \text{D.S., 2, 4}$$

We have now deduced r *on the basis of* the assumption (a). We end the scope of the assumption here; that is, we terminate the use of the assumption. Consequently, we write one final step, namely,

$$6.\ (a \supset r) \qquad\qquad \text{C.P., 3–5}$$

We join the assumption (a) to the result deduced, r, by $\supset$ and write C.P., indicating the use of the method of conditional proof (which runs from step 3 through step 5).

For a final illustration, consider the argument form

$$1.\ (lh')'$$
$$2.\ (h' + p)$$
$$3.\ (e \supset p') \qquad /(l \supset e')$$

Following the procedure outlined, the steps of the proof are as follows. The student should supply the justification for each step.

$$4.\ (l)$$
$$5.\ (l' + h)$$
$$6.\ (h)$$
$$7.\ (p)$$
$$8.\ (e')$$
$$9.\ (l \supset e')$$

EXERCISE SET 12–5

For the following arguments, give either a proof of invalidity or a conditional proof of validity.

a. If the television receiver is not operating properly, then one of the tubes is faulty. If the television receiver's screen shows a clear picture, then an audio tube is responsible for the difficulty. If one of the tubes is faulty and an audio tube is responsible for the difficulty, then the cost of repair is low. Consequently, if the television receiver is not operating properly and the receiver's screen shows a clear picture, then the cost of repair is low.

b. If Spinoza is a Jew, then he is a scholar in Old Testament studies. If Spinoza is a convert to Christianity, he is a scholar in Old Testament studies. Therefore, if Spinoza's not being a Jew implies that he is a convert to Christianity, then he is a scholar in Old Testament studies.

c. If π is a rational number, then it is the ratio c/d. If π is not a rational number, then it is the value of $\sqrt{2}$. Hence, if π is neither rational nor irrational, it is the value of $\sqrt{2}$.

d. If the cafeteria is closed and its alarm system is broken, it is a good mark for a thief. If it is a good mark for a thief, then the absence of a guard implies that it will be broken into. Therefore, if the cafeteria is closed, then if the alarm system is broken and there is no guard present, it will be broken into.

e. If the law forbids polygamy, then John has committed a crime and been judged guilty of it. If the law forbids arson, then John has committed another crime and been acquitted of it. Consequently, if the law forbids polygamy or arson, John has committed one crime or another.

f. Linda is not a secretary. Hence, if Linda is a secretary and a pilot and a radio operator, she is intelligent.

g. Linda is a secretary. Hence, if Linda is a secretary and a pilot and a radio operator, she is intelligent.

h. Susan is a mathematician and a mother, although she is not married. If she is a mathematician or a mother, she is unreasonable. If she is unreasonable or emotional, then she is a mother or not a mathematician. Hence, Susan is married or she is a mother.

i. If Margaret is not a native of Germany, then she is not able to speak German and Hungarian. If she is a native of Germany, then she is able to speak German and French. Consequently, if she is a native of Germany if and only if she is able to speak German, then she is able to speak Hungarian and French.

j. Jesus is not divine, or his message being radical implies that if he is sincere he is deceived. The message is radical. It cannot both be that he is sincere and not insane. Hence, Jesus is not divine or he is deceived.

RECOMMENDED FOR FURTHER STUDY

For a presentation of certain topics of our Chapter 12 in terms of Boolean relations and operations, the student may refer to H. N. Lee's *Symbolic Logic* (New York, 1961), Chapters 8 and 9.

A somewhat more advanced discussion of certain methods of proof can be found in J. M. Anderson and H. W. Johnstone's *Natural Deduction* (Belmont, Calif., 1962), Chapters 2, 3, and 4; and in C. I. Lewis and C. H. Langford's *Symbolic Logic* (2d ed.; New York, 1959), Chapter 7.

A. N. Prior's *Formal Logic* (2d ed.; Oxford, 1962), Part I, Chapters 1 and 2, discusses the statement calculus and some methods of proof. It makes use of the Polish notation (*Łukasiewicz*).

We can also recommend the presentations in H. Reichenbach's *Elements of Symbolic Logic* (New York, 1947), Chapter 2; and in Alice Ambrose and Morris Lazerowitz's *Fundamentals of Symbolic Logic* (rev. ed.; New York, 1962), Chapters 6 and 7.

13

Statement Functions and Arguments

13–1. SINGULAR AND CATEGORICAL STATEMENTS

The discussion of logic from Chapter 6 through Chapter 12 has been an examination of one division of modern logic, the *statement calculus*. It is called the *statement calculus*, since in it we handle statements *as units*. Thus, the statement "John is a lawyer," symbolized by p, was examined in relation to other statements, q, r, and s. We did not go into a study of the internal structure of "John is a lawyer." Our apparatus permits us to prove the validity of many arguments in which we deal with statements as units.

There are arguments, however, that cannot be analyzed by the procedures we have thus far advanced. For example, the syllogistic argument

> All lawyers are eloquent.
> James is a lawyer.
> ―――――――――――――
> Hence, James is eloquent.

could be symbolized so that its form is displayed as

> 1. (p)
> 2. (q)
> ―――――――
> Hence, (r)

The **alf** for the argument form is $[(pq) \supset (r)]$. Whether we use a truth-table, the shorter truth-table method, the algebraic method, or the axiomatic proof of validity, the argument is shown to be invalid. Intuitively, however, it seems valid. The methods we have at hand take no account of the fact that the statements in the two premises are related by the common middle term, "lawyer." This is a feature of the structure of the argument that we neglect when we deal with statements only as units.

If we devise additional symbols and rules, we can display the form of the argument in such a way as to acknowledge relationships that were unexpressed by our earlier symbols and rules. In this way, we open a whole new field of logical study and analysis and put ourselves in a position to give proofs of validity and invalidity for many new kinds of arguments. This division of logic is termed the *functional calculus*.

The basic natures of the statements that will be involved in the kinds of arguments we will shortly encounter are indicated by these examples:

(I)   Betty is a secretary.
(II) Joan is not a mother.
(III) All women are lovely.
(IV) No friend is discourteous.

In statements (II) and (IV), logical negation appears. Through Chapter 12, we used the prime mark (′) as a symbol for this operation. Because of certain features of the new symbolism we are about to adopt, the use of this mark sometimes becomes awkward. From here on, for convenience, we will use the *tilde* ($\sim$) for negation. Thus, the negation of p is now written $\sim p$.

Statements of types (I) and (II) have in their subject position the names of individuals—"Betty" and "Joan." In English, an individual is generally denoted by a *proper name* (Betty) or by a *descriptive phrase* such as, "The writer of the Greek comedy, *The Clouds*" (Aristophanes). These statements generally have in their predicate position a *common name* (mother), an *adjective* (irritable), or a *verb* (runs); that is, some term that expresses a property or properties ~~possessed by the subject~~. Statements of types (I) and (II) are called, as we have indicated in Chapter 6, *singular statements*. In type (I), the property of being a secretary is *affirmed* as applying to Betty. In type (II), the property of being a mother is *denied* of Joan. These two types are, respectively, the *singular affirmative* and *singular negative categorical statements* we discussed in Chapter 6.

In order to symbolize such statements, we use capital letters, such as A, B, C, . . . , to denote properties, and lower-case letters, such as a, b, c, . . . , to denote individuals. The lower-case letters are employed as subscripts on the capitals. Thus, for the two statements given above, we write: (I), S_b; (II), $\sim M_j$. Similarly, "The writer of the Greek comedy, *The Clouds*, is vicious" is symbolized by V_w. "Elston is generous" becomes G_e, and "Harry is not a pilot" becomes $\sim P_h$.

The student will remember that the singular statements of types (I) and (II) affirm and deny, respectively, group or set membership. "Betty is a secretary" means that Betty is a member of the group or set of secretaries. "Joan is not a mother" means that Joan is affirmed not to be a member of the group or set of mothers. Using the symbol "ϵ" to denote "is a member of," we can also symbolize (I) and (II) by $(b \; \epsilon \; S)$ and $\sim(j \; \epsilon \; M)$.

These singular statements, symbolized in the manner we have indicated, can be related by the logical connectives with which we are familiar. Given the following symbols

Symbol	Meaning
a	Alexander
b	Betty
c	Carl
P	pilot
M	mother
B	blue-eyed

the following logical formulas express the statements listed beside them:

Formula	Statement
$(P_a B_a)$	Alexander is a blue-eyed pilot.
$(P_a \sim M_b)$	Alexander is a pilot and Betty is not a mother.
$(P_c + B_c)$	Carl is a pilot or he is blue-eyed.
$(M_b \supset P_a)$	If Betty is a mother, then Alexander is a pilot.
$\sim(P_c M_c)$	Carl is not both a pilot and a mother.

These five formulas can also be expressed thus:

$$[(a \in P) \cdot (a \in B)]$$
$$[(a \in P) \cdot \sim(b \in M)]$$
$$[(c \in P) + (c \in B)]$$
$$[(b \in M) \supset (a \in P)]$$
$$\sim[(c \in P) \cdot (c \in M)]$$

In summary, singular statements affirm or deny group or set membership, or affirm or deny properties of individuals. From them, we can construct compound statements.

What can we say about statements of types (III) and (IV), such as "All women are lovely" and "No friend is discourteous"? In Chapter 6, we indicated that such categorical statements as "All women are lovely" assert that all members of the group or set of women are *included in* the group or set of lovely things. Said another way, the statement affirms that *any arbitrarily selected* woman is lovely. We need, therefore, symbols for arbitrarily selected individuals. Let the Greek letters α, β, and γ serve for this purpose. Thus, while a, b, and c denote some *particular individuals*, α, β, and γ designate any *arbitrarily chosen individuals*.

With this notation, the statements of types (III) and (IV) can be symbolized this way:

(III) $(W_\alpha \supset L_\alpha)$, read "If α is a woman, then α is lovely."

(IV) $(F_\beta \supset \sim D_\beta)$, read "If β is a friend, then β is not discourteous."

In both forms, α and β are arbitrarily selected individuals. Type (III), of course, is a *universal affirmative* statement; and type (IV) is a *universal negative* statement.

We previously indicated (Chapter 6) that the universal affirmative and universal negative statements can also be interpreted as statements of *group* or *set inclusion* and *group* or *set exclusion*. Thus, "All women are lovely" means that the group or set of women is included in the group or set of lovely things. "No friend is discourteous" means that the group or set of friends is excluded from the group or set of discourteous persons. Using the ε-notation, we can, therefore, write

(III) $[(\alpha \epsilon W) \supset (\alpha \epsilon L)]$, read "If any arbitrarily selected individual, α, is in the group 'women,' then the arbitrarily selected individual, α, is included in the set of lovely things."

(IV) $[(\beta \epsilon F) \supset \sim(\beta \epsilon D)]$, read "If any arbitrarily selected individual, β, is in the group 'friends,' then the arbitrarily selected individual, β, is not included in the group of discourteous persons."

In summary, we now have the symbols

Particular Individuals	*Arbitrarily Selected Individuals*
$a, b, c, d, \ldots$	$\alpha, \beta, \gamma, \ldots$

Properties or Groups
$A, B, C, \ldots$

that, along with conventions for using them and the basic logical connectives, permit us to symbolize the internal structures of statements.

13–2. STATEMENT FUNCTIONS

Let us examine again a singular statement such as "Harold is a lawyer," which has the form L_h. The statements "James is a lawyer," "William is a lawyer," etc., have the forms L_j, L_w, $\ldots$ These statements have the same form except for the subject name. Let us now replace the subject name by a variable, x. This gives L_x. The variable x takes on values, which in this case are individual names. The *domain* of x is a group of individuals. While L_j is true or false and is therefore a statement, L_x is not reckoned as true or false, because we do not know for which individual x stands. We call L_x a *statement function*.

The situation just described is similar to this one in algebra. We count $2 = 4/2$ to be true and $3 = 4/2$ to be false. But the expression $2x = 4$ is itself neither true nor false. We say that $2x = 4$ is *a function of* x. For some values of x, such as $2, 6/3$, or $8/4$, the function becomes a true statement; but for other values of x, such as $3, 4$, or 5, the function becomes a false statement.

The statement function, L_x, generates true statements for some values of x, such as Abraham Lincoln, and false statements for other values of x, such as John L. Sullivan. Thus, by *substitution* we produce statements from statement functions.

AL was a lawyer, but is he a l.? Something on tense?

In the case of any statement function, the variable x (or y, or z, . . .) takes on values in a designated domain. For L_x, presumably the intended domain of x is human persons. Sometimes the domain of a function is specifically described, as when in mathematics we read, "In the domain of positive integers, $ax = xa$." In the larger number of cases, however, the intended domain of the variable(s) must be inferred from the context. If one attempts to substitute for x a value from outside the domain, he gets a meaningless expression, such as "NaCl is a lawyer." If x takes on values within the designated or intended domain, the statement function yields true statements or false statements. Since x in L_x may take on any value in the domain (of significance), it is called a *free variable* or an *unbound variable*.

Since L_x yields true statements for some values of x and false statements for other values of x, the *range of the function* comprises two values: true (1), and false (0). The statement functions "x is a mechanic," "x is red-haired," and "x is a teacher" have the range $\{1, 0\}$. Some functions will have the range $\{1\}$, such as "x is a biped," where the domain of x is human persons. Other functions have the range $\{0\}$, such as "$x^2 = 2$," where the domain of x is the positive integers.

We can, of course, have compound statement functions, such as $(M_x T_x)$, where M represents the property of being a mathematician and T represents the property of being a teacher. In $(M_x T_x)$, the domain of x is, we judge, human persons. The range is $\{1, 0\}$; for some persons are mathematicians and teachers, while others are not both at the same time. If E represents the property of being an even number and O represents the property of being an odd number, then $(E_x O_x)$, where the domain is the integers, has the range $\{0\}$, while $(E_x + O_x)$ has the range $\{1\}$.

Now let us relate the concept of statement function to the universal categorical statements. Instead of writing $(W_a \supset L_a)$ or $(W_\alpha \supset L_\alpha)$, we write a similar expression with a variable x in the position held by a or α: $(W_x \supset L_x)$. This last expression is read, "If x is W, then x is L." Interpreting W as representing the set of women and L as standing for the set of lovely beings, we have a statement function. The domain of x is judged to be human persons. Similarly, $(F_y \supset \sim D_y)$ is a statement function with free variable y, where y has as its domain human persons, F stands for the set of friends, and D represents the set of discourteous beings.

By substituting values for the variables, we get statements such as

$x = a$: If Alice is a woman, Alice is lovely.
$x = b$: If Betty is a woman, Betty is lovely.
$y = a$: If Alice is a friend, Alice is not discourteous.
$y = h$: If Harry is a friend, Harry is not discourteous.

Presumably some of these statements are true, while others are false. Therefore, the range for both $(W_x \supset L_x)$ and $(F_y \supset {\sim}D_y)$ is $\{1, 0\}$.

Let the domain of x be the positive integers. Consider the statement function $[(2 = 3) \supset (x = 7)]$. Since the antecedent of the conditional $(2 = 3)$ is always false, the statement function will under any substitution for x yield a true statement. Thus, the range of this function is $\{1\}$.

The statement functions used thus far have specified a particular property or set of things, such as $(W_x \supset L_x)$ in which W stands for the group or set of women, and L symbolizes the set of lovely beings. Symbols can be used to designate any property or set. Usually, Φ and Ψ have been used to stand for unspecified properties or sets in statement functions. Thus, Φ or Ψ can have in the subscript position three sorts of things:

Particular Individuals: $a, b, c, \ldots : (\Phi_a, \Phi_b, \Phi_c)$.
Arbitrarily Selected Individuals: $\alpha, \beta, \gamma, \ldots : (\Phi_\alpha, \Phi_\beta, \Phi_\gamma)$.
Variables: $x, y, z, \ldots : (\Phi_x, \Phi_y, \Phi_z)$.

Given a statement function, such as Φ_x, $(\Phi_x\Psi_x)$, $(\Phi_x + \Psi_x)$, or $(\Phi_x \supset {\sim}\Psi_x)$, we can produce statements from these functions by substitution, assigning values to the variable x from its domain of significance. Every statement function generates a family of statements. The range of a statement function will be either $\{0, 1\}$, or $\{0\}$, or $\{1\}$.

13–3. QUANTIFIERS AND GENERAL STATEMENTS

In Section 13–2, we introduced the concept of a statement function. The expression "x is a novelist" is such a function. It is not a statement, for the function itself, containing the free variable x, cannot be said to be true or false. When the variable takes on a specific value, such as $x =$ A. J. Ayer, then the statement function yields the statement "A. J. Ayer is a novelist," which is false.

There is another very important way, besides substitution, by which to produce statements from statement functions. This is by employing *quantifiers*. One such quantifier is the phrase "for all values of x," which we adjoin to the statement function. For x, a domain is either explicitly stated or understood. Doing this, we get

For all values of x, x is a novelist.

This is a statement and it is false. Assuming x refers to the domain of humans, it asserts that everybody is a novelist. "For all values of x" is symbolized by "$(\forall_x)$"; and since it refers to all values of a domain, it is called the *universal quantifier*. If N stands for a novelist, the statement above is represented by

$$(\forall_x)N_x$$

on p. 167 capital letters were to denote properties

The x in this statement is a *bound* variable, not a free variable. It is bound by the *universal quantifier*, $(\forall_x)$. Or, expressed another way, we say that x in the statement function N_x falls within the scope of the quantifier $(\forall_x)$.

"For all values of x, x is not a prophet" ("Nobody is a prophet") can be symbolized by $(\forall_x) \sim P_x$. "Nobody flies" can be designated by $(\forall_x) \sim F_x$. "For all values of x, x is a male and x is a biped" is represented by $(\forall_x)(M_x B_x)$. "Everyone is religious or emotional" can be expressed by $(\forall_x)(R_x + E_x)$.

We can adjoin the $(\forall_x)$ to a function such as $(W_x \supset L_x)$ as well as to one such as N_x. Thus, $(\forall_x)(W_x \supset L_x)$ is "For all values of x, if x is a woman, then x is lovely"; that is, "All women are lovely." $(\forall_x)$ $(W_x \supset L_x)$ is a statement, a universal affirmative statement. Similarly, $(\forall_x)(F_x \supset \sim D_x)$ is the symbolic form of the statement, "No friend is discourteous."

The statements

$$(\forall_x)\Phi_x$$
$$(\forall_x)(\Phi_x \supset \Psi_x)$$
$$(\forall_x)(\Phi_x \supset \sim\Psi_x)$$

are called *general statements*; and they are produced from statement functions by generalization (achieved by adjoining the quantifier). We have now succeeded in symbolizing statements of types (III) and (IV) in Section 13–1.

Now we must do a similar thing for statements of types (I) and (II) in Section 13–1. Those statements were ones such as could be generated from statement functions like "x is a golfer" and "x is not a mechanic." Instead of substituting individual names for x, we adjoin the quantifier, "There is an x such that," symbolized by "$(\exists_x)$." As a result, we have

$(\exists_x)G_x$, "There is an x such that x is a golfer," and
$(\exists_x) \sim M_x$, "There is an x such that x is not a mechanic."

These are called *existential statements*, and the quantifier is known as the *existential quantifier*. But they are general statements, for they mean, respectively, "*Someone* is a golfer" and "*Someone* is not a mechanic." Their sense is different from "Harry is a golfer" and "Joe is not a mechanic." The difference is that between a situation in which you can say "John stole my pen" and one in which you can say "Someone stole my pen." Symbolically, the latter are S_j and $(\exists_x)S_x$, respectively. The statements $(\exists_x)\Phi_x$ and $(\exists_x)\sim\Psi_x$ are true or false. The variable x is a bound variable. A domain is either explicitly stated or understood for x.

The statement "There is an x such that x is not liquid" can be symbolized by $(\exists_x)\sim L_x$. Now consider, "There is not an x such that x is not a liquid." The student should study these two statements. Let him symbolize the second one and clearly express the difference between the two. Let him also symbolize "It is not the case that everybody is rich," "It is not the case that nobody is sober," and "There is not an x such that x is liquid."

EXERCISE SET 13–3

A

1. Symbolize the following statements by the use of statement functions and quantifiers, choosing appropriate symbols for the sets or properties mentioned.

   a. Everything is spiritual.

   b. All spiritual beings are wise.

   c. Something is metallic.

   d. Some metal is liquid.

   e. No fox is a bird.

   f. Unless a man is a mathematician, he fails to understand Plato.

   g. Only poets are inspired.

   h. Nothing is material.

   i. Olives and onions are tasty.

   j. Every rational creature who can speak is sane.

   k. If a man is a Christian or a Jew, he is a monotheist.

   l. Some man is not a lawyer and not a mechanic.

   m. It is not the case that there is no blackbird that is not black.

   n. All students but Freshmen are admitted.

   o. A merchant is harassed, if he has employees.

   p. Only physicists and chemists understand the theory of relativity.

   q. All integers are rational numbers, and some real numbers are not integers.

   r. A number is prime, if and only if it is odd.

   s. No historian is reliable, if he does not follow the theories of Toynbee.

   t. There is a man such that, if he is a philosopher, he is insane.

   u. Some insane man is a philosopher.

   v. If a compound contains carbon or hydrogen, then it is not radioactive.

   w. If a man writes a novel, then if he sells many copies, he is both happy and rich.

   x. Nothing is both animate and not sentient.

   y. If someone took my pen, then everybody is a thief.

   z. If Aristotle is just, everybody is just.

2. Express in English, choosing meanings for the properties A, B, C, . . . :

a. $(\forall_x)A_x$

b. $\sim(\forall_x)\sim B_x$

c. $[(\exists_y)C_y \cdot (\exists_z)D_z]$

d. $(\forall_s)\sim E_s$

e. $[(\exists_y)A_y \cdot \sim(\forall_y)\sim A_y]$

f. $\sim(\exists_z)\sim F_z$

g. $[(\forall_r)C_r \cdot \sim(\forall_t)D_t]$

h. $[(\forall_x)A_x \cdot (\forall_y)B_y]$

i. $(\exists_z)(B_z D_z)$

j. $(\forall_x)(A_x \sim B_x)$

k. B_x

l. $(C_y D_z)$

m. $(C_z + E_x)$

n. $(\sim E_x \sim F_x)$

o. $[A_x \cdot (\exists_y)B_y]$

B

3. Are these statements or statement functions?

a. Somebody is a murderer.

b. If everybody is religious, someone is religious.

c. If everybody is sane, then x is sane.

d. $(\exists_x)(P_x \sim C_x)$

e. $(\forall_x)(A_y \supset P_x)$

f. $(\forall_y)(A_x \supset P_x)$

g. $(\exists_x)G_x$

h. $(\forall_x)(\forall_y)[(xy) = (yx)]$

i. $(\exists_x)(\forall_y)[(xy) = (yx) = (y)]$

j. Plato is a politician.

k. Aristotle is a scientist, and there is no philosopher.

l. $(\forall_x)[(xz) = (x)]$

m. If z is a physicist, z is compassionate.

n. Elmer is a man who entered the ministry.

o. _____ was the philosopher who wrote *Metaphysics*.

p. Pittsburgh is between _____ and New York City.

q. $x/y = z$.

4. Making a judgment about the domain of these functions, what are their ranges?

a. $(p \supset q)$

b. $[(p) + (pq)]$

c. (pp')

d. $\{[(p \supset q) \cdot (q')] \supset [p']\}$

e. $\{[(r') + (rs)] + [r]\}$

f. $\{[(p \supset q) \cdot (q \supset r)] \supset [r \supset p]\}$

g. x is an integer and x is a square root of 2.

h. x is a male person or x is a female person.

i. x is a radioactive compound and x is a carbon compound.

j. If x is a human person, then x is a lawyer.

k. x is not a rational number and not a square number.

l. If x is located below the earth's crust and above the earth's crust, x is lighter than air.

13–4.   QUANTIFIER NEGATION

Using our new notations to express singular and categorical statements [types (I), (II), (III), (IV), discussed in Section 13–1], we write four fundamental general statements that will be used extensively in analyzing arguments.   Their symbolic expression is followed by a translation into English.

Universal Affirmative: $(\forall_x)(\Phi_x \supset \Psi_x)$—"All Φ's are Ψ's," or "For all values of x, if x is Φ, then x is Ψ."

Universal Negative: $(\forall_x)(\Phi_x \supset \sim\Psi_x)$—"No Φ is a Ψ," or "For all values of x, if x is Φ, then x is not Ψ."

Existential Affirmative: $(\exists_x)(\Phi_x\Psi_x)$—"Some Φ is Ψ," or "There is an x such that x is Φ and x is Ψ."

Existential Negative: $(\exists_x)(\Phi_x\sim\Psi_x)$—"Some Φ is not Ψ," or "There is an x such that x is Φ and x is not Ψ."

The word "some" that is used means *at least one and possibly all.* Thus, $(\exists_x)(M_xL_x)$ may mean "One metal, at least, is liquid," "Four metals are liquid," "The majority of metals are liquid," or, possibly, "Every metal is liquid."   The student must carefully note that the $(\exists_x)$ establishes an *indefinite reference* to at least one or more individuals.

A special characteristic of the universal affirmative and negative statements should be noted.   Suppose the set Φ from which the values of x are to be chosen is an empty set, such as "four-headed foxes" or "integral square roots of 2."   Then there are no true substitution instances (all are false) for the function Φ_x.   Since Φ_x is the antecedent of a hypothetical or conditional in both the universal affirmative and negative statements, then the hypothetical or conditional statement is in all cases true.   Universal statements of this kind about empty sets are always true.   For example, "All integral square roots of 2 are prime numbers" is a true statement.   Conversely, if we know simply that a statement $(\forall_x)(\Phi_x \supset \Psi_x)$ is true, we cannot tell whether or not there are individuals with properties Φ and Ψ.   The universal statements are, therefore, hypothetical.

In contrast, existential affirmative and negative statements, using the quantifier $(\exists_x)$, *do assert that there is at least one individual or particular thing* with (or without) the properties Φ and Ψ.   The statement $(\exists_x)$

(M_xL_x) may be false, but it asserts that there is an individual or particular entity that is metallic and liquid. On the other hand, $(\boldsymbol{\forall}_x)(M_x \supset L_x)$ does not assert that there is an entity of any kind—it says *if* an x is metallic, *then* it is liquid.

Certain relations obtain among universal and existential statements. We will examine some of these relations. $(\boldsymbol{\forall}_x)(\Phi_x \supset \Psi_x)$ means that, if any x has the property Φ, it has the property Ψ (all Φ's are Ψ's). $(\boldsymbol{\exists}_x)$ $(\Phi_x \sim \Psi_x)$ says that there is an x that has the property Φ but not the property Ψ. If it is true that all metals are liquid, then it is false that there is a metal that is not liquid, and vice versa. The two assertions are contradictory. Thus, we write

$$(\boldsymbol{\forall}_x)(\Phi_x \supset \Psi_x) \; \underline{\quad\quad} \; \sim(\boldsymbol{\exists}_x)(\Phi_x \sim \Psi_x)$$

$$\sim(\boldsymbol{\forall}_x)(\Phi_x \supset \Psi_x) \; \underline{\quad\quad} \; (\boldsymbol{\exists}_x)(\Phi_x \sim \Psi_x)$$

Similarly, $(\boldsymbol{\forall}_x)(\Phi_x \supset \sim\Psi_x)$ means that, if any x has the property Φ, it does not have the property Ψ (no Φ is a Ψ). But, $(\boldsymbol{\exists}_x)(\Phi_x\Psi_x)$ asserts that there is an x that has both properties. If it is true that no odd integer is divisible by 2, then it is false that some odd integer is divisible by 2, and vice versa. We have, then,

$$(\boldsymbol{\forall}_x)(\Phi_x \supset \sim\Psi_x) \; \underline{\quad\quad} \; \sim(\boldsymbol{\exists}_x)(\Phi_x\Psi_x)$$

and

$$\sim(\boldsymbol{\forall}_x)(\Phi_x \supset \sim\Psi_x) \; \underline{\quad\quad} \; (\boldsymbol{\exists}_x)(\Phi_x\Psi_x)$$

These relationships will be denoted by **Q.N.**, which abbreviates *quantifier negation*.

Since the formulas expressing **Q.N.** are interchange expressions, we may substitute the statement on the one side of the interchange sign for the one on the other side. For example, "For all values of x, if x is an elephant, then x is a mammal" can be replaced by "It is not the case that there is an x such that x is an elephant and not a mammal." "Some doctor is not intemperate" can be replaced by "It is not the case that all doctors are intemperate." Similarly, "Some metal is liquid" is interchangeable with "It is not the case that no metal is liquid." In this manner, any existential statement (of the type under consideration) can be expressed in universal terms. And any universal statement (of the type under consideration) can be expressed in existential terms.

The four formulas designated by **Q.N.** will be viewed and used as the interchange expressions in the reference list in Section 10–8. We will need them in proving the validity of arguments that contain quantified statements.

EXERCISE SET 13–4

1. Produce the statement in symbolic form that contradicts:

a. $(\forall_x)(B_x \supset \sim C_x)$

b. $\sim(\exists_x)(D_xE_x)$

c. $\sim(\forall_x)\sim(G_x \supset H_x)$

d. $(\exists_x)K_x$

e. $\sim(\exists_x)\sim(J_xK_x)$

f. $\sim(\forall_x)L_x$

g. $(\exists_x)(P_x\sim M_x)$

h. $(\forall_x)[(S_x) \supset (E_xH_x)]$

i. $(\forall_x)[(P_xS_x) \supset (B_x)]$

j. $(\forall_x)(\Phi_x \supset C \Psi_x)$

2. Produce in English the statement that contradicts:

a. No fox is an elephant.

b. Everything has mass.

c. There is no golden mountain.

d. Someone is a teacher and a preacher.

e. Everything that is liquid is acid.

f. A triangle is equilateral, if and only if it is equiangular.

g. Some mechanic is not a pilot.

h. Every writer is a poet, if he writes in verse.

i. Every politician is a statesman, unless he is expedient.

j. There is a book and it is printed in movable type and it is over 600 years old.

13–5.   RULES OF INFERENCE

In Chapters 11 and 12, we discussed how one can make valid inferences and prove the validity of arguments by making use of certain simple valid argument forms. These were listed in Section 10–8. The simple valid argument forms are *rules of inference*. Given $(p \supset q)$ and (p) as asserted, *modus ponens* is a rule by which we assert q. Using the axiomatic method of proof described in Section 12–4, we might at some point in a proof sequence have steps 7 and 8, thus,

$$7. \ (a' + b)$$
$$8. \ (a)$$

In step 9, therefore, we write

$$9. \ (b) \qquad \text{D.S., 7, 8}$$

Here we are using D.S. as a rule for making the inference from steps **7** and 8, considered together, to step 9.

We shall continue to use these rules of inference. When we deal with arguments involving quantified statements, however, we need four additional rules of inference.   Why is this so?   Consider the argument

> No German is a philosopher.
> All mathematicians are Germans.
>
> Hence, no mathematician is a philosopher.

With our apparatus of functions and quantifiers, we can now express symbolically the form of this argument, thus,

1. $(\forall x)(G_x \supset \sim P_x)$
2. $(\forall x)(M_x \supset G_x)$ $/(\forall x)(M_x \supset \sim P_x)$

Intuitively, we judge the argument to be valid.   Moreover, we may argue that from $(G_x \supset \sim P_x)$ and $(M_x \supset G_x)$ we can infer by H.S. $(M_x \supset \sim P_x)$.   Such an argument overlooks that these expressions are quantified (and the quantifier tells us, to put it simply, how many of each class we are talking about).   In $(\forall x)(G_x \supset \sim P_x)$, the quantifier $(\forall x)$ binds *both* occurrences of the variable x.   This means that the formula $(\forall x)(G_x \supset \sim P_x)$ is a *unit* and cannot itself be considered a compound statement, $[(G_x) \supset (\sim P_x)]$.   Hence, H.S. cannot be employed as just suggested. We need, therefore, some rules for modifying or transforming the quantified universal and existential statements so that they can be displayed as compound statements.   Then we can use the simple argument forms (rules of inference) listed in Section 10–8.   The four new rules of inference referred to will achieve this for us.

Suppose we have a universally quantified expression given.   Let us take a simple example, $(\forall x)\Phi_x$.   The variable x may take on any value in the domain—all substitution instances are true, assuming $(\forall x)\Phi_x$ is asserted.   We can, therefore, infer from $(\forall x)\Phi_x$ the statement Φ_α, where α is any *arbitrarily selected individual* in the domain.   It is also acceptable to infer from $(\forall x)\Phi_x$ a substitution instance in which x takes on some particular value, a, b, . . .   This rule of inference is called *universal instantiation* (**U.I.**).   We can write it thus:

$$\textbf{U.I.} \qquad \frac{(\forall x)\Phi_x}{\text{Hence, } \Phi_\alpha} \quad \text{or} \quad \frac{(\forall x)\Phi_x}{\text{Hence, } \Phi_a}$$

For example, from $(\forall x)(B_x \supset C_x D_x)$, we can infer

$$(B_\alpha \supset C_\alpha D_\alpha) \qquad (B_a \supset C_a D_a)$$
$$(B_\beta \supset C_\beta D_\beta) \qquad (B_b \supset C_b D_b)$$
$$(B_\gamma \supset C_\gamma D_\gamma) \qquad (B_c \supset C_c D_c)$$
$$. \ . \ . \ . \ . \ . \qquad . \ . \ . \ . \ . \ .$$

These substitution instances that result from **U.I.** are compound statements to which the interchange expressions and elementary argument forms of Section 10–8 are applicable.

Restrictions? (No nesting of quantifiers) — but
no polyadic predicates
no def of wff either)

nested quantifiers mentioned
but not stated on p. 195

STATEMENT FUNCTIONS AND ARGUMENTS   179

Second, consider the statement Φ_α (*not, however,* Φ_a). Since α denotes any arbitrarily selected individual in the domain, we stipulate that from Φ_α we can infer $(\mathbf{V}_x)\Phi_x$. This rule is called *universal generalization* (**U.G.**).

$$\text{U.G.} \qquad \frac{\Phi_\alpha}{\text{Hence, } (\mathbf{V}_x)\Phi_x}$$

For example, from "*Any* planet travels around the sun in an elliptical orbit," we can infer "*All* planets travel around the sun in elliptical orbits." But, inasmuch as a denotes a particular individual, *we cannot* infer $(\mathbf{V}_x)\Phi_x$ from Φ_a. From "Mars travels around the sun in an elliptical orbit," we cannot conclude "All planets travel around the sun in elliptical orbits."

There is, however, a general statement that can be inferred from Φ_a, namely, $(\mathbf{\exists}_x)\Phi_x$. "Mars travels around the sun in an elliptical orbit" can justifiably be restated in the general form, "Some planet travels around the sun in an elliptical orbit." This mode of inference is called *existential generalization* (**E.G.**). Of course, if we had Φ_α, we can similarly infer $(\mathbf{\exists}_x)\Phi_x$.

$$\text{E.G.} \qquad \frac{\Phi_a}{\text{Hence, } (\mathbf{\exists}_x)\Phi_x} \qquad \text{or} \qquad \frac{\Phi_\alpha}{\text{Hence, } (\mathbf{\exists}_x)\Phi_x}$$

Finally, if we are given the statement $(\mathbf{\exists}_x)\Phi_x$, which asserts that there is an x such that x has the property Φ, we can at least conclude Φ_a, where a stands for the "one" individual of the "at least one and maybe all" referred to in the general statement. This rule is called *existential instantiation* (**E.I.**).

$$\text{E.I.} \qquad \text{or} \qquad \frac{(\mathbf{\exists}_x)\Phi_x}{\text{Hence, } \Phi_a}$$

This last rule (**E.I.**) must be used with caution. Suppose the domain about which we are speaking is the class of government officials and we are considering two existential statements:

$(\mathbf{\exists}_x)P_x$, There is (in the set of government officials) a President.

$(\mathbf{\exists}_x)S_x$, There is (in the set of government officials) a Secretary of Agriculture.

We cannot instantiate both existential statements with the same value for x. Otherwise, we would get from $(\mathbf{\exists}_x)P_x$, P_r, and from $(\mathbf{\exists}_x)S_x$, S_r, where r is one individual, say, Franklin D. Roosevelt. The result would be that we would be asserting that Franklin D. Roosevelt is the President and Franklin D. Roosevelt is the Secretary of Agriculture. This may very well be false, even though $(\mathbf{\exists}_x)P_x$ and $(\mathbf{\exists}_x)S_x$ are each true. In order to protect against this error, we stipulate that when two or more existential statements appear in a single argument context and **E.I.** is applied in two or more cases, different values of x (constants) must be used in the several cases of **E.I.**   More generally, in any case of application of **E.I.**, a value must be used for x that has not appeared earlier in the context of the argument.   Thus, using our previous example, $(\exists_x)P_x$ can be existentially instantiated P_r; but in the same argument context, $(\exists_x)S_x$ will be existentially instantiated S_w, or by some other value for x besides r.

13–6.   PROOFS FOR SIMPLE ARGUMENTS INVOLVING QUANTIFIED STATEMENTS

The interchange expressions, **Q.N.**, and the four rules of inference, **U.I.**, **U.G.**, **E.G.**, and **E.I.**, are now added to the principles listed in Section 10–8.   With these additions to our apparatus for giving proofs, we can now use the axiomatic method on arguments that contain statements with the general forms $(\forall_x)\Phi_x$ and $(\exists_x)\Phi_x$.

Consider the argument

> All lawyers are eloquent and courteous.
> Some pilot is a lawyer.
> _____
> Hence, some pilot is courteous.

The argument form, where $L_x = x$ is a lawyer, $E_x = x$ is eloquent, $C_x = x$ is courteous, and $P_x = x$ is a pilot, is

> 1. $(\forall_x)(L_x \supset E_xC_x)$
> 2. $(\exists_x)(P_xL_x)$ $/(\exists_x)(P_xC_x)$

When an argument form possesses both existential premises and universal premises, it is advisable, in light of the *restriction on* **E.I.** described in Section 13–5, to instantiate the existential statements before the universal ones.   Following the axiomatic method of proof outlined in Section 12–4, we proceed in this way:

> 3. (P_aL_a) E.I., 2
> 4. (L_a) Simpl., 3
> 5. $(L_a \supset E_aC_a)$ U.I., 1
> 6. (E_aC_a) M.P., 4, 5
> 7. (C_a) Simpl., 6
> 8. (P_a) Simpl., 3
> 9. (P_aC_a) Conj., 7, 8
> 10. $(\exists_x)(P_xC_x)$ E.G., 9

For a second example, we choose

> No Buddhist believes in the trinity.
> All Christians believe in the trinity.
> If a man is not a Christian, he is not a Methodist.
> _____
> Hence, no Methodist is a Buddhist.

The form of the argument, where $B_x = x$ is a Buddhist, $T_x = x$ believes in the trinity, $C_x = x$ is a Christian, and $M_x = x$ is a Methodist, is

1. $(\mathbf{\forall}_x)(B_x \supset \sim T_x)$
2. $(\mathbf{\forall}_x)(C_x \supset T_x)$
3. $(\mathbf{\forall}_x)(\sim C_x \supset \sim M_x)$ $/(\mathbf{\forall}_x)(M_x \supset \sim B_x)$

The proof is as follows:

4. $(B_\alpha \supset \sim T_\alpha)$ U.I., 1
5. $(C_\alpha \supset T_\alpha)$ U.I., 2
6. $(\sim C_\alpha \supset \sim M_\alpha)$ U.I., 3
7. $(\sim T_\alpha \supset \sim C_\alpha)$ Trans., 5
8. $(B_\alpha \supset \sim C_\alpha)$ H.S., 4, 7
9. $(B_\alpha \supset \sim M_\alpha)$ H.S., 8, 6
10. $(M_\alpha \supset \sim B_\alpha)$ Trans., 9
11. $(\mathbf{\forall}_x)(M_x \supset \sim B_x)$ U.G., 10

The proof of validity for

> Every metal is liquid.
> Some non-liquid is a metal.
> _____
> Hence, all acids are carbon compounds.

is as follows:

1. $(\mathbf{\forall}_x)(M_x \supset L_x)$
2. $(\mathbf{\exists}_x)(\sim L_x M_x)$ $/(\mathbf{\forall}_x)(A_x \supset C_x)$
3. $(\sim L_a M_a)$ E.I., 2
4. $(M_a \supset L_a)$ U.I., 1
5. (M_a) Simpl., 3
6. (L_a) M.P., 4, 5
7. $(\sim L_a)$ Simpl., 3
8. $\{[L_a] + [(\mathbf{\forall}_x)(A_x \supset C_x)]\}$ Add., 6
9. $(\mathbf{\forall}_x)(A_x \supset C_x)$ D.S., 7, 8

The student should state, after a study of this proof, why the argument can be proved valid, even though the conclusion deals with a subject matter seemingly quite different from that of the premisses. He should also express, in a logical formula, his statement about the argument form.

EXERCISE SET 13–6

Construct proofs of validity for these arguments:

a. No college student is able to earn $5,000 per year.   John is a college student. Therefore, John is not able to earn $5,000 per year.

b. If a thing is not liquid, it is not viscous. Oil is viscous. Consequently, it is liquid.

   c. Every philosopher is courteous or compassionate. Some historian is a philosopher. There are no compassionate people. Hence, some historian is courteous.

   d. All automobiles are mechanically defective vehicles. It is not the case that there is a mechanically defective vehicle that is not a low-priced item. Hence, all automobiles are low-priced items.

   e. Apples and oranges are nourishing. Some apple is green. Hence, some green apple is nourishing.

   f. All men die, and Elijah was a man. Therefore, Elijah died.

   g. Some students with ability are failing logic, because all who have passed our admission exams are students with ability, and some who are failing logic have passed our admission exams.

   h. No generous person is dishonest. Susan and Dan are generous. Therefore, Susan is honest.

   i. Since all Texans are proud, and no proud person is unpatriotic, no Texans are unpatriotic.

   j. Some teachers are taking advanced work. Other teachers are taking refresher courses. All teachers must have a teacher's certificate. Hence, some taking advanced work have a teacher's certificate.

   k. Every Sophomore takes the course in English grammar. No one who takes the course in English grammar participates in intramural sports. Hence, no Sophomore participates in intramural sports.

13–7.   THE PROOF OF INVALIDITY

We have presented the technique for proving the validity of simple arguments involving quantified statements. What happens if an argument is advanced that is invalid? Given the form of an argument, we may try for a long time to construct a sequence of steps in order to arrive at the conclusion and do so without success. After repeated failures, we do not know whether (1) the argument is valid but we have been unable to discover a proof sequence, or (2) the argument is invalid and there is no sequence of inferences that constitutes a demonstration. Of course, in the case of a valid argument, there may be a number of different sequences of steps of valid inference that result in the given conclusion. It is desirable to have a proof of invalidity for arguments involving quantifiers similar to that which we used in the statement calculus (Section 12–2). By an adaptation of the technique used in Section 12–2, we can construct a proof of invalidity that will be helpful in analyzing arguments that contain quantified statements.

First, we must say a few more things about substitution instances of general statements. Since $(\forall_x)\Phi_x$ is universal, asserting that the statement holds for every value in the domain, it holds for a, and for b, and for c, etc. In other words, instead of writing $(\forall_x)\Phi_x$, we can write out the enumeration of the instances for which the statement holds:

$$(\mathbf{\forall}_x)\Phi_x \underline{\quad\quad} (\Phi_a \cdot \Phi_b \cdot \Phi_c \cdot \Phi_d \cdot \, \ldots)$$

The quantified statement can be replaced by the *conjunction* of all its substitution instances. Thus, "For all values of x, if x is a single digit integer, then its square is less than 100," $(\mathbf{\forall}_x)(S_x \supset L_x)$, where the domain is prescribed as 1, 2, 3, 4, 5, 6, 7, 8, 9, we have

$$(\mathbf{\forall}_x)(S_x \supset L_x) \underline{\quad\quad} [(S_1 \supset L_1) \cdot (S_2 \supset L_2) \cdot (S_3 \supset L_3) \cdot (S_4 \supset L_4) \cdot$$
$$(S_5 \supset L_5) \cdot (S_6 \supset L_6) \cdot (S_7 \supset L_7) \cdot (S_8 \supset L_8) \cdot (S_9 \supset L_9)]$$

In the case of $(\mathbf{\exists}_x)\Phi_x$, which asserts that *at least* one member of the domain has the property Φ, the general statement can be replaced by the *disjunction* of its substitution instances.

$$(\mathbf{\exists}_x)\Phi_x \underline{\quad\quad} (\Phi_a + \Phi_b + \Phi_c + \, \ldots)$$

For example, consider "There is an x such that x times x equals 9," $(\mathbf{\exists}_x)N_x$, where the domain for x is the three integers, 1, 2, 3.

$$(\mathbf{\exists}_x)N_x \underline{\quad\quad} (N_1 + N_2 + N_3)$$

In attempting to show that an argument is invalid, we are looking for a case in which the premises can be true while the conclusion is false. To achieve this objective, the following steps or procedures should be followed:

(I)   We replace the quantified statements by their substitution instances.

(II) If any individual or singular constant is stated in the argument, it should be employed as a substitution instance throughout the attempt to prove invalidity. Thus, the singular statement "Socrates is a man," (M_s), will provide us with s, which should be used as a substitution instance.

(III) By the use of an individual constant, either mentioned in the argument or selected as a substitution instance, we test for invalidity in a case where the domain has one member.

(IV) If the proof of invalidity fails in (III), we then attempt the proof of invalidity in a case where the domain has two members. This failing, we proceed to try the case where the domain has three members, and so on.

(V)   In constructing the proof of invalidity, singular statements are never expanded. Universal statements are expanded to more than one case by employing conjunction; thus, $[(S_a \supset B_a) \cdot (S_b \supset B_b)]$. Existential statements are expanded to more than one case by employing disjunction; thus, $[(S_a \cdot B_a) + (S_b \cdot B_b)]$.

As a first illustration of these procedures, let us consider

Every politician is irritable.
Every politician is expedient.

Hence, every irritable person is expedient.

The argument form is

1. $(\mathbf{\forall}_x)(P_x \supset I_x)$
2. $(\mathbf{\forall}_x)(P_x \supset E_x)$ $/(\mathbf{\forall}_x)(I_x \supset E_x)$

Assuming a domain of only one member, a, we have

1. $(P_a \supset I_a)$
2. $(P_a \supset E_a)$

Hence, $(I_a \supset E_a)$

Following the procedure of Section 12–2, we discover that with the assignment of truth-values, $I_a = 1$, $E_a = 0$, $P_a = 0$, the premises are both true and the conclusion is false. Thus, we have found an instance, and we need find only one, in which the original argument can have true premises and a false conclusion. It is, therefore, invalid.

For a second example, let us examine this argument:

Some sugar is a carbon compound.
Some hydrogen compound is a carbon compound.

Hence, some sugar is a hydrogen compound.

The argument form is

1. $(\mathbf{\exists}_x)(S_x C_x)$
2. $(\mathbf{\exists}_x)(H_x C_x)$ $/(\mathbf{\exists}_x)(S_x H_x)$

Assuming a domain of only one member, a, we discover that

1. $(S_a C_a)$
2. $(H_a C_a)$

Hence, $(S_a H_a)$

is valid, because we cannot make $(S_a H_a)$ false and both $(S_a C_a)$ and $(H_a C_a)$ true, without assigning contradictory values to some statement. The student should show this in detail. Therefore (Rule IV), we try a domain with two members, a and b. In this case, we have for the substitution instances

1. $[(S_a C_a) + (S_b C_b)]$
2. $[(H_a C_a) + (H_b C_b)]$

Hence, $[(S_a H_a) + (S_b H_b)]$

We make the conclusion false by the assignment $S_a = 1$, $S_b = 0$, $H_a = 0$, and $H_b = 1$. Now, if we choose $C_a = 1$ and $C_b = 1$, the premisses are true, while the conclusion is false. There is a case, then, when the truth of the premisses of the original argument does not force the conclusion to be true. The argument is invalid.

Let us examine one final argument.

> Some philosophers are scientists.
> All scientists understand mathematics.
> Plato was a philosopher.
> _____
> Therefore, Plato understands mathematics.

The argument form is

1. $(\exists x)(P_x S_x)$
2. $(\forall x)(S_x \supset M_x)$
3. (P_p) $/(M_p)$

Assuming a domain of one member and following the procedure in (II), we discover that

1. $(P_p S_p)$
2. $(S_p \supset M_p)$
3. (P_p) $/(M_p)$

appears valid. Assigning $M_p = 0$, we cannot make $(P_p S_p)$ true.

We now proceed to a case where the domain has two members. In this case, we have for the substitution instances

1. $[(P_p S_p) + (P_a S_a)]$
2. $[(S_p \supset M_p) \cdot (S_a \supset M_a)]$
3. $[P_p]$ $/[M_p]$

We make the conclusion false. The premisses are made true if $P_p = 1$, $M_p = 0$, $S_p = 0$, $P_a = 1$, $S_a = 1$, and $M_a = 1$. We have discovered a case where the truth of the premisses does not compel a conclusion that is true. The argument is invalid.

In arguments with existential premisses, it is generally advisable to make an assumption of a domain with as many members as there are existential premisses.

By the application of these procedures, we can decide whether an argument is invalid or not. Between the two techniques—the axiomatic proof of validity, and the proof of invalidity—we can arrive at a sure judgment about the correctness of an argument.

Why not give the upper bound on the size of the universe wh. needs to be considered?

(Bernays - Schönfinkel)

+Leblanc rev Copi (
(Copi p. 85)

EXERCISE SET 13–7

Produce proofs of invalidity wherever possible for the following arguments. If any prove too difficult to symbolize, they should be handled after Section 13–8.

a. $(\forall_x)(G_x \supset \sim H_x)$
   $(\forall_x)(J_x \supset \sim H_x)$ $/ (\forall_x)(G_x \supset \sim J_x)$

b. $(\exists_y)(B_y C_y)$
   $(\exists_z)(B_z D_z)$ $/ (\exists_y)(C_y D_y)$

c. $(\forall_x)(R_x \supset \sim Q_x)$
   $(\exists_y)(S_y \sim Q_y)$ $/ (\exists_z)(R_z S_z)$

d. Every dog is vicious or unpredictable. Some cat is vicious. Some buffalo is unpredictable. Hence, some cat is not a buffalo.

e. Any student of Aristotle becomes a Christian, if his study is profound. A student's study is profound or he is a student of Aristotle. James does not become a Christian. Hence, it is not the case that James's being a student of Aristotle is equivalent to his being a profound student.

f. Any experiment that fails is ill-conceived. If anything is ill-conceived or improperly handled, it fails. Therefore, every experiment is improperly handled.

g. Anybody who breaks a law or is humble is the subject of feelings of inferiority. If a person does not like his neighbors, then he is not humble. Everyone who is the subject of feelings of inferiority is humble. Someone breaks a law. Hence, someone is the subject of feelings of inferiority and does not like his neighbors.

h. All teachers who read their lectures are teachers of great scholarship. All teachers of great scholarship are teachers with a profound respect for the truth. Hence, some teachers with a profound respect for the truth are teachers who read their lectures.

i. No student or professor lacks respect for truth. All criminals and spies lack respect for truth. Therefore, some students are not criminals and spies.

j. Any two men who disagree over whether the pitch was a strike or ball cannot both be wrong. John and James disagree on whether the pitch was a strike or ball. Therefore, John and James cannot both be wrong.

13–8. PROOFS FOR EXTENDED ARGUMENTS INVOLVING QUANTIFIED STATEMENTS

We need no additional apparatus for proving the validity or invalidity of extended or complex arguments. The devices discussed in Sections 13–1 through 13–7 will suffice. The student may have to acquire by practice the facility of handling arguments with many premises or with premises that are complex in structure. The purpose of this section is to give him some examples of the analysis of such arguments and to lead him to the point where he can undertake such analyses himself.

Arguments expressed in English may use grammatical modes of expression that present difficulty in arriving at the proper symbolization of the forms of the statements. A few of these occur frequently enough to deserve mention here. The problem is one of grasping the *meaning* of the English statement and expressing exactly the same meaning in the symbols of logic. There are no mechanical procedures that are universally applicable.

Frequently, we encounter statements such as, "Only Freshmen are admitted to the dance." It means "All who are admitted to the dance are Freshmen," $(\forall x)(A_x \supset F_x)$. Similarly, "None but the intelligent understand the theory of relativity" means "All who understand the theory of relativity are intelligent," $(\forall x)(U_x \supset I_x)$.

The statement "All students except Sophomores are eligible" means "If a student is not a Sophomore, then he is eligible; and if he is a Sophomore, then he is not eligible." Symbolically, it is $\{[(\forall x)(\sim S_x \supset E_x)] \cdot [(\forall x)(S_x \supset \sim E_x)]\}$. It can also be expressed by $(\forall x)(\sim S_x \supset\subset E_x)$.

In summary fashion, some other types of statements, along with their symbolic formulations, are

James is a minister, but he drinks.	$(M_j D_j)$
Harry is a banker, although he lies.	$(B_h L_h)$
A Buick is an automobile.	$(\forall x)(B_x \supset A_x)$
A man can vote, only if he is a citizen.	$(\forall x)(\sim C_x \supset \sim V_x)$
A man can vote, if and only if he is a citizen.	$(\forall x)[(C_x \supset V_x) \cdot (\sim C_x \supset \sim V_x)]$
Integers are never prime numbers.	$(\forall x)(I_x \supset \sim P_x)$
A robin is not carnivorous.	$(\forall x)(R_x \supset \sim C_x)$
The penguin is a bird.	$(\forall x)(P_x \supset B_x)$
Apples and pears are fruits.	$(\forall x)(A_x + P_x \supset F_x)$
Not all bankers are sane.	$(\exists x)(B_x \sim S_x)$
No mechanic who is dexterous will be injured.	$(\forall x)(M_x D_x \supset \sim I_x)$
A man is happy, unless he is ill.	$(\forall x)(\sim I_x \supset H_x)$
Not every student who is a pilot is careful.	$(\exists x)(S_x P_x \sim C_x)$
Paintings are sometimes beautiful.	$(\exists x)(P_x B_x)$
A philosopher is tender-minded or rebellious.	$(\forall x)(P_x \supset T_x + R_x)$
If Harry goes to the meeting, then if he speaks he is fired.	$[G_h \supset (S_h \supset F_h)]$
Any historian is a teacher if he writes.	$(\forall x)[H_x \supset (W_x \supset T_x)]$

It is, of course, impossible to give an exhaustive or completely organized listing.

We now illustrate the axiomatic proof of validity for somewhat lengthy or complex arguments. Consider this argument:

> If anyone steals an automobile, then if he is not
> intelligent, he does not escape and go unpunished.
> A person escapes or is not shrewd.
> If a person goes unpunished, then he has guilt feelings
> and makes society suffer.
> If a person has guilt feelings, he is religious.
> Some stupid person stole an automobile.
> _____
> Hence, some religious person is not shrewd.

We choose the following symbols:

$S_x = x$ steals an automobile	$T_x = x$ is shrewd
$I_x = x$ is intelligent	$G_x = x$ has guilt feelings
$U_x = x$ goes unpunished	$W_x = x$ makes society suffer
$E_x = x$ escapes	$R_x = x$ is religious

The argument form is, then,

1. $(\forall_x)[(S_x) \supset (\sim I_x \supset \sim E_x U_x)]$
2. $(\forall_x)(E_x + \sim T_x)$
3. $(\forall_x)(U_x \supset G_x W_x)$
4. $(\forall_x)(G_x \supset R_x)$
5. $(\exists_x)(\sim I_x S_x)$ $/(\exists_x)(R_x \sim T_x)$

The proof follows:

6.	$(\sim I_a S_a)$	**E.I.**, 5
7.	$(G_a \supset R_a)$	**U.I.**, 4
8.	$(U_a \supset G_a W_a)$	**U.I.**, 3
9.	$(E_a + \sim T_a)$	**U.I.**, 2
10.	$[(S_a) \supset (\sim I_a \supset \sim E_a U_a)]$	**U.I.**, 1
11.	(S_a)	Simpl., 6
12.	$(\sim I_a \supset \sim E_a U_a)$	M.P., 10, 11
13.	$(\sim I_a)$	Simpl., 6
14.	$(\sim E_a U_a)$	M.P., 12, 13
15.	(U_a)	Simpl., 14
16.	$(G_a W_a)$	M.P., 8, 15
17.	(G_a)	Simpl., 16
18.	(R_a)	M.P., 7, 17
19.	$(\sim E_a)$	Simpl., 14
20.	$(\sim T_a)$	D.S., 9, 19
21.	$(R_a \sim T_a)$	Conj., 18, 20
22.	$(\exists_x)(R_x \sim T_x)$	**E.G.**, 21

We take as a second example this argument:

Everyone who appreciates poetry is both a philosopher
and a religious person.
Only those who understand Plato and are emotionally sensitive
are philosophers.
Kant is not emotionally sensitive.

Hence, Kant is not a person who appreciates poetry or he is
a mathematician.

Adopting the symbols

$P_x = x$ appreciates poetry $U_x = x$ understands Plato
$Q_x = x$ is a philosopher $E_x = x$ is emotionally sensitive
$R_x = x$ is a religious person $M_x = x$ is a mathematician
k = Kant

the argument form and the proof of validity are

1. $(\mathbf{\forall}_x)(P_x \supset Q_x R_x)$
2. $(\mathbf{\forall}_x)(Q_x \supset U_x E_x)$
3. $\sim E_k$ $/(\sim P_k + M_k)$

4. $(P_k \supset Q_k R_k)$ **U.I.**, 1
5. $(Q_k \supset U_k E_k)$ **U.I.**, 2
6. $(\sim P_k + Q_k R_k)$ D.C., 4
7. $[(\sim P_k + Q_k) \cdot (\sim P_k + R_k)]$ Distr., 6
8. $(\sim P_k + Q_k)$ Simpl., 7
9. $(\sim Q_k + U_k E_k)$ D.C., 5
10. $[(\sim Q_k + U_k) \cdot (Q_k + E_k)]$ Distr., 9
11. $(\sim Q_k + E_k)$ Simpl., 10
12. $(P_k \supset Q_k)$ D.C., 8
13. $(Q_k \supset E_k)$ D.C., 11
14. $(P_k \supset E_k)$ H.S., 12, 13
15. $(\sim P_k)$ M.T., 3, 14
16. $(\sim P_k + M_k)$ Add., 15

As a final example, let us consider this argument:

If someone is both a minister and a physicist, then
Harry's contention is wrong.
If Harry's contention is wrong or exaggerated, then
everybody who is a scientist is religious.
Only poets are religious.

Consequently, if someone is both a minister and a physicist,
then all scientists are poets.

Specifying the symbols

$M_x = x$ is a minister $S_x = x$ is a scientist
$P_x = x$ is a physicist $R_x = x$ is religious
$W_x = x$'s contention is wrong $Q_x = x$ is a poet
$E_x = x$'s contention is exaggerated

the argument form and proof are

1. $\{[(\exists x)(M_x P_x)] \supset [W_h]\}$
2. $[(W_h + E_h) \supset (\forall x)(S_x \supset R_x)]$
3. $(\forall x)(R_x \supset Q_x)$ $/\{[(\exists x)(M_x P_x)] \supset$
                                              $[(\forall x)(S_x \supset Q_x)]\}$

4.	$(\exists x)(M_x P_x)$	Assumption
5.	(W_h)	M.P., 1, 4
6.	$(W_h + E_h)$	Add., 5
7.	$(\forall x)(S_x \supset R_x)$	M.P., 2, 6
8.	$(S_\alpha \supset R_\alpha)$	U.I., 7
9.	$(R_\alpha \supset Q_\alpha)$	U.I., 3
10.	$(S_\alpha \supset Q_\alpha)$	H.S., 8, 9
11.	$(\forall x)(S_x \supset Q_x)$	U.G., 10
12.	$\{[(\exists x)(M_x P_x)] \supset [(\forall x)(S_x \supset Q_x)]\}$	C.P., 4–11

EXERCISE SET 13–8

C

For the following arguments, construct either a proof of invalidity or an axiomatic proof of validity.

a. Anyone who reads Freud fails to understand him unless he has psychiatric training. Everybody who reads Freud and misunderstands him contributes to his own ill-health. Only those who understand Freud are mature. Not everyone with psychiatric training is mature. Some mature person reads Freud. Hence, someone with psychiatric training contributes to his own ill-health.

b. Disciples of Jesus and disciples of Gandhi respect human personality. If a man is a disciple of Gandhi, he believes in non-violence. Only those who believe in peace are disciples of Jesus. Believing in peace is equivalent to believing in non-violence. Someone who respects human personality believes in peace. Someone who respects human personality believes in non-violence. Therefore, some disciple of Jesus is a disciple of Gandhi.

c. If Linda left the room, then Linda is under suspicion. Anyone who does not lie is not under suspicion, if he is guilty. Linda is guilty or she knows who committed the crime. Anybody who knows who committed the crime is fearful. A person is fearful only if he lies. Linda did not lie. Therefore, Linda left the room and she is guilty.

d. Some artist is not capable of abstract thought. Someone capable of abstract thought is a painter of miniatures. Some painter of miniatures is an artist. No painter of miniatures is an artist, if he is capable of abstract thought. Therefore, there is a painter of miniatures who is capable of abstract thought and is not an artist, and there is a painter of miniatures who is an artist and is not capable of abstract thought.

e. Every valid argument is sound. If an argument is sound, it is convincing, and vice versa. No convincing argument is advanced by a philosopher, unless it is an attempt to appear scholarly. Anselm's argument for God is advanced by a philosopher and it is valid. Consequently, Anselm's argument for God is a convincing argument attempting to appear scholarly.

f. If a person is a student, then if he is in good health or not disabled, he takes physical education. Everybody is in good health or he does not take physical education. Someone is a student and is disabled. Consequently, there is a person such that if he is disabled he is in good health.

g. If anyone steals an automobile, then if he is not intelligent, he does not escape and he is arrested. If a person is arrested, then he cannot hold office or leave the country. Some stupid person stole an automobile, and some intelligent person cannot leave the country. Therefore, some intelligent person does not hold office.

h. If everybody is religious, then someone is inspired and is not Christian. If it is not the case that everybody who is inspired is a Christian, then everybody who is religious believes in fictions. Hitler is religious. Therefore, Hitler believes in fictions.

i. Everybody who votes but does not read the newspapers is contributing to political confusion. Unless a person votes, he contributes to apathy among our citizens. No one reads the newspapers without being deceived. Only those who read the newspapers vote. Consequently, everybody contributes to apathy among our citizens.

j. No one applies for a marriage license if he doesn't intend to get married. Anybody who applies for a marriage license is emotionally unbalanced, if he does so contrary to his parent's wishes. John doesn't intend to get married, but he is emotionally unbalanced. Mary applies for a marriage license, even though she does so contrary to her parent's wishes. Therefore, John applies for a marriage license and Mary is emotionally unbalanced.

RECOMMENDED FOR FURTHER STUDY

For more technical discussions of some of the topics treated in our Chapter 13, we recommend J. M. Anderson and H. W. Johnstone's *Natural Deduction* (Belmont, Calif., 1962), Chapter 5; Alonzo Church's *Introduction to Mathematical Logic* (Princeton, N. J., 1956), Volume I, Chapter 3; Patrick Suppes' *Introduction to Logic* (Princeton, N. J., 1957), Chapters 3 and 4; and A. N. Prior's *Formal Logic* (2d ed.; Oxford, 1962), Part I, Chapters 3 and 4. These sources adopt at some points a mode of symbolization that is somewhat different from ours.   For this reason and because of the advanced level of the presentations, the student may have to acquaint himself with the discussions in them prior to the chapters we cite.

Supplementary studies at a less advanced level may be found in I. M. Copi's *Symbolic Logic* (New York, 1954), Chapter 4; and in J. C. Cooley's *A Primer of Formal Logic* (New York, 1942), Chapters 4 and 5.

14

Some Directions for Further Study

Beyond the elementary level, the study of logic can be pursued in many different, exciting directions.

Those who have a passion for elegance and rigor can again go over the ground we have covered, developing the operations of logic in a more exact manner and in an axiomatic fashion. This is generally done in the opening chapters of textbooks on symbolic logic. The field of logic, however, is very broad and rich—one can move into new areas of study instead of doing better the job we have now finished.

In Chapters 7–12, we developed in a semirigorous manner the *statement calculus*. Chapter 13 discussed a part of what is involved in the *functional calculus*. A few additional notions involved in it will be advanced in Section 14–1. There is a third major division of modern logic—the *relational calculus*—that handles statements involving relations, such as "father of," "between," and "loves." Some basic concepts about relations will be discussed in Section 14–2.

The whole of the logic we have developed is based on two truth-values, 1 and 0. Such a logical system is called *two-valued*. But, one can construct three-valued logics, four-valued logics, . . . , or *n*-valued logics. This is another fertile field for investigation that we will introduce in Section 14–3.

Beyond these areas, there are other divisions and domains of logical study such as modal logic and intuitionistic logic. One also can engage in an investigation of certain applications of logic to science and other disciplines. Logical apparatus and logical modes of inference are found in use in mathematics and among the empirical sciences. If the student proceeds to the study of Part III, he will be introduced to some of these uses of logic. More specifically, an important application of logic is found in switching circuits and the "adding" units of digital computers. Section 16–7 will discuss this topic briefly. Moreover, much of the contemporary literature in the field of philosophy presupposes a knowledge of the basic forms and apparatus of symbolic logic.

In this chapter, in order merely to point out some of the directions in which the student may advance in his understanding and use of logic, we discuss briefly four topics: multiply general statements, relations and some of their properties, n-valued logics, and postulates for a logical system. In each case, of course, only very elementary notions are presented.

14–1.   MULTIPLY GENERAL STATEMENTS   *if nesting of quantifiers*

Both for the development of the science of logic itself and for the purpose of relating logic to certain applications in the scientific process, we must be in a position to handle statements that involve more than one variable. Recalling the terminology of Sections 13–2 and 13–3, our statement functions frequently contain not merely one variable (x), but two variables (x, y), three variables (x, y, z), or more. Consequently, our general statements make use of corresponding numbers of universal and existential quantifiers. As simple examples, we can cite from algebra an expression such as:

$$x + y = 5$$

which involves two variables, and from a physical science an expression such as:

$$V \cdot P = k \cdot T$$

a law of gases, which contains three variables (V = volume, P = pressure, T = temperature, k = a constant). Furthermore, the common modes of speech frequently contain two or more variables. The statement "If somebody stole my pen, everybody in the room is responsible" contains two variables under the use of the terms "somebody" and "everybody." Similarly, the statement "If there are at least two metals that are liquid, then every metal expands with a rise in temperature" involves three variables.

Let us begin by considering the statement function

$$x \text{ observes } y$$

which contains two variables, x and y. If the universal quantifier is applied to the variable x, we get

$$(\forall_x)O_{xy}$$

that is, "Everybody observes y." But this is still a statement function, not a statement, for the variable y is not bound. We have a statement, only if y also is bound by a quantifier. This can be done by universally quantifying the free variable; thus,

$$(\forall_y)(\forall_x)O_{xy}$$

Now we have the symbolic form of the statement "Everybody observes everybody," if we agree that the variables x and y range over the domain of persons.

But, such variables can also be quantified existentially. The statement

$$(\exists_x)(\exists_y)O_{xy}$$

is, in English, "There is an x and there is a y such that x observes y"; that is, "Somebody observes somebody." Similarly,

$$(\forall_x)(\exists_y)O_{xy}$$

and

$$(\exists_x)(\forall_y)O_{xy}$$

mean, respectively, "Everybody observes somebody" and "Somebody observes everybody."

Multiply general statements can, of course, be much more complex than the examples we have employed. But, this very simple understanding of this kind of logical expression will suffice for our purposes. The rules of inference that we introduced in Section 13–5 can, with certain restrictions, be used for analyzing arguments that involve multiply general statements.

The other thing that we should perhaps do at this time is to indicate how certain statements from everyday speech, from mathematics, and from the empirical sciences are expressed in our logical language.

The statement "Somebody stole my pen" can be expressed, of course, by $(\exists_x)S_x$, where S_x stands for "x stole my pen." On the other hand, "Somebody stole my pen and somebody stole my wallet" will be expressed by $[(\exists_x)S_x \cdot (\exists_y)W_y]$ or $(\exists_x)(\exists_y)(S_xW_y)$, where W_y stands for "y stole my wallet" and we agree that x and y are not necessarily the same. "If there are at least two metals that are liquids, then every metal expands with a rise in temperature" can be symbolized by

$$\{[(\exists_x)(\exists_y)(M_xL_xM_yL_y)] \supset [(\forall_z)(M_z \supset E_z)]\}$$

where M_x means "x is a metal," L_x means "x is a liquid," and E_z means "z expands with a rise in temperature." The statement "Every man is a biped, or some biped is not rational" may be expressed by

$$\{[(\forall_x)(M_x \supset B_x)] + [(\exists_y)(B_y{\sim}R_y)]\}$$

where M_x stands for "x is a man," B_x stands for "x is a biped," and R_y stands for "y is rational."

Now let us illustrate how certain statements in mathematics can be expressed in our logical language. The statement "The sum of any two integers is another integer" can be expressed in this way:

$$(\forall_x)(\forall_y)(\exists_z)(x + y = z)$$

where the variables x, y, and z range over the domain of integers. That is, "For any x and for any y, integers, there is an integer z such that $(x + y)$ is equal to z. The statement "There is an element, zero, such that any integer multiplied by zero yields zero" can be symbolized in this manner:

$$(\exists_0)(\forall_x)(x \cdot 0 = 0)$$

Similarly, the laws of commutation and distribution for algebra can be expressed thus:

$$(\forall_x)(\forall_y)(x + y = y + x)$$
$$(\forall_x)(\forall_y)(x \cdot y = y \cdot x)$$
$$(\forall_x)(\forall_y)(\forall_z)[x(y + z) = (xy + xz)]$$

What about statements in the factual or empirical sciences? Here the situation is more complicated, and we do not have available all the apparatus we would need to give completely formal expression to scientific statements. The direction, however, in which one can move is indicated by the following examples. The statement "If one measure of length is greater than a second, and this second measure is greater than a third, then the first is greater than the third" can be given logical expression by

$$(\forall_x)(\forall_y)(\forall_z)\{[(x > y) \cdot (y > z)] \supset [x > z]\}$$

where x, y, and z are variables in the domain of measures of length and $>$ is a sign for "greater than." The statement "If every metal is a conductor of electrical current, then there is something that is not a metal" can be formulated in symbols thus:

$$\{[(\forall_x)(M_x \supset C_x)] \supset [(\exists_z){\sim}M_z]\}$$

"If one hamster is the sire of a second hamster, and the second hamster is the sire of a third, then the first hamster is not the sire of the third" can be formulated in this way:

$$(\forall_x)(\forall_y)(\forall_z)(S_{xy}S_{yz} \supset {\sim}S_{xz})$$

In manners such as these, many statements in everyday language, in mathematics, and in the empirical sciences can be given logical expression. Arguments that involve multiply general statements can be analyzed for validity, once the appropriate procedures have been developed. From such a basis as we have briefly described here, the student may proceed to a further, detailed investigation of the functional calculus. And he may inquire into the many uses to which it is put in the formulation of mathematical and scientific structures.

EXERCISE SET 14–1

A

1. Express in multiply general logical formulas the following assertions, choosing and identifying symbols for the various relations, properties, or functions expressed in the assertions.

    a. There is at least one dog and at least one cat.

    b. There are at least two books on the shelf.

    c. Everybody loves someone.

    d. Paul loves everybody.

    e. Everybody loves Walt.

    f. John loves at least one person.

    g. Nobody loves everybody.

    h. If Bill loves everybody, somebody is a saint.

    i. If everyone at the party is happy, somebody is not at the party.

    j. Something is male and something is female.

    k. If any integer is equal to a second, and the second is equal to a third, then the first is equal to the third.

    l. If somebody is an artist, then all philosophers are not artists.

    m. If Louise is an artist, then everybody loves poetry.

    n. If all integers are prime, then all integers are odd.

    o. If all acids are hydrogen compounds, and all chlorine compounds are non-metallic, then some hydrogen compound is non-metallic.

    p. If somebody is a thief, and somebody is wealthy, and somebody is red-haired, then not everybody is a wealthy, red-haired thief.

    q. If all circles are conic sections, then some conic section is a point.

2. In the discussion, we gave a logical formulation for the law of distribution in algebra (multiplication over addition). Is there a second one, for the distribution of addition over multiplication? (There are *two* laws of distribution in logic for the operations $\cdot$ and $+$.) Can you give a logical expression that formulates the idea that the other law of distribution in algebra does or does not hold?

3. Let K_{xy} be the statement function "x outlives y." Write English sentences that correspond to the following formulas.

    a. $(\exists_x)K_{xy}$

    b. $(\exists_x)(\forall_y)K_{xy}$

    c. $(\forall_x)(\forall_y)K_{xy}$

    d. $(\forall_y)(\forall_x)K_{xy}$

    e. $(\exists_x)(\exists_y)K_{xy}$

    f. $\{[(\exists_x)(\exists_y)K_{xy}] \supset [(\forall_x)(\forall_y)K_{xy}]\}$

    g. $\{[(\forall_x)(\forall_y)K_{xy}] \supset [(\forall_y)(\forall_x)K_{xy}]\}$

    h. $\{[(\exists_x)(\exists_y)K_{xy}] + [(\forall_x)(\forall_y) \sim K_{xy}]\}$

B

4. Give a logical formulation of the statement that there is among the integers an element 1 such that any integer multiplied by 1 yields that same integer.

Also formulate the statement that, given any rational number, there is an inverse of that rational number such that the rational number multiplied by its inverse yields 1.

14–2. RELATIONS

Many statements and arguments, both in common discourse and in scientific discourse, contain *relational terms*. This was indicated by some of the examples used in Section 14–1.

In everyday discourse, we employ relational statements such as:

> John is the *father of* Harry.
> Chicago is *between* New York City *and* San Francisco.
> James *loves* Alice.
> Carol *purchases* potatoes *from* Joe *for* five cents.

In the domain of mathematics, relational statements such as the following occur:

> 27 is *greater than* 26.
> x is *equal to* y.
> Equilateral triangles are *equivalent to* equiangular triangles.
> b is the *successor of* a.

And in the empirical sciences, we often find relational statements of this sort:

> The gas is *inside of* the chamber.
> The beaker is *to the left of* the burner.
> The technician *observes* the reaction.
> The gas pressure is *inversely proportional to* its volume.

A whole logic of relational statements comparable to the logical system developed in Chapters 7–13 can be constructed for arguments involving statements of the kinds listed above. We cannot undertake that extensive task here. We can, however, present a few notions related to such a logic, in order to illumine further how the science of logic can be developed and how its applications can be extended to various scientific domains.

From the list of statements given above, the student can infer that some relations demand two terms in order to establish a meaningful statement, that others demand three terms, and that yet others demand four or more terms. A two-termed relation is called *dyadic*. A three-termed relation is called *triadic*. Using lower case letters, $a, b, c, \ldots$, to denote individuals, as we did earlier, we now adopt the *convention of designating relations* by upper case letters, $A, B, C, \ldots$ We shall write the terms in the relation *in order* as subscripts to the symbol for the relation. Thus, the first four examples given above will be symbolized

$$F_{jh}$$
$$B_{cns}$$
$$L_{ja}$$
$$P_{cpjf}$$

For purposes of general discussion, we will refer to a relation, R. As the student recognizes from Chapter 13, the terms designated for R may be particular individuals (a, b, . . .), arbitrarily selected individuals (α, β, . . .), or variables (x, y . . .).

By adopting these conventions, we can symbolize some argument forms that contain relational statements. For example, the argument

> Everybody who loves Carol hates Joe.
> Alice loves Carol.
> _____
> Therefore, Alice hates Joe.

can be symbolized in this way:

1. $(\mathbf{\forall}_x)(L_{xc} \supset H_{xj})$
2. L_{ac} $/H_{aj}$

The student should construct the proof of validity for this argument, employing the procedures of Chapter 13.

The argument

> 5 is greater than 3.
> 3 is greater than 1.
> _____
> Hence, 5 is greater than 1

has as its form:

1. $G_{5,3}$
2. $G_{3,1}$ $/G_{5,1}$

A little further on in our discussion, we will indicate that this is an enthymeme of a sort and describe the premiss that must be added in order to give a proof of validity.

By additional symbolic devices, similar to those just introduced, we can symbolize relational arguments in general. The axiomatic proof procedure set forth in Chapters 12 and 13 is applicable to them.

A knowledge of certain special features of relations is helpful and sometimes necessary in order to analyze many arguments. Since relations occur so frequently in everyday speech and in technical discourse, a knowledge of some of their properties is extremely valuable. On the basis of such a knowledge, a vast range of scholarly literature—from psychology to mathematics and physics—becomes more comprehensible than it would otherwise be.

Some dyadic relations are called *reflexive*. A reflexive relation is one in which the same individual can stand in both positions for the two terms. Thus, "equals" is reflexive, for we can always write $x = x$. If a relation is such that the same individual can never stand in both positions, it is called *irreflexive*. For example, "father of" is irreflexive; for we cannot assert "James Johnson Jones is the father of James Johnson Jones" without violating the sense of the relation. Symbolically, we express these properties thus:

$$(\forall_x)R_{xx} \qquad (Reflexive)$$
$$(\forall_x)\sim R_{xx} \qquad (Irreflexive)$$

Symmetry is another property of some relations. A relation is *symmetric* if when one individual is related to another by the relation, then the second is also related to the first by it. For example, if "$2 = 8/4$," then "$8/4 = 2$." If a relation is such that an interchange of the individuals is never possible, the relation is *asymmetric*. Since we are dealing with two entities in a dyadic relation, we must introduce two variables and two quantifiers in order to express these properties in the apparatue of logic. A reference to the discussion in Section 14–1 should make ths symbolization in this case clear.

$$(\forall_x)(\forall_y)(R_{xy} \supset R_{yx}) \qquad (Symmetric)$$
$$(\forall_x)(\forall_y)(R_{xy} \supset \sim R_{yx}) \qquad (Asymmetric)$$

We read the first of these, "For all values of x and for all values of y, if x is related to y, then y is related to x." The second is expressed, "For all values of x and for all values of y, if x is related to y, then y is not related to x."

Finally, some relations are *transitive*. If one individual is related to a second by such a relation, and the second is related to a third by it, then the first is always related to the third by it. "Greater than" is transitive. If $5 > 3$ and $3 > 1$, then $5 > 1$. A relation is *intransitive* when the first term is never related to the third, on the basis of the condition stated above. For instance, "father of" is intransitive. If Joe is the father of Harry, and Harry is the father of Alexander, then it is not the case that Joe is the father of Alexander. These properties may be expressed symbolically in the following manner.

$$(\forall_x)(\forall_y)(\forall_z)(R_{xy}R_{yz} \supset R_{xz}) \qquad (Transitive)$$
$$(\forall_x)(\forall_y)(\forall_z)(R_{xy}R_{yz} \supset \sim R_{xz}) \qquad (Intransitive)$$

Returning to the argument above that involved the relation "greater than" and adding the additional premiss that expresses the idea that "greater than" is transitive, we have

1. $G_{5,3}$
2. $G_{3,1}$
3. $(\mathbf{\forall}_x)(\mathbf{\forall}_y)(\mathbf{\forall}_z)(G_{xy}G_{yz} \supset G_{xz})$ $/G_{5,1}$

The proof of validity is

4. $(G_{5,3} G_{3,1} \supset G_{5,1})$ **U.I.**, 3 ($x = 5; y = 3; z = 1$)
5. $(G_{5,3} G_{3,1})$ Conj., 1, 2
6. $(G_{5,1})$ M.P., 4, 5

It is possible to show that certain connections exist among reflexivity, symmetry, and transitivity. For instance, given that a relation, R, is transitive and irreflexive, we can demonstrate that it is asymmetric. Thus,

1. $(\mathbf{\forall}_x)(\mathbf{\forall}_y)(\mathbf{\forall}_z)(R_{xy}R_{yz} \supset R_{xz})$
2. $(\mathbf{\forall}_x)\sim R_{xx}$ $/(\mathbf{\forall}_x)(\mathbf{\forall}_y)(R_{xy} \supset \sim R_{yx})$
3. $(R_{\alpha\beta}R_{\beta\alpha} \supset R_{\alpha\alpha})$ **U.I.**, 1 ($x = \alpha; y = \beta; z = \alpha$)
4. $\sim R_{\alpha\alpha}$ **U.I.**, 2
5. $\sim(R_{\alpha\beta}R_{\beta\alpha})$ M.T., 3, 4
6. $(\sim R_{\alpha\beta} + \sim R_{\beta\alpha})$ D.M., 5
7. $(R_{\alpha\beta} \supset \sim R_{\beta\alpha})$ D.C., 6
8. $(\mathbf{\forall}_x)(\mathbf{\forall}_y)(R_{xy} \supset \sim R_{yx})$ **U.G.**, 7

By reason of its ability to express relations and their properties and as a result of its capacity for analyzing arguments containing relational statements, logic can bring within the domain of its control vast areas of everyday language and of scientific discourse that lie beyond the control of classical logic.

EXERCISE SET 14–2

B

1. Construct proofs of validity for the following arguments.

    a. Anybody who left the building was observed by John. Anyone John observes John hates. Harry left the building. Hence, John hates Harry.

    b. If everybody respects Alice, then Harry respects Alice. If Harry respects Alice, then Harry does not offend her. If Harry does not offend Alice, then everybody respects Harry. Therefore, if anyone respects Alice, he respects Harry.

    c. Point a is to the left of point b. Any point to the left of b is above it. Any point to the left of a is above it. Point c is to the left of point a. Therefore, point c is above point a.

d. The area of the floor in the room is equal to the area of one wall in the room. The area of this one wall of the room is equal to the area of the driveway. The area of the driveway is equal to the area of the sidewalk from the house to the street. Hence, the area of the floor in the room is equal to the area of the sidewalk from the house to the street. (Use E to symbolize the relation "equal to.")

C

e. No one who dislikes Joe and is intelligent is a brother of Harry. Someone is a brother of Harry and dislikes Joe. Hence, someone who dislikes Joe is not intelligent.

f. Only those who are inconsiderate criticize the President. If a person is resourceful and loves the U.S.A., he criticizes the President. Anybody who loves the U.S.A. is not inconsiderate. Therefore, anybody who is resourceful does not love the U.S.A.

g. John can outrun anybody on the French team. Somebody on the French team can outrun Harry. If anybody can outrun John he can outrun Harry. Anybody on the German team can outrun John. Hence, anybody on the German team can outrun Harry.

2. Prove that every asymmetric relation is irreflexive.

3. Given that a relation R is transitive and symmetric, show that this assertion holds for R: $(\forall_x)(\forall_y)(R_{xy} \supset R_{xx})$.

4. Given that a relation R is intransitive and symmetric, show that this assertion holds for R: $(\forall_x)(\forall_y)(R_{xy} \supset \sim R_{xx})$.

5. Show that the biconditional $(\supset\subset)$, which is defined by $[(p \supset q) \cdot (q \supset p)]$, is reflexive, symmetric, and transitive. Use an informal type of argument.

14–3. N-VALUED LOGICS

The system of logic we have studied so far is based on the stipulation that a statement shall have one or the other of two truth-values, 1 and 0. This stipulation seems acceptable, perhaps because we have developed a mind-set or orientation that inclines us to feel that the simple division, "true" *versus* "false," is in some sense "real." Moreover, we are sometimes aware that certain phenomena in nature are two-valued. For example, certain kinds of switches are either "on" (which we might denote by 1) or "off" (which we might denote by 0). The female egg is either impregnated or not. A few domains of common and scientific experience display this two-valued structure, and consequently the logic we have developed can be effectively applied to them.

But, in the general area of human experience and of scientific investigation, we more often come across domains or problems that display a three-valued, four-valued, . . . , or n-valued structure. For example, plane triangles (Euclidean) exhibit a threefold division, mutually exclusive and exhaustive, into isosceles, equilateral, and scalene triangles. In elementary mathematics, we deal with finite sets of, say, three, four, seven, or eleven members. And in certain areas of scientific work and construction, switches may be fashioned to have, let us say, four operating positions; or cams in certain machinery may have eight faces. The data of common and scientific experience are only occasionally two-valued; they are more frequently many-valued. It is this sort of situation, combined with purely theoretical logical interest in some investigators, that led to the development of n-valued logics. At this point there opens before the student of logic a whole new world for investigation, research, and adventure.

The simple notions that we introduce here will serve only to point to the horizon, beyond which this new world of logic lies. Let us begin by assuming that a statement can have, instead of two truth-values (1 and 0), three truth-values. A statement p will then have this truth-table:

	(p)
Case 1:	3
2:	2
3:	1

where the values that p can assume are 3, 2, and 1.

Now if we consider two statements, p and q, collectively, we must write in a truth-table all the combinations of the values possible for the two statements. They will be in number $3^2 = 9$. Thus,

	(p)	(q)
Case 1:	3	3
2:	3	2
3:	3	1
4:	2	3
5:	2	2
6:	2	1
7:	1	3
8:	1	2
9:	1	1

For n statements, considered collectively, the number of rows in the truth-table is 3^n. (The student should write the formula that gives the number of rows in the truth-table for, not a two-valued or a three-valued logic, but an m-valued logic.)

In addition to statement symbols, we require some connectives or operations (analogous to $'$, $\cdot$, $+$, etc., in the two-valued logic). Let us define several *unary operations* (that is, operations on a single statement, just as the prime mark in the two-valued logic applied to a single statement). Symbolizing them by U_1 and U_2, we define the results of their operations on a statement p in this way:

(p)	$U_1(p)$	$U_2(p)$	(Definitions)
3	2	1	
2	2	2	
1	2	3	

In other words, the operation U_1 on a statement changes every one of its values to the value 2. The operation U_2 on a statement interchanges the values of 3 and 1 but leaves 2 unchanged.

Our two-valued logic also had some *binary operations* (that is, operations connecting two statements, such as · and +). It will be useful to have some binary operations in the three-valued logic we are building. Let us define two of them, designating them by o and *. We stipulate that the result of connecting two statements by o shall be the smaller of the two values of the two statements. In the case of *, the result shall be the larger of the two values. The truth-table giving the definitions for these operations is, therefore,

(p)	(q)	$(p \text{ o } q)$	$(p * q)$	(Definitions)
3	3	3	3	
3	2	2	3	
3	1	1	3	
2	3	2	3	
2	2	2	2	
2	1	1	2	
1	3	1	3	
1	2	1	2	
1	1	1	1	

We can now write truth-tables for statement formulas in this logic, just as we did for such formulas in the two-valued logic. For example, the logical formula $[(q \text{ o } U_1p) * (p)]$ has this truth-table:

(p)	(q)	U_1p	$(q \text{ o } U_1p)$	$[(q \text{ o } U_1p) * (p)]$
3	3	2	2	3
3	2	2	2	3
3	1	2	1	3
2	3	2	2	2
2	2	2	2	2
2	1	2	1	2
1	3	2	2	2
1	2	2	2	2
1	1	2	1	1

If we define equivalence in this logic to mean that two formulas have, in every case, the same truth-values, we can see that $(p * U_1q)$ and $U_2(U_2p \text{ o } U_1p)$ are equivalent in value and constitute interchange forms. This is indicated by the following truth-table:

(p)	(q)	U_2p	U_1p	$(U_2p \text{ o } U_1p)$	$U_2(U_2p \text{ o } U_1p)$	U_1q	$(p * U_1q)$
3	3	1	2	1	3	2	3
3	2	1	2	1	3	2	3
3	1	1	2	1	3	2	3
2	3	2	2	2	2	2	2
2	2	2	2	2	2	2	2
2	1	2	2	2	2	2	2
1	3	3	2	2	2	2	2
1	2	3	2	2	2	2	2
1	1	3	2	2	2	2	2

equivalent

Different three-valued logics can be constructed, depending upon the number and nature of the operations stipulated. These systems will exhibit different characteristics. Some of them are, for example, *functionally complete*. This means that, for any truth-table column we write (having a choice of 3, 2, or 1 for each row), we can write a formula in the system that has this column as its truth-table. In a three-valued logic, there are, as we said earlier, 3^n rows in the truth-table, where n is the number of statements considered. There are 3^{3^n} possible columns (with 3, 2, or 1 in each row), where there are n statements to consider. Thus, if $n = 2$, the truth-table has 9 rows; and the total number of possible truth-tables is $3^{3^2} = 19,683$. In other words, there are 19,683 logically distinct truth-functions (or families of truth-functions) that can be written, if the logic is functionally complete.

Proceeding along lines like these, one can develop other logics than the two-valued one constructed in Part II.

EXERCISE SET 14–3

C

1. For a two-valued logic, a truth-table has 2^n rows. The number of distinct truth-functions is 2^{2^n}. Thus, for two statements ($n = 2$), there are four rows in the truth-table, and there are sixteen distinct truth-functions (or families of truth-functions) corresponding to the sixteen ways in which 1 and 0 can be arranged in the four rows of the truth-table. In the following display, some of these sixteen possible truth-table entries are given, along with a simple truth-function corresponding to each. The student should complete the display.

p	q	$(p + p')$	(pp')	$(p + q)$	$(p'q')$	(p)	(p')	(pq)
1	1	1	0	1	0	1	0	1
1	0	1	0	1	0	1	0	0
0	1	1	0	1	0	0	1	0
0	0	1	0	0	1	0	1	0
		1.	2.	3.	4.	5.	6.	7.

In the cases of the seven truth-tables given in the display, the student should write alternative truth-functions for the ones given.

2. Defining o and * as above for a three-valued logic, choose unary operations different from our U_1 and U_2. Write three formulas in the logic you construct and produce their truth-tables.

3. In the three-valued logic defined in the text, o and * were stipulated as giving, respectively, the minimum and maximum values of the statements joined by them. The student should construct a three-valued logic, using our U_1 and U_2; but he should employ one binary operation, $\square$. It shall mean that one *adds arithmetically* the truth-values of the statements it joins; and if the result is greater than 3, the value of $(p \square q)$ is what remains after 3 is subtracted from the sum. In other words, $\square$ specifies *addition modulo 3*. Thus,

(p)	(q)		$(p \square q)$
3	3	(6 =)	3
3	2	(5 =)	2
3	1	(4 =)	1
2	3	(5 =)	2
2	2	(4 =)	1
2	1	(3 =)	3
1	3	(4 =)	1
1	2	(3 =)	3
1	1	(2 =)	2

The student should write three formulas in this logic and construct their truth-tables. The formula $(U_1 p \square U_1 q)$ has the value 1 in every row of its truth-table. Can you discover a peculiar property that it has?

14–4. SOME REMARKS ABOUT POSTULATES IN LOGICAL SYSTEMS

In Chapters 7–12 we developed the apparatus of logic for the statement calculus. In doing this, our chief objective was to produce a set of logical formulas, rules of procedure, and techniques of inference and proof for the purpose of analyzing the validity of arguments. We attempted to employ as much symbolism and rigor as seemed appropriate and feasible, considering that this is a first course in logic. As the student has proceeded with his study, he has undoubtedly recognized at one point or another that our procedure was not as rigorous as it could have been. Furthermore, it was not as economical as it could have been.

One of the ways of introducing rigor, economy, and elegance into a logical system is to develop it in an *axiomatic* or *postulational* manner. Obviously, we are not about to undertake that task here—it would require a book in itself. But the beginning student should be introduced to the idea of a postulational method and to certain criteria for assessing sets of postulates in a logical (or mathematical) system.

Let us open the topic by referring to two situations with which the student is familiar. First, he will recall that in plane (Euclidean) geometry the presentation of the subject was launched by listing at the outset certain definitions (for example, definitions for "point" and "line") and certain unproved statements such as "The whole is equal to the sum of its parts" and "Through a point external to a given line there can exist one line parallel to the given line." These unproved statements were called *axioms* or *postulates*. From them and the definitions of the primitive terms, the theorems of plane geometry were proved. Just as it is necessary to have certain terms in a language for which no verbal definitions are given (Chapter 3), if we are to avoid circularity, so it is necessary in any deductive system to have some unproved statements (postulates), if circularity is to be avoided in the presentation of proofs or in the development of the theory of the system.

Another way to approach this matter is to recall that after developing by the truth-table technique certain logical formulas, we listed in Section 10–8 twenty simple argument forms and interchange expressions. Subsequently, we constructed proofs of validity by appealing to these twenty basic assertions or expressions. Informally, we were using them as postulates for our various demonstrations and arguments. The student will remember that at that juncture in our presentation we remarked that there was nothing necessary about the list being twenty in number. We could have had fewer than twenty, but then our proofs would have been longer and more complex. We could have had more than twenty; but then perhaps it would have been too great a burden for us to keep in mind, say, twenty-five or thirty expressions. The fact that the selection of twenty was somewhat arbitrary or was based on pedagogical factors is indicated by the frequent contentions among students (1) that, say from $[(pq) \supset (r)]$, by the use of D.M., Assoc., D.C., and Rule of Substitution, they can deduce Exp.; or (2) that, say, since from $(p \supset rs)$, by the application of D.C., Distr., and Simpl., they can deduce $(p \supset r)$, we might properly add to our list the simple argument form $(p \supset rs) \vdash (p \supset r)$.

If one undertakes to construct a logical system in a completely formal and rigorous manner, among other things he will want to begin with a set of postulates that contains enough statements so that he can develop the full scope of the logical theory but that contains no more statements than are necessary to do the job. In their *Principia Mathematica*,[1] Bertrand Russell and A. N. Whitehead constructed the theory of the statement calculus from five postulates, namely,

$$\text{(I)} \quad (p + p \supset p)$$
$$\text{(II)} \quad (q \supset p + q)$$
$$\text{(III)} \quad (p + q \supset q + p)$$
$$\text{(IV)} \quad [p + (q + r)] \supset [q + (p + r)]$$
$$\text{(V)} \quad [q \supset r] \supset [(p + q) \supset (p + r)]$$

[handwritten margin note: Opposite page → No comment on the redundancy of IV]

The student should compare this list with our array in Section 10–8, and especially with Taut., Add., Comm., and Assoc. in that list. Another formal system of logic devised by J. B. Rosser develops the theory of the statement calculus from three postulates:

$$(p \supset pp)$$
$$(pq \supset p)$$
$$[p \supset q] \supset [(qr)' \supset (rp)']$$

These two examples will serve to illustrate the nature of the economy that may be achieved in a set of postulates for the statement calculus. A number of other factors must be taken into consideration in constructing a system of logic postulationally and with rigor: the nature of undefined terms, rules of inference and substitution, rules for deciding what is and what is not a formula in the system, the distinction between an object language and a metalanguage, and so on. We cannot venture to discuss these here.

Attending simply to the list of postulates for a logical or formal system, what are some criteria for assessing such a set of primitive statements? One thing we require of a set of postulates is that they be *consistent*. Recalling our discussion of arguments with inconsistent premises in Section 11–5, the student can quickly appreciate the necessity for this requirement. If a set of postulates contains an inconsistency, any statement can be deduced from the postulates. It must be impossible to prove both some statement and also its negation on the basis of the postulates. If we can prove both p and p', then we can prove z, any statement whatsoever; thus,

1.	(p)	
2.	(p')	$/(z)$
3.	$(p + z)$	Add., 1
4.	(z)	D.S., 2, 3

[1] Bertrand Russell and A. N. Whitehead, *Principia Mathematica* (2d ed.; Cambridge: The University Press, 1950).

This means that any statement can be asserted in the system, even if it has no connection whatsoever with the postulates.

A second criterion for a set of postulates is *independence*. This has to do with whether or not some postulate in the set of postulates can be proved on the basis of the remaining ones. When each postulate cannot be proved by the use of the others, we say that the postulates are independent. In the case of the *Principia* postulates, given above, it was shown that postulate (IV) could be proved by using (I), (II), (III), and (V). As a matter of elegance and economy, independence is desirable in a set of postulates. It is not, however, necessary; and a lack of independence among the postulates does not affect consistency.

There are several other criteria for assessing sets of postulates that we cannot discuss here. The student interested in pursuing this matter further will want to consult the suggested readings given at the conclusion of the chapter.

EXERCISE SET 14–4

C

1. Let R_{xy} be a statement function of two variables. Consider the following three statements as a set of postulates for a system.

$$(\forall_x) \sim R_{xx}$$
$$(\forall_x)(\forall_y)(R_{xy} \supset \sim R_{yx})$$
$$(\forall_x)(\forall_y)(\forall_z)(R_{xy}R_{yz} \supset R_{xz})$$

Prove that the postulates are dependent by deducing one of them from the other two. *Tarski*

2. The E. L. Post criterion for consistency is that any system is consistent if it contains a formula that cannot be proved in the system. Given the consistent postulates p, q, and r, give a formula that cannot be proved.

3. Consider the following statements as a set of postulates.

$$[p \supset (p \supset q)] \supset [p \supset q]$$
$$[(p \supset q) \cdot (q \supset p)] \supset [p \supset q]$$
$$[p \supset (q \supset p)]$$
$$[p \supset p]$$

By the use of the Rule of Substitution and our other rules and principles in Part II, prove that the fourth postulate is dependent.

4. Consider the following statements as a set of postulates.

$$[(p + p) \supset p]$$
$$[p \supset (p + q)]$$
$$[(p + q) \supset (q + p)]$$
$$[p \supset q] \supset [(r + p) \supset (r + q)]$$
$$[p \supset (p')']$$

Show that the fifth postulate is dependent.

5. Consider the following statements as a set of postulates.

$$[(p + p) \supset p]$$
$$[p \supset (p + q)]$$
$$(p + q) \supset (q + p)$$
$$[p \supset q] \supset [(r + p) \supset (r + q)]$$
$$[(p') \cdot (p')']$$

Show that this is an inconsistent set of postulates.

RECOMMENDED FOR FURTHER STUDY

In the *Journal of Symbolic Logic*, Vol. 27, No. 4 (December, 1962), pp. 409–22, William H. Jobe develops the structure of an *n*-valued logic and gives a proof of functional completeness for it. His article is "Functional Completeness and Canonical Forms in Many-Valued Logics." For an extended discussion of many-valued logics, the student may refer to J. B. Rosser and A. R. Turquette's *Many-Valued Logics* (Amsterdam, 1952). He should be able to follow the presentation in Chapters 1 and 2.

H. N. Lee's *Symbolic Logic* (New York, 1961), Chapter 3, "Properties of Relations," can be consulted with profit. Bertrand Russell's *Introduction to Mathematical Philosophy* (New York, 1920), Chapters 5 and 6, "Kinds of Relations" and "Similarity of Relations," gives a more sophisticated discussion of relations than we have advanced.

Raymond L. Wilder's *Introduction to the Foundations of Mathematics* (New York, 1952), Chapter 2, "Analysis of the Axiomatic Method," contains a good treatment of consistency, independence, and completeness of axiom systems. For a discussion of criteria for postulates within the framework of mathematics, the student may turn to E. R. Stabler's *An Introduction to Mathematical Thought* (Reading, Mass., 1953), Chapter 8.

Part III
DEDUCTIVE LOGIC AND SCIENCE

15

Some Factors in the
Scientific Process

15–1. INTRODUCTION: IS SCIENCE PURELY INDUCTIVE?

One of the common ways in which man's function as a user of symbols manifests itself is in deductive thinking. In Parts I and II, we studied some of the features of deductive thinking. Man's brain is continuously producing concepts and symbols that find expression in myths and music, in sacraments and rituals, and in logical and mathematical operations. Our study of logic in Part II was an examination of one of the ways in which man brings some of this conceptual wealth to expression in logical symbols.

The material in the previous chapters can be described as a treatment of deductive logic in a modern idiom. But, for many, the word "deduction" suggests a form of thinking that is less productive and rewarding than empirical or inductive modes of thought. The striking achievements of modern science rest, it is claimed, upon inductive reasoning. Many consider themselves to be disciples of a "scientific" or "inductive" logic. Others are motivated by a desire to master this "more rewarding" inductive form of logical thought.

The daily impact of modern technology upon us all, the tremendous progress of modern science, and the prominence of scientific language and comment in our daily lives make it advisable that we gain some understanding of the nature of the scientific enterprise. For the greater number of students, who are not already beginning scientists or who will not be involved in a further examination of science, Part III will provide an overview of deductive logic in relation to the scientific process.

Many who live in this scientific age and who benefit from the achievements of modern technology do not understand the processes of science and are deceived by the "common coin" on the subject passed by the man on the street. Today men generally extol and revere science, although they often do not understand it—and this blind faith often turns out to be costly.   Unfortunately, the word "science" has become an emotionally loaded term.   Scientific activity takes on, for many, the characteristics of a religion.   "Scientifically tested," "endorsed by men of science," and "established by scientific research" are typical of the phrases used frequently and insistently by commercial and political propagandists, by businessmen and clergymen, and by housewives and students. Such expressions can, of course, be used properly and wisely.   On the other hand, they are often used to persuade, to confer prestige on some idea or product, or to advance unscientific and unwise objectives.   Even more tragic is the perverse use of the name of science to try to make some contemporary viewpoint—in politics, economics, religion, etc.— appear to be a superior or final truth.

Since much of the "common coin" of science is counterfeit, the student who is not involved in the sciences must be notified of its circulation and become acquainted with some of the genuine currency in the scientific process.   But, we must caution the student about the limits of our presentation.   We will discuss in a very elementary way a contemporary interpretation of the scientific process, giving attention chiefly to the role deductive logic plays in it.   For some students, our presentation will simply indicate directions for further, technical study.

The philosophy or logic of science is not, as is sometimes assumed, a rigid or well-defined area of analysis and study.   Deductive logic and epistemology, as well as the special sciences themselves, such as psychology, physics, and physiology, make their contribution to the understanding of the scientific process.   But, any careful examination indicates that science is not a *single* method or technique.   To suppose that all the sciences proceed by one precise technique of observation, analysis, and generalization is to fail to appreciate the differences among the physical, social, and mathematical sciences, or even the differences that exist within a given discipline such as physics.   History, sociology, and archaeology are sciences, just as are astronomy, mechanics, and chemistry. In its various expressions, science reflects processes of investigation and discovery that display both *common* and *diverse* elements.   Although the techniques and tools of the sciences are highly various, one thing common to all of them, whatever be the differences among them, is the use of the principles of deductive logic.

A misconception that must be discarded for a proper understanding of scientific processes is that they are "inductive" or "empirical," while non-scientific disciplines are "deductive" or "theoretical."   This bifurcation reflects a failure to recognize the dominant role that deduction and theory plays in even the most elementary scientific studies.   Hypothesis and theory are indispensable for the astronomer who searches for data about Mars or for the botanist who seeks to identify and classify the flora of the Andes.   As a matter of fact, often in the history of science an ingenious hypothesis or new theory has been the instrument by which a whole new area of knowledge and research has been opened to investigation.   New theories in science have frequently produced revolutions in man's thoughts and daily actions.   The Copernican theory transformed astronomy, rocked the church and traditional philosophy, and modified man's whole perspective on his world.   Darwin's theory of evolution transformed biology and radically changed man's evaluation of himself and of his society.   In physics, theories of light by Max Planck, the theory of relativity by Einstein, and the theory of the nuclear structure of the atom by Niels Bohr are a few of the hypotheses that have made the twentieth century a new scientific era.   It is deductive logic that does business in the abstract ideas that constitute the theories of the various sciences.

Moreover, deductive logic is employed by any scientist who utilizes mathematics in handling data.   It is used by anyone who infers from a general scientific principle or law.   Students of algebra will recall employing laws of association, commutation, and distribution similar to those we have discussed in Part II.   Furthermore, patterns of argument such as Disjunctive Syllogism and Hypothetical Syllogism are used by the scientist as he employs mathematics and makes other sorts of inferences in his investigations.

The contention that induction is the basic method of thought or procedure in science *cannot be adopted without qualification, if it can be accepted at all.*   Whether there is such a thing as *pure induction*, starting with the particular and reasoning to a general rule, is highly questionable, as we will indicate through our examinations of facts and generalizations. *The principal mechanics of thought or inference in the scientific process is deduction*, which we have discussed in Part II.   Here in Part III we will present some of the ways in which deductive logic functions as the instrument of reasoning in the scientific process.

15–2. THE FACT

Facts, it is said, are the building blocks of the empirical sciences.   The emphasis upon factual data was one of the important factors in the development of modern science.   The modern scientific movement is distinguished, in part at least, by facts that are established by impartial observation.   Facts, which are in some sense rooted in sensory data and are made precise by highly developed methods for quantification, are tested by ongoing experience and experiment before they are accepted as building blocks of knowledge in science.

The scientific accent upon factual data has permeated contemporary Western life and culture.   Children are trained to be "factually ori-

[Handwritten at top: Is a "scientific" fact a fact that is known by scientists to be a fact? Or is it a fact that is relevant to the ~~esp~~ investigations of scientists, whether known or unknown?]

ented." Congressmen and businessmen demand "the facts." Laymen often contend that "the true facts" have not been given to them by specialists in some areas. The public demands that "the facts" be presented in a trial, and competent lawyers and judges struggle to ascertain what these facts are. Responding to a general demand and their own desire to make their discipline "scientific," historians try to produce a record of the past that is "factual." The nature of a fact in history, law, psychology, chemistry, or astronomy is, however, very difficult to define. Frequently, factual data among the sciences are more difficult to describe or define than are abstract ideas and logical principles.

Nevertheless, the modern world has profited greatly from science's emphasis on factual data. In general, the orientation toward facts that has infused our society has been salutary. But, among laymen there has developed an uncritical and confused understanding of the nature of factual data, especially as they appear in the scientific process. Frequently, we hear references to the "simple facts." On occasions, students may ask that their teachers give them the "simple facts," devoid of any theory or interpretation. And some students have naïvely contended that they are interested only in science where men handle simply factual data. This widespread plea for the "simple facts" is understandable but hopeless, for a careful consideration reveals that facts are not easy to ascertain and they are seldom simple.

From a scientific perspective, what are the marks of a fact? Is it something that is observable? Yes, a scientific fact is the result of observation of some sort. Without further specification or qualification, however, this criterion would permit a mirage, the redness of the Fall leaves, an hallucination, and the solid state of a table to be facts.

The qualification is sometimes advanced that a scientific fact is physical or directly observable. But, are physicists and chemists dealing with facts when they make assertions about electrons and neutrons? Are psychologists referring to facts when they speak of complexes and manias? Is it a fact that Jones has an I.Q. of 160, or that the writer of *Romeo and Juliet* was an actor as well a playwright? In some sense such statements are factual ones or represent attempts to present factual data; yet, the data referred to are not properly described as physical and directly observable. Although a fact is frequently not physical and often only indirectly observable, it is at some level rooted or grounded in perception of sensory data. We perceive a precipitate formed in a beaker, we examine the patterns on an X-ray film, or we note the velocity of the rotating vanes of a radiometer. In general, in some context, we deal with perceived sensory data. We cannot enter the epistemological, metaphysical, and psychological issues that are involved in this matter. It is sufficient here to emphasize that knowledge in the scientific process is based on factual data that are the result of some kind of apprehension of sensory data.

In observation that establishes or creates a fact, man does not just "reflect," as in the case of a mirror-image, what is given to him. He is not passive—a Lockean "blank tablet" upon which external structures and events simply leave their marks. In the observation and definition of a fact, man is involved as *an instrument*. Man's capacities for awareness, perception, and definition are, of course, limited. In receiving what is presented to him or observed by him, he functions within the limits his nature and nervous system impose. If dogs do not have the capacity to deal with color or to think in terms of cause-effect relations, then whatever apprehensions of data occur in them will always be conditioned by the absence of these two factors. Similarly, man's limitations, whatever they be, affect his awareness of and handling of data. The limits of the visual spectrum among electromagnetic waves is a case in point. The nature of a scientific fact is always in part determined by the nature of man, who is the *instrument for the reception of data*.

In his handling of data, man is much more, however, than a limited instrument of perception. He is *active* in the process of apprehending data. He does more than merely respond to "outside" stimuli. Man *attacks* both "internal" and "external" stimuli. He *approaches* and *manipulates* what is presented to him. This approach or attack plays its part in determining what a scientific fact will be.

Man's attack upon stimuli is always an attack from some perspective, from some specific physical, emotional, and intellectual orientation. Each man possesses a history of past experiences. Each is the result of a process of cultural conditioning. In many instances, his experiences are not ones of his own choosing. In other cases, they are. In either case, they result in a "mind-set" or perspective from which the approach to present stimuli is made. The mind-set of the twentieth-century schoolboy makes it obvious to him, as he watches a boat disappear, that there is a curvature of the earth's surface. But, a learned Greek of Plato's Academy, observing the sail of an inbound vessel, sensed no data that suggested to him the curvature of the earth. The facts of human anatomy are quite different for the layman, for the general student of biology, and for the specialist in physiology. These differences are based on other factors besides variations in interests, in depth of investigations, and level of acquired information. Among these other factors are the varied perspectives and mind-sets that have been developed by experience and education among the perceivers. They, too, determine how things are "seen."

Our general world-view, whether rational or non-rational, is also a part of the orientation or perspective from which we attack stimuli.

Convinced that the "natural" state of affairs was one of rest, Aristotle attacked and interpreted the facts of motion quite differently from a modern physicist. And, when in the fourteenth and fifteenth centuries men were moved to take the contrary position, namely, that the "natural" state of affairs was one of motion, the factual data related to motion in nature became quite different from what Aristotle knew. Louis Agassiz, not accepting Darwin's evolutionary world-view, saw some facts different from those Darwin apprehended. Science acknowledges the pervasive influences of such a world-view, but it insists that any prevailing *scientific* world-view must be logical or rational. One of the chief demands made in the scientific process is that the approach to and investigation of facts be logical and rational, insofar as this is possible.

Other factors also shape the nature of scientific facts. Observing involves an *interest* or an *intent* on the part of the investigator. While it is true that interests and intents are conditioned by past experiences, they are also modified or shaped by present emotions, temporary concerns, passing hypotheses, or chance. Who has not, under the influence of some emotion or interest, glanced at a vague representation and observed one thing (a small black spot, apprehended as an insect), and a few moments later in a second glance, reflecting a different interest or feeling, sensed the object to be something else (a small black spot, apprehended as an ink stain)? With a particular hypothesis dominating the mind, factual data with certain characteristics appear that are modified when they are viewed under the influence of another interest or from the perspective of another hypothesis.

Another aspect of human interest or intent in relation to factual data is man's desire to manipulate or control what he encounters. The purpose of modern science is not merely to *understand* experience or data, but to *control* it. This has been made abundantly clear by the important place taken by controlled experimentation in the modern scientific process. Roger and Francis Bacon were among the pioneers who first emphasized the importance of experiment or manipulation in the construction of scientific knowledge. Mathematics and deductive logic have been employed in the scientific process to advance man's control of the world. Factual data and factual knowledge that emerge from man's intent to control the world have been in some measure shaped by that intent.

A fact always emerges in a context. We have already indicated that this context involves man as an instrument of perception and man as an agent of attack upon stimuli. Furthermore, factual data are conditioned by human experiences, fashioned by man's intellectual structure, and influenced by human intentions. But, in addition, a fact always appears in the context of other facts, generalizations, and relations. An isolated fact is non-existent. The fact that sodium chloride is completely ionized in the solid state appears in the context of a host of other facts, generalizations, and relations related to sodium, chloride, sodium chloride, ionization, the solid state, and so on. Thus, another distinctive feature of the scientific process is the constant reappraisal to which the context of a given fact is subjected. Through this regular re-examination, the accuracy and reliability of facts are maintained or improved.

The scientific process is characterized by an insistence upon impartial observation in the endeavor to establish facts. Partiality and impartiality are, of course, matters of degree and are relative to each other; but this does not mean that there is not a clear distinction between the person who observes with discernable bias and the impartial observer. The biased observer not only entertains a theory, but he strongly and unswervingly believes in it; as a result, he sees as a fact what will fit into or buttress his theory. Under the influence of strong belief and emotion, he robs the data of their integrity and makes them submit to his theory. An impartial observer will also have a hypothesis in mind and a prevailing mind-set; but he has no purpose that corrupts, no emotional commitment that blinds, and no determination to refuse to modify his beliefs. His search for the facts is disinterested—as disinterested, at least, as any human investigation can be. Of course, in their research scientists fall short of the ideals of impartial observation and disinterestedness; but this by no means diminishes the significance or relevance of these ideals in the prosecution of scientific inquiries.

Scientists and philosophers of science have emphasized the social or communal nature of the scientific process. One weakness of traditional philosophy and science was their tendency to interpret scientific investigation as chiefly a private or personal enterprise. Descartes, Hegel, and many others display this perspective. In contrast, contemporary science insists that the search for knowledge is, explicitly or implicitly, a collective or group enterprise. The greater number of successes in the prosecution of modern scientific tasks has resulted from cooperation among many inquirers. Modern scientific research is so complex and demands so many different tools, conceptual and mechanical, that it generally requires the combined resources of a community of investigators. Moreover, scientific knowledge and factual data emerge in a historical and contemporary community. A fact, in the scientific sense, is not a private experience. A scientific community has given birth to it, possesses it, and uses it. What one man offers as a candidate for factual status must be corroborated or checked by many impartial observers. Personal discoveries must be ones that, under similar conditions, others can discover and confirm. Scientific facts are interpersonal and have a historical and public character.

The public or communal character of factual data in science has resulted in certain distinct benefits. First, through a recognition of the public character of facts, the goal of impartial observation is increasingly achieved. The subjective and personal biases that produce biased observations are limited or checked in an interpersonal context. If interpersonal agreement about the nature of a fact cannot be achieved, the phenomenon is generally rejected. Second, the involvement of a community of investigators in a scientific enterprise is a condition for the corroboration or verification of reports of facts and for establishing their reliability. In brief, a fact is said to be reliable if, time after time, as impartial observers confront it, they find it to appear the same or to yield the same measurement. Scientific facts are distinguished by their reliability in contrast to the "facts" cited by the man on the street or by the casual observer. Third, the cross-fertilization among ideas, the cooperative endeavors, and the increased scope of investigation that is possible in a community of investigators or in a collective search for knowledge have been important factors in the rapid strides taken in modern science and technology.

A scientific fact is made precise by highly refined methods for observation and quantification. Precision and reliability clearly distinguish scientific facts from other so-called "facts." For many persons, it may be a fact that the room is "hot"; but for a scientist it is a fact that the room's temperature is 100.6 degrees Fahrenheit. For more advanced scientific purposes, the description of the room's temperature and of the attendant conditions will be given in even more precise terms. Precision of factual data is dependent upon refined observational techniques, highly developed procedures for quantification, careful and detailed delineations of the contexts of the data, and so forth. A drive in the direction of greater and greater precision in the observation and description of factual data is an important characteristic of the scientific process.

As we have remarked, one of the chief features of a scientific fact is that it is quantified. The common-sense terms of "heavy," "bright," "rapid," etc., are replaced by quantitative terms, such as "kilogram," "milligram," "miles per second," "ampere," "cycles per second," etc. This quantification of data is a factor in achieving precision in science and in constantly reconstructing facts in more meaningful and useful ways. Through quantification, the scientist's manipulation of facts and his descriptions of their interconnections are made easier.

Whenever in the scientific process a fact is determined or established, whatever be the terms by which it is described, it is a tentative definition or determination. No conditions of observation or quantification are complete, final, or perfect. The scientific process is a continuous one. The established scientific facts of today are subject to change tomorrow. And, since one fact never stands in isolation from other facts, investigations of materials that are seemingly remote from what we are examining may bring about significant changes in our understanding of the latter. Any given factual data are always relative to other data and are always open to reconstruction or reinterpretation. The very nature of the process of science does not permit us to declare any fact to be absolute.

While many other things can be said about the nature of a fact in the scientific process, we conclude this section with a summary of some of the characteristics of a scientific fact. A scientific fact is:

1. At some level rooted or grounded in perception of sensory data;
2. The result of impartial or disinterested observations;
3. Conditioned by man as instrument for its reception, and by the attack man makes from his framework of experience, including his world-view, his feelings and motives, and his categories of thought;
4. Established in the context of other facts, generalizations, and relations;
5. Always the object of attention by a community of investigators;
6. Always tested in ongoing experience, experiments, or both;
7. Always interpersonal;
8. As precise as possible;
9. Quantified; and
10. Tentative, not absolute.

15–3.   GENERALIZATION

The last section described certain features of a scientific fact and indicated something of its limitations and relativity. In passing, we have simply alluded to the role of induction or generalization in the scientific process. A brief examination of this matter is desirable.

The contention that in science observations or statements expressing them inherently contain within themselves the grounds for expressing general or universal statements is a questionable one. This presumed movement from the particular to the general is what the term "induction" is generally supposed to designate. The inductive process is often described as if the scientist, beginning with a clean slate, examines a series of particulars and *from them* draws forth a general statement. The problem of generalization is highlighted in "induction by simple enumeration"—the question as to how, or when, in counting black crows, we can affirm the universal statement, "All crows are black." The empirical side of science says in existential spirit, "This is another black crow," and the rational side proclaims in abstractions, "All crows are black." It *appears as if* the scientist begins with particulars and basic or existential statements and then simply derives from them universal statements or general laws.

On the contrary, logical formulations and abstractions that are so common and necessary to the scientific process are *brought to* the observed data or particulars in order to interpret them and in order to manipulate them. Generalizations or laws *do not arise from the particulars themselves* in some secret manner—as if by some sort of spontaneous generation within the core of sensory data or by some kind of conceptual partheno-genesis. Generalizations or concepts *do not come from observed data; they are brought to them.* This is one reason why in the problem of "induction by simple enumeration" we are unable to suggest how or when the particulars enumerated lead us to a generalization; for, in fact, they do not. Bertrand Russell is correct when he remarks that "what is called induction appears . . . to be either disguised deduction or a mere method of making plausible guesses."[1]

In the problem of induction by simple enumeration, we confront two issues: (1) whether or not generalizations or universal assertions *arise from* specific factual data and the existential statements that express them; (2) given a generalization or universal assertion, can it be *justified* or *warranted* by appeal to factual data or the existential statements that express them? We have briefly responded to the first issue in accord with a contemporary scientific perspective. With regard to the second, we must recognize that, except for the few cases in which one can canvass each and every instance referred to by a universal statement, generalizations or universal statements cannot be logically justified by invoking factual data because of our inability to investigate each and every instance referred to or because of the limitations in time, energy, and scope of inquiry that attach to human investigations. This idea was expressed earlier when, in Section 13–5, we indicated that the inference from Φ_a or from $(\exists_x)\,\Phi_x$ to $(\forall_x)\Phi_x$ was unjustified.

Ordinarily, a scientist approaches a particular set of data with a hypothesis, or several possible hypotheses or concepts, already in mind. These concepts, hypotheses, or tentative generalizations are a part of the context within which he examines the data or particulars. He has already made judgments about the possible category or hypothesis to use in dealing with the data before him. It, of course, helps to make the observed data meaningful. Hypotheses may be repudiated because they lack coherence or are inconsistent with related materials. They may be rejected on the ground that they lack scope in descriptive capacity or because they fail to relate meaningfully to other descriptive generaliza-tions. A hypothesis may also not be precise enough to be of any signifi-cance and will be cast aside for this reason. Or, a complex hypothesis may be discarded because there is a simpler one available that is just as

[1] Bertrand Russell, *The Principles of Mathematics* (New York: W. W. Norton & Co., Inc., 1937), p. 11.

adequate for describing or interpreting the data under consideration. These and other possible criteria play their roles in the rejection of some hypotheses and the acceptance of others as the scientist deals with his data.

The particular data in an area of scientific inquiry are examined in the light of some tentative generalizations. These tentative generalizations may be about a highly limited set of data of a comparatively simple nature; for example, "All students in this class who are failing rank in the lowest one-fourth of the student body on the basis of entrance scores." In other cases, they refer to a wider and more complex range of data; for instance, "The shortest wave visible in the spectrum has a wave length of about 0.0004 mm. and the longest has a wave length of about 0.0007 mm." The factual data are examined by means of such generalizations. They seem to confirm or deny a tentative generalization used in understanding or interpreting them. Thus, we are "induced" by the particulars *to affirm or deny* the generalization. However, we do not "induce" the generalization *from the particulars.* As a result of examining particulars from the perspective of a selected general hypothesis, we may be induced to restructure this hypothesis or to advance a new one. Contrary to the conventional understanding of the situation, what takes place in *induction or generalization may be described as a process of moving from a general hypothesis to the examination of particulars, with the result that one may be induced by the data to assert or deny the hypothesis in use.*

The history of science offers abundant testimony for this interpretation of induction or generalization. When Joseph Priestley on August 1, 1774, generalized that the "air" he had produced was air free of phlogiston, or was "dephlogisticated air," he brought a tentative generalization to the interpretation of the data before him. For example, a mouse lived in the gas for twice as long as it did in an equal amount of common air; and in the gas, red-hot wood sparkled. Although Priestley failed to realize the importance of his discovery, Lavoisier (1743–1793) later confirmed the results and named the gas "oxygen." Lavoisier's hypothesis that oxygen played a role in the respiration of both plants and animals was subsequently employed to arrive at new understandings and interpretations of a wide range of data. The particular data confirmed a hypothesis brought to the data, and the confirming experiences "induced" the investigator to continue the hypothesis in use as a "theory." Continued confirmation establishes such a theory as a "law."

Success in scientific discovery or generalization involves more than a constant handling of particulars and a continuing review of factual data. There are no established rules for scientific discovery or generalization. The scientist must possess *imagination* and a *facility for making plausible guesses.* At this point, *the scientific process is creative*; it is not a rote procedure. Imaginative hypotheses should be at one's disposal as he examines observed data. Many of these imaginative hypotheses will, of course, prove worthless in handling particular data. But, often a knowledgeable guess, an intuitive insight, or a clever analogy enables one to achieve a creative and useful inductive synthesis.

Mendelejeff (1834–1907), by his arrangement of known elements in order of their atomic weights, hypothesized unknown elements with certain properties. His generalizations were the basis for the reinterpretation of certain data and for the discovery of new elements. By a stroke of creative imagination, Kepler (1571–1630) brought the concept of the ellipse to certain astronomical data in order to interpret the movements of the planets. Mendel (1822–1884) shrewdly hypothesized that the concept of dominance would meaningfully interpret the data secured from his examination of the growth of garden peas. The data confirmed this generalization for him; and, after further testing, the hypothesis became known as the law of dominance in heredity.

Generalizations or inductive syntheses are almost always based on a limited number of particulars. Yet scientific generalizations are, in a real sense, universal statements. Science insists that any generalization be subject to testing and future experience. As they emerge in the scientific process, new data may challenge old generalizations, as the history of science so clearly reveals. Scientific generalizations, then, must not be taken as absolutes. They do not constitute a permanent foundation for knowledge, but only a temporary one. When we build the superstructure of knowledge on such foundations, we should be aware of the fact that those foundations may soon need to be replaced or repaired.

In closing this section, we should note that men of science always caution themselves and others against too hastily accepting a generalization as established. The communal nature of the scientific process is one protection against such hasty acceptance. And, the demand that any generalization must be corroborated in experiment or experience is a safeguard against its being too hastily accepted or becoming too firmly entrenched. The willingness to test and check generalizations against additional data is one of the reasons that science can advance sound, valuable, and useful assertions.

15–4. CAUSE AND EFFECT

The man on the street, the philosopher, and the scientist all speak of cause and effect relations. They do not all, however, mean the same thing by this term. Perhaps no one can escape using this category because it is rooted in a "primitive animal faith." But there are many different interpretations of its nature, its operations, and its foundations.

The meaning of causality in philosophy and science has been a debatable topic for a very long time. Various thinkers, from ancient times to the present—Aristotle, Aquinas, Descartes, Spinoza, Hume, Kant, and others—have discussed it in detail. An attempt to resolve the philosophical issues related to the idea of causality is not within the scope of our study. Nonetheless, one's philosophical position on this matter does condition how he understands the nature and functions of the idea of cause in the scientific process. For example, if we agree with Kant that the cause and effect relation is a category of the human understanding that is used to handle materials received in sensation, then we understand causality and the law of causality to be projections of the human mind; and we must remain agnostic about its reality apart from the knowing mind. According to Kant, science will always be deterministic and will always speak in terms of cause, because the knowing mind will have it no other way. On the other hand, if we agree with Hume, the property of necessity is removed from our understanding of a cause-effect relation; and we understand the relation to refer to the constant conjunction of two events, A followed by B, which psychologically conditions us to think of A "causing" B. Consent to other philosophical notions of causality will lead to yet different views about the nature and role of cause in the scientific process.

Scientists themselves have also pondered the nature and role of causality. The various interpretations advanced by men of science are the concern of the history and philosophy of science. The student may be surprised to learn that certain scientific disciplines, such as physics, rarely use the term. Those in the field of science who do use the category of causality have differing conceptions about its meaning. The differences relate, not only to the "kinds" of causes, but to the question at what level of reality a cause is "operative." It would be outside the scope of our discussion—as well as excessively bold—for us to attempt to solve the problems centering on the use of this category in the scientific process. For the non-scientific student and the beginning student in logic, it will be appropriate and sufficient simply to emphasize a few of the issues related to this matter and voice certain warnings.

The terms "cause" and "effect" seem most useful at the practical level and in the domain of everyday life. "The failure of the brakes caused the accident," "Death was caused by cancer," and "The student's failure was caused by his unwillingness to study" are meaningful and useful assertions. Whether or not "cause" is a satisfactory term in science is another question. Contrary to popular views and attitudes, causal terminology enjoys a limited use in the scientific process. When it is used, it is frequently employed with a very special sense. "Cause-effect relation" is a term similar to "solid," "substance," and "the present," which are useful and meaningful in common communication but which are not transferable to the scientific process unless they are very carefully redefined. In general, we discover that terms other than "causality" express better what the scientist intends to say.

Certainly, in the modern scientific process the idea that a single causal chain leads to a given event is rejected. A given phenomenon or happening is not viewed as the result of a linear development of a series of previous events, termed "antecedent causes." An event occurs in a *field* or *context* of events, each of which, in one sense or another, can be termed "a cause." From this perspective, we would speak of many causes. An event occurs in the context of a set of conditions. When we speak of *the* cause of an event, we have generally selected some one factor from a complex context of factual details and conditions and labeled it "the cause." Oversimplification is, thus, inescapable.

N. R. Hanson points out that:

> Causal connexions are expressible only in languages that are many-levelled in explanatory power. This is why causal language is diagnostic and prognostic, and why the links-in-a-chain view is artificial. This is why within a context the cause-words are not "parallel" to the effect-words, and why causes explain effects but not vice versa. For "cause"-words are charged; they carry a conceptual pattern with them.[2]

> This is the whole story about necessary connection. "Effect" and "cause," so far from naming links in a queue of events, gesture towards webs of crisscrossed theoretical notions, information, and patterns of experiment. In a context and by way of a theory, certain effect-words inevitably follow the utterance of certain cause-words. . . .
> Causes certainly are connected with effects; but this is because our theories connect them, not because the world is held together by cosmic glue.[3]

Hanson's contentions that cause-words reflect a conceptual pattern and are connected to effect-words because our theories so connect them provide an orientation for understanding the category of cause and effect as an expression of a predictive situation. Certain scientists interpret a causal explanation as one by which they can make successful predictions from a hypothesis. The "law of gravity" ($s = \frac{1}{2}gt^2$) is used as a basis for predicting how a body will fall toward the earth's surface (in a vacuum), and the predictions are successful. Gravitational force (expressed in the acceleration constant, g) is termed the "cause" of the body's fall. Predictions of this sort take on a deductive character. In another instance, a similar situation may be expressed, "If I have an acid, then the litmus paper turns red; I have an acid; therefore, the litmus paper should turn red." This deductive prediction is corroborated by experi-

---

[2] N. R. Hanson, *Patterns of Discovery* (Cambridge: The University Press, 1958), p. 60.

[3] *Ibid.*, p. 64.

ence. As a consequence, we are led to say that the presence of acid is the "cause" of the litmus paper turning red.

In certain areas of scientific inquiry, causality is viewed in a statistical manner. A certain correlation between two sets of statistical data is the basis for calling one set a cause of the other. Thus, if there is a high positive statistical correlation between overweight and heart attacks, then overweight is listed as a cause of heart attacks. If there is a high positive statistical correlation between the taking of a certain drug and the birth of deformed children, then the drug is termed a cause of these deformities.

Any talk about cause and effect relations should be recognized as talk about abstractions. The event called *cause* and the event called *effect* are isolated facts, selected from the complex context of events that is actually experienced or known. What this means is to some extent sensed by the soldier who, imbedded in a complex web of events, has his arm shot off in battle. The cause was the machine gun fire. But if he had not stooped to tie his shoe laces, if he had not received his orders, if he had not been so slow in executing them, or if any of many other conditions had not obtained, the event would not have occurred. To speak of the machine gun fire as the cause of the injury is to oversimplify a complex situation by isolating and abstracting one connection or relation from many others.

Scientists frequently use causality as a *methodological* rule or principle, setting aside theoretical or philosophical issues and questions. They make a distinction between causality as a working principle and causality as metaphysically interpreted. This is a justifiable and useful distinction. As a working principle or methodological rule, causality serves as a functionally useful tool for manipulating factual data and for suggesting interrelations among events. The ordinary reader of scientific literature does not always recognize this. Because of the knotty problems connected with cause and effect, it seems best to assume that a scientist is using the principle of causality as a methodological rule, unless we are informed otherwise.

15–5. NECESSARY AND SUFFICIENT CONDITIONS

Some of the problems one encounters in dealing with causality in science have been suggested in Section 15–4. As we indicated, we cannot involve ourselves in the scientific and philosophical debates over the meanings of "cause." Very often people connect cause-effect relations with necessary and sufficient conditions, or at least they connect talk about the one with talk about the other. Consequently, we should make a few remarks about the formulations of necessary and sufficient conditions as deductive principles in the scientific process.

The ideas of necessary and sufficient conditions are categories drawn from logic and mathematics for use in treating or rationalizing empirical data. They are methodological principles. They have their roots in

deductive reason. Moreover, it is possible to speak about their meanings
and functions without involving ourselves in the philosophical debates
over the nature of cause-effect relations. The student may be aware of
the use of these ideas in mathematics, as in the case of the assertion that
a plane figure being a circle is a sufficient condition for equal chords
intercepting equal arcs. In handling the conditional statements in Part
II, we had already employed the terms "condition" and "necessary condition." In the empirical sciences, these words are also used; and they
are employed with beneficial results. We encounter such statements as
"A voltage applied to a lamp circuit is a necessary condition for the illumi-
nation of the lamp."

Simply stated, among the empirical sciences, one phenomenon, A, is
said to be a *sufficient condition* for another, B, if when A occurs, then B
occurs. Thus, igniting a match in a gas-filled room or chamber is a
sufficient condition for an explosion. Or, building up excessive pressure
within a closed chamber is a sufficient condition for an explosion. Similarly, boiling perchloric acid is a sufficient condition for an explosion.
Obviously, there are other conditions that are followed by an explosion.
When we assert *one* phenomenon to be a sufficient condition for another,
we admit the possibility of *other* conditions for the event specified. Now
the connection affirmed between any one of several sufficient conditions
and the resulting event can be expressed by the logical formula $(A \supset B)$,
which we express as "If A, then B."

Now, when we assert that one phenomenon, A, is a *necessary condition*
for another, B, we mean that, without A, there is no occurrence of B (but
we recognize that A is not the only factor that is necessary for the occurrence of B). Thus, the presence of sulphuric acid (H_2SO_4) in a beaker is
a necessary condition for the production of hydrogen gas (H_2); but it is
not all that is needed. We require, in addition, such things as the presence of a metal, say, metallic zinc (Zn), giving the reaction conventionally
denoted by

$$H_2SO_4 + Zn \rightarrow ZnSO_4 + H_2$$

In this case, sulphuric acid is a necessary condition for the appearance
of hydrogen gas; that is, if H_2SO_4 is *not* present, then H_2 is *not* present.
Consequently, we logically formulate a necessary condition between two
phenomena, A and B, in this way: $(A' \supset B')$. The concepts of necessary
condition $(A' \supset B')$ and sufficient condition $(A \supset B)$ are extensively used
in the scientific process.

In a few cases, we also want to express the idea that one phenomenon,
A, is *both* a necessary *and* a sufficient condition for another phenomenon,
B. This is formulated, as one may easily surmise, by a conjunction of
the two formulations already advanced: $[(A \supset B) \cdot (A' \supset B')]$. From

one point of view, scientific inquirers have as their ideal objective the formulation of necessary and sufficient conditions among phenomena. But, they can rarely be justifiably formulated in the empirical sciences. One generally has to be content (due, among other things, to the multiplicity of relevant factors in empirical situations) with either the formulation of a necessary condition or the formulation of a sufficient condition. In the formal discipline of mathematics, necessary and sufficient conditions occur more frequently, as in such a simple assertion as that two lines (l_1 and l_2) in a plane being parallel is a necessary and sufficient condition for the equality of the alternate interior angles (α and β) formed by a transversal (t) cutting them.

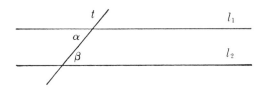

The logical symbolization of necessary, sufficient, and necessary and sufficient conditions depicts the *logical* or *mathematical* relations that prevail between two categories. No metaphysical, epistemological, or theological significance is carried by the symbols; and the student should not read any such meanings into them. If a scientist, as an individual, entertains such meanings, they will have to be made known by additional assertions on his part. The logical formulations for necessary and sufficient conditions express relations established in deductive logic at the level of conceptualization. They can sometimes be *applied to* connections among empirical data; but the question of their application, whether successful or unsuccessful, is quite another matter than the logical or mathematical relations expressed in the formulations.

EXERCISE SET 15–5

Symbolize the following statements:

a. An inductance in an electrical circuit is a necessary condition for a time lag.

b. A current flowing in a wire is a sufficient condition for a voltage drop across its terminals.

c. At least one good eye is a necessary condition for visual perception.

d. A sufficient condition for offering a course in social problems is the enrollment of at least three students.

e. A necessary and sufficient condition for a dyadic relation to be irreflexive is that it be intransitive.

15–6. PREDICTION

Science is marked by the desire to predict and control the future as well as by the desire to know and describe phenomena of the past and present. Perhaps it can be said that scientists desire to "know" the future in a way parallel to their knowing the past. They predicate that, if their generalizations are adequately descriptive of past and present particulars, then future particulars should conform to those generalizations. Hoping or believing that future data will conform to their generalizations, but ready to readjust them if the data do not, scientists undertake to manipulate the world and to control future events.

Scientific predictions are made as precise as possible. The greater their precision, the greater are the chances of exercising control over the world and of achieving a wider and deeper knowledge of its structure and functions. Predictions are precise to the extent that the facts and generalizations upon which they are based are precise, and to the degree that mathematical and logical rigor have been employed in the deductions related to them. This element of precision is one of the factors that clearly distinguishes scientific prediction from the primitive or speculative predictions of seers and fortune-tellers, in the past and the present. Loosely defined, vague, or ambiguous predictions, such as those of the famous oracles of Delphi, are hard to falsify. Clarity and precision are features of scientific predictions. The traditional weather prophet may not be "wrong" as often as the scientific weatherman, because the latter's demands are more precise than the former's. The "prophet's" warning that a storm is coming may be judged fulfilled if it rains or storms within two weeks. But scientific prediction calls for thunderstorms of a certain severity as a frontal system passes through a city between the hours of six and eight on a given evening.

Scientific predictions are or should be stated in such terms that the conditions for falsifying them are obvious or are easily determined. A precipitate forms in the solution, or it does not. An electrical current appears in the circuit and registers on the meter, or it does not. The vaccine provides immunity from polio in 95 per cent of those receiving it, or it does not. Experiments based on hypotheses express predictions that are framed so that the conditions for falsifying them are clearly understood and are capable of achievement. Tests applied to predictions made from hypotheses are attempts to falsify them. One might go so far as to say that a necessary condition for a genuine scientific hypothesis is that it be capable of being falsified.

Scientific prediction involves numerous assumptions. It is based on assumptions about the quality and reliability of past observations and generalizations. A more basic assumption is deposited in the conviction

But if this is a book on logic should it not consider
as exactly as possible what sort of validation such a principle
has?

FACTORS IN THE SCIENTIFIC PROCESS   231

that what has prevailed in the past will be found to hold for the future. This is often called the *postulate of predictive uniformity*. It is a practical conviction. Better said, it is a methodological rule or axiom, just as is causality. It is a heuristic principle. Philosophically, one may theorize about it in terms of the idea of an orderly or designed universe or the idea of a mathematical matrix of probabilities. In actual scientific work, however, it is simply a very useful tool to use in inquiry.

Probably the primary role of prediction in the scientific process is one of testing or corroborating generalizations or hypotheses. Experimentation and prediction go hand in hand. In experimentation, the scientist undertakes to control the world. In doing this, he is guided by certain ideas, ideals, and expectations—hypotheses that are either loosely framed or set forth in a highly articulated manner. In any case, his thinking or conjecturing about the future results of his manipulative endeavors constitutes prediction, implicitly or explicitly. Earlier we said that a scientific fact or generalization becomes established because it stands the test of experience, experiment, or both. In experimental situations, we have a controlled environment that is not usually present in ordinary experience. Under controlled conditions of experiment, we predict by making deductions from a generalization or hypothesis. The predictions from it must be such that it can be sustained or falsified in a community of investigators.

Thus, drug X is asserted to be 80 per cent effective in eliminating cancerous growths in rats within three months. We predict that, given a collection of 200 rats possessing cancerous growths, the administration of the drug will within three months eliminate all signs of cancerous growth in at least 160 rats. The presence of cancerous tissue in, say, 90 per cent of the rats at the close of the three-month period means that the prediction fails. The generalization is thus falsified.

A closer examination of this matter is desirable. A theory, hypothesis, or generalization is in some sense universal in scope, or at least it involves some universal statements. A universal quantification is found among the statements that constitute the hypothesis. "Arsine is an extremely poisonous gas," "All crows are black," and "Electrolysis of water increases the concentration of molecules containing deuterium" are universal in character and would be symbolized by the use of the universal quantifier ($\forall_x$). But, how do we test a universal statement? Only in the case of a universal with a restricted domain does one have a universal statement where he can examine every instance indicated. Human experience is limited. No one has experienced all crows—past, present, and future— and discovered that each and every one is black. By appeal to empirical data, universal statements such as "All crows are black" cannot be proved.

Proof is found at the rational or logical level. We may *rationally* or *logically* compare a generalization with other generalizations and in the process prove or disprove it. Generalizations may be compared with singular, particular, and existential statements. These may contradict or deny the generalizations. Science has been marked by its practice of testing generalizations by experimentation based on prediction. If from a generalization (in connection with other premises, some of which may be existential) we deduce instances or particular conclusions that are specifically predictive, then a unique opportunity is provided for verifying the predicted instance or particular conclusion. Observers can be prepared for the occurrence of the predicted event. Its occurrence verifies the specific prediction, which in turn testifies to or corroborates the generalization from which it was deduced. The failure of the prediction to be realized falsifies the generalization from which it was made.

If, for example, our generalization is "No metal is liquid," then we deductively predict that the next metal or any future metal we examine will not be a liquid. This prediction is falsified when we encounter mercury. We reject the generalization from which the prediction was made. If our generalization is "All planets travel about their suns in elliptical orbits," then we may proceed to make specific predictions, in keeping with other necessary information, about the orbital paths of Mercury, Jupiter, etc. Our specific predictions being fulfilled, we then continue to use the generalization until it is rejected by the failure of some additional predictions or by the adoption of a different generalization that is more in accord with the data. Notice that, in this case, our experience (so far) bears out the generalization; but the generalization is *not proved*, rationally or by experience.

Let us examine this matter of experimentally testing generalizations by looking more closely at some of the logical operations that are involved. Symbolically, we express "All crows are black" by

$$1. \ (\mathbf{\forall}_x)(C_x \supset B_x)$$

where C_x means "x is a crow" and B_x means "x is black." Perhaps we add to this universal statement, the additional statement

$$2. \ (\mathbf{\exists}_x)(C_x)$$

and advance the conclusion

$$\text{Therefore, } (\mathbf{\exists}_x)(C_x B_x)$$

The simple proof of the validity of this argument will provide us with a further display, in skeletal form, of what we do in scientific observation, experimentation, and prediction.

3. (C_a) E.I., 2
4. $(C_a \supset B_a)$ U.I., 1
5. (B_a) M.P., 4, 3
6. $(C_a B_a)$ Conj., 3, 5
7. $(\exists x)(C_x B_x)$ E.G., 6

What we do in the second premiss is to assert the existence of a crow; and, as indicated by steps 3–7, we conclude that there is a crow that is black. Construed as a device for testing the generalization, the second premiss is conceived as referring to the future experience of the next crow we encounter. Our conclusion is, then, interpreted as a prediction that this next crow will be black.

One of the major functions of prediction in the scientific process is to exercise control over and to manipulate things in the universe. Prediction is a factor in manipulating metals, fuels, guidance mechanisms, etc., in the air and space sciences. It plays its role in manipulating drugs, blood, the functions of the body's organs, etc., in research on the human anatomy. The whole structure of modern applied science and technology is crucially dependent upon predictions made by deductive inferences from generalizations.

15–7.   VERIFICATION AND CORROBORATION

The words "verification" and "corroboration" have been used in our discussion of some of the factors in the scientific process. These terms are not synonymous and should not be used interchangeably. The distinction between them, therefore, should be clarified.

Verification means the process of demonstrating or establishing something to be true. "Verification," "verifiable," "veridical," and "verify" are words that refer to the establishment of truth. In the scientific process, this demonstrating or establishing is supposed to be achieved through appeal to observed data and experience. "This is water" is verified by common sense and experimental procedures that establish the assertion as true.

Corroboration is the process of confirming or buttressing a statement asserted. In the process of corroboration, nothing is proved or established as true. Corroborative data support but do *not demonstrate.* The discovery that some particular cancer was caused by a virus corroborates but does not prove the statement, "All cancers are caused by viruses."

Both verification and corroboration refer to the testimony that future experience brings to our statements. Experience or observation that has not been preceded by a prediction or has not been anticipated by some generalization is a fleeting, somewhat mysterious thing. A statement referring to it cannot be verified—perhaps it can, in a way, be corroborated by future experiences that appear to be similar to the earlier one. We look at the night sky and by chance observe what seems to be a flaming meteor. In a second, it is gone. Did we see a meteor, or did we see some other sort of phenomenon? Or, was it an optical illusion? We may consult with friends or companions to determine whether they too saw something in the sky. By such means, which involve additional or future observations, we may corroborate or confirm the particular observation we made. Not being prepared for the experience, we could not try to establish a context for demonstration, if indeed that were possible at all. Singular, particular, or existential statements made about past observations are not directly verifiable; they can only be indirectly corroborated.

Predictive statements are unique. In general, statements of prediction in science are not universal statements, but existential ones. They are deduced from a set of assumptions that includes universal statements, but they refer to a specific existential event in the future. Such predictions provide us with carefully defined situations for testing.

Universal statements, generalizations, or theories are generally not verifiable (except in such special circumstances as attach to a statement like "All ten marbles in this box are green").

It is the *singular, particular,* or *existential* statement that is, in general, verifiable. From the generalization "All paper burns when a lighted match is held to it" and the existential statement "There is a piece of paper to which a lighted match is held," we may proceed to deduce that there is a piece of paper to which a lighted match is held and which burns.

$$1. \ (\forall x)(P_x L_x \supset B_x)$$

$$2. \ (\exists x)(P_x L_x) \qquad /(\exists x)(P_x L_x B_x)$$

Expressed in predictive terms, we are arguing: "*If* all paper burns when a lighted match is held to it, and *if* in the future there is a specific piece of paper to which a lighted match is held, *then* that piece of paper will burn." We assert this with regard to factual data, using the existential form to do so.

When the actual test is performed and we observe the occurrence of the event that was predicted, we may say that the predictive existential statement is verified. The predictive statement can be verified, because before it occurred we were able to establish controlled conditions under which we and others could impartially observe what would happen. The event, impartially observed by a number of investigators, shows that the prediction was not in error. But, the general statement or hypothesis "All paper burns when a lighted match is held to it" is not verified. The successful prediction corroborates it. We noted in Chapter 13 that, logically, universal generalization (**U.G.**) does *not* permit the inferences

$$\Phi_a, \text{ hence } (\mathbf{\forall}_x)\Phi_x$$

and

$$(\mathbf{\exists}_x)\Phi_x, \text{ hence } (\mathbf{\forall}_x)\Phi_x$$

The burning of the paper referred to above would be symbolized by

$$(\mathbf{\exists}_x)(P_xL_xB_x)$$

Universal generalization does *not* permit us to assert $(\mathbf{\forall}_x)(P_xL_x \supset B_x)$. However, $(\mathbf{\forall}_x)(P_xL_x \supset B_x)$ was the generalization from which the prediction was made. This general statement has not been proved logically and it has not been proved in fact, since all instances of paper have not been subjected to the proper test. The general statement "All paper burns when a lighted match is held to it" has been corroborated in one instance. The experiment or test and the resulting existential assertion $(\mathbf{\exists}_x)(P_xL_xB_x)$ buttress or help to support the general assertion. One such experiment is not a very significant buttressing of the generalization, but numerous such successful experiments will lend additional support to or increase our confidence in the generalization.

If at a later date, we predict that, given the same conditions, another bit of paper will burn and it does not, the predictive statement is falsified, and, in addition, *the general statement from which it was deduced is falsified*. The existence of paper that will not burn under the specified conditions is a contradiction of the assertion that all paper burns under these conditions. We have seen earlier that, logically, $(\mathbf{\forall}_x)(\Phi_x \supset \Psi_x)$ is contradicted by $(\mathbf{\exists}_x)(\Phi_x \sim \Psi_x)$; or, in terms of our example, $(\mathbf{\forall}_x)(P_xL_x \supset B_x)$ is contradicted by $(\mathbf{\exists}_x)(P_xL_x \sim B_x)$.

A verified prediction supports a theory or generalization only tentatively. Given the limited character of human experience, individual or communal, corroboration can never establish certainty or constitute proof. The degree of corroboration increases as the number of corroborating instances increases, but no number of corroborating instances verifies a theory or generalization. In science, theories or generalizations are not directly demonstrated or verified; they are indirectly corroborated.

RECOMMENDED FOR FURTHER STUDY

N. R. Hanson's *Patterns of Discovery* (Cambridge, 1958) is particularly valuable and stimulating in its handling of observation and facts.

Karl R. Popper's *Conjectures and Refutations* (New York, 1962) is a worthwhile treatise; it explains the role of conjectures as a normal element in advancing scientific knowledge.

Three stimulating chapters on topics related to our discussion can be found in Bertrand Russell's *Mysticism and Logic and Other Essays* (New York, 1957)—

"The Relation of Sense-data to Physics," "On the Notion of Cause," and "Knowledge by Acquaintance and Knowledge by Description."

Part IV, "Empirical Knowledge," of W. H. Werkmeister's *The Basis and Structure of Knowledge* (New York, 1948) can be recommended for its discussion of scientific categories and principles in terms of specific scientific data and examples.

The student is also encouraged to read such works as Karl R. Popper, *The Logic of Scientific Discovery* (New York, 1959); Ernest Nagel, *The Structure of Science* (New York, 1961); H. L. Searles, *Logic and Scientific Methods* (2d ed.; New York, 1956); and Ernst Mach, *The Analysis of Sensations* (New York, 1959).

16

Principles of Deduction in the Scientific Process

The use of logical concepts and modes of thought is natural to man, the symbol-maker. Indeed, it is necessary in man's endeavor to develop his understanding of nature and to extend his control over the world.

Among other things, the language of logic (1) gives clear and exact expression to the distinctive human capacity for conceptualization, (2) confers upon man an otherwise unattainable computational power and control over the world, (3) uses symbols that are unambiguous and operations that are precise, (4) leads to demonstrations that are rigorous, and (5) has a capacity for widespread applications because of the abstract concepts in which it deals. In this chapter, we are interested chiefly in the last point: the applications of deductive logic, especially in the scientific process. How are the principles of deduction used in the scientific process? We shall be able, of course, to cite only a few examples of such applications and interpretations. We will *not* undertake a thorough discussion of what has traditionally been called *inductive logic* or *scientific method*.

In the enterprise of constructing knowledge in the scientific process, one of the tools man uses is his capacity for deductive reasoning. We examined the apparatus of deductive logic in Part II. As man reflects upon his experience and manipulates the factual data in his sciences, he employs the modes of conceptualization and patterns of deductive thought that we have discussed. Deductive thinking is an integral and necessary part of the scientific process. In the following sections, we shall select for discussion a few of the functions of deductive logic in the scientific process.

16–1. DEDUCTIVE LOGIC AND MATHEMATICS—THE LANGUAGES OF SCIENCE

By providing concepts for organizing and interpreting factual data, mathematics has played a very significant role as a scientific language.

The ancient Greeks were perhaps the first to understand mathematics as a deductive system, while recognizing that it was useful in conceptualizing and ordering observed data. The Pythagoreans categorized reality in terms of numbers and made significant contributions to number theory. Euclidean geometry, deductively developed, was used as an instrument for dealing with the world. Later, Ptolemaic astronomy employed the concepts of the circle and the sphere to interpret some of the structures and movements in the world system. In the early modern period, Kepler used the concept of the ellipse to describe planetary movements. Nicholas of Oresmus and Rene Descartes invented analytical geometry, a creative synthesis of algebra and geometry, which permitted quantitative calculations of the properties of geometric structures. In time, differential and integral calculus appeared (Leibniz and Newton); and the analysis involved in the use of differential equations became possible. It is no accident that, at the time when a whole set of new mathematical disciplines was invented, the foundations of modern empirical science were laid. The new mathematical languages of the fourteenth through the seventeenth centuries made modern science possible. Their categories and functions were used as instruments of description and explanation for the data of the physical universe. The classical Galilei-Newtonian system, which emerged as the culmination of this new science and which prevailed for so long, was chiefly a deductively elaborated system of abstract concepts.

One of the notable features of the new science that appeared in the time of Galileo (1564–1642) and Kepler (1571–1630) was the fusion of *mathematical and logical deductions* with a *new emphasis on observation and measurement*. Leonardo da Vinci, Galileo, Brahe, Pascal, Kepler, and others proclaimed that scientific knowledge must be fashioned in face of natural phenomena and be erected on the firm foundation of facts. Galileo required that the scientific enterprise begin with "sensible experiments." Leonardo remarked that the sciences are futile if they do not originate and terminate in observation.

At the same time, the flourishing of the new languages of modern mathematics and logic, among which we find Descartes' analytic geometry, provided these pioneers with new kinds of conceptual apparatus and deductive tools for expressing the "laws of nature" and for making accurate measurements and calculations. In the thirteenth century, Roger Bacon insisted that mathematics was the gateway and key to the sciences. Leonardo was as insistent upon the use of mathematical and logical demonstrations as upon beginning with observations. There was no true science without mathematical and logical descriptions or deductions. Galileo maintained that nature was written in mathematical language. "Without mathematics I am blind," he asserted.

The dual accent on observation or measurement and on mathematical or logical formulations was one of the striking features of the scientific method conceived at the outset of the modern period. The method of the new science demanded a fusion of empirical and rational factors. It married abstractions to phenomenal data. Logically stated, it combined intensional and extensional elements. Although the relationship between abstractions and deductions, on the one side, and observations and measurements, on the other side, remains to some extent a non-rational wedding of category and form to observable data, this union of the rational and empirical is still a dominant feature of contemporary scientific enterprises.

In this union, logic and mathematics have proved themselves to be the languages or instruments par excellence for investigating and manipulating the physical world. Thus, the principles of deductive reasoning in logic and mathematics have become an essential and distinctive part of the modern scientific process. As a working hypothesis, science assumes either that some form of orderliness prevails in the world or that the world displays some meaningful statistical correlations among sets of events. Inasmuch as scientific investigators proceed on such an assumption, they discover that the rational structures of mathematical systems can be used as models for talking about the world or can be used as tools for manipulation and prediction.

Mathematics, aided by logic, is essential to the development of the precision and predictive power that are so important in modern science. Scientific facts, generalizations, and predictions are distinguished by their precision. Mathematical languages provide men with the conceptual tools for establishing exact standards for measurement, calculation, and defining relations. No longer is speed described as "fast" or "slow"; weight described as "heavy" or "light"; and force defined as "great" or "small." The interrelations of mass, velocity, acceleration, force, and so on, could be quantitatively specified, after the invention of the proper mathematical languages.

Mathematics also provided a means by which precision and definiteness were introduced into areas that formerly had been described by theological or metaphysical terms. Thus, the idea of cause could now be expressed and characterized in logical or mathematical terms instead of in terms of necessary forces and hidden powers. Energy could be described and calculated in terms of mathematical symbols rather than in terms of anthropomorphic categories. The objectives in inquiry for knowledge could be spelled out in mathematical expressions and quantitative factors rather than in teleological and religious ideals.

The languages of logic and mathematics also prove valuable to science by providing an avenue for discovering and describing interrelations among concepts and data. They help men to sense and to formulate interrelations that are not clear to common-sense observation. For example, by their aid we can give a precise definition of equality in mathematics; or we can express the ideas that the relation "greater than" is irreflexive, asymmetric, and transitive, and that the relation "similar to" is reflexive, symmetric, and transitive. The powers of logic and mathematics have led to manifold scientific discoveries that would otherwise have either been impossible or long delayed.

The successes of mathematics and logic as the languages of science are so startling as to mystify us. Little significant progress in modern science would have been possible without them. Yet, they are man-made tools. They are a striking testimony to the creative power of man's capacities for conceptualization and for the use of symbols. It was the felicitous dual emphasis on mathematics or logic and on observation or empirical data that gave rise to modern science.

16–2.   HOW DEDUCTIVE LOGIC SERVES MATHEMATICS

Logic and mathematics are the clearest and most powerful languages used in the scientific process. An argument has been under way for years among philosophers and mathematicians about the relations between symbolic logic and mathematics. Which, for example, is prior to the other? We will not enter into this sort of debate, inasmuch as our purposes will not be served by involving ourselves in the controversy. Quite apart from the issues that are in question, it is clear that the principles of deductive logic are employed in mathematical systems and deductions. And, since mathematics is so widely used in scientific formulations and deductions, we must briefly indicate how deductive logic at this point performs its functions in mathematics and in the scientific process. This we will do by the use of examples.

First, we call attention to the fact that the steps in mathematical deductions in the sciences are connected to one another by the conditional connective. For example, when in algebra the student writes

$$2y + x = 6$$
$$2y = 6 - x$$
$$y = (6 - x)/2$$

what is meant is "*If* $2y + x = 6$, *then* $2y = 6 - x$; and *if* $2y = 6 - x$, *then* $y = (6 - x)/2$." Written explicitly, we have

$$[2y + x = 6] \supset [2y = 6 - x]$$
$$[2y = 6 - x] \supset [y = (6 - x)/2]$$
$$\overline{\text{Hence, } [2y + x = 6] \supset [y = (6 - x)/2]}$$

By way of illustration, this will indicate that mathematicians typically employ the conditional statement of logic in their deductions. Moreover, it also indicates that the elementary valid argument forms (Section 10–8) are employed in mathematical inferences. Hypothetical Syllogism, of course, was used in the example just given.

The importance of the hypothetical statement in mathematics is also accented by the fact that many theorems and statements in mathematical systems are hypothetical assertions. For example, "If a circle is cut by two equal chords, then the arcs intercepted by these chords are equal." "If $y = x + 2$ and $2y = 3x + 8$, then $x = -4$ and $y = -2$."

In our earlier definition and discussion of the hypothetical statement, we pointed out that the formula $(p \supset q)$ is reckoned true when the antecedent is false. Among the theorems of mathematics, we find situations in which this occurs. The mathematician refers to them by saying that the theorems are *vacuously satisfied*. For example, the statement "If x is an even prime number greater than 2, then the set of prime numbers has a finite number of members" is reckoned true because there is no x such that it is an even prime number and is greater than 2.

Mathematicians also make use of many interchange expressions, such as those that are listed in Section 10–8. Many statements and theorems are, as we said, in hypothetical form. They have the form $(p \supset q)$. Often it is easier to work with $(\sim q)$ as an assumption than it is to work with (p). After showing that $(\sim q \supset \sim p)$, the investigator contends that he has proved $(p \supset q)$. This is an appeal to the law of transposition. Framed a slightly different way, it is an appeal to *modus tollens*. Thus, perhaps instead of proving "If $m^2 = 2$, then m is not rational," he demonstrates that "If m is rational, then $m^2 \neq 2$."

The frequent use of *reductio ad absurdum* as a method of proof in mathematics draws upon certain logical principles and procedures. In a system we are given, say, postulates $(P_1, P_2, \ldots , P_k)$. We wish to prove the theorem X. *Reductio ad absurdum* consists in adding $(\sim X)$ to the postulates (that is, we assume the theorem is not true). We then have postulates $(P_1, P_2, \ldots , P_k, \sim X)$. If we can deduce a contradiction from the postulates, we take it as evidence that $(\sim X)$ is false; that is, (X) is true. Assuming that the denial of a contradiction is true and may be used as a premiss, we have

1. $(P_1 \cdot P_2 \cdot \ldots \cdot P_k \cdot \sim X) \supset (r \sim r)$
2. $\sim (r \sim r)$

3. $\sim (P_1 \cdot P_2 \cdot \ldots \cdot P_k \cdot \sim X)$ M.T., 1, 2
4. $(\sim P_1 + \ldots + \sim P_k + X)$ D.M., 3

Since, however, the postulates $P_1, P_2, \ldots , P_k$ are reckoned true, X is true by D.S.

Finally, we can suggest that in elementary arithmetic and algebra, as well as in higher mathematics, one implicitly uses statement functions and quantifiers. When the student learns that $(2 + 3 = 3 + 2)$, $(4 + 3 = 3 + 4)$, $(7 + 1 = 1 + 7)$, etc., and moves to the general idea that the sum of two numbers is the same, regardless of the order of summation, he is in an informal manner saying,

$$(\forall_x)(\forall_y)(x + y = y + x)$$

where the domain for x and y is the integers, the rational numbers, or the real numbers. This is, of course, the law of commutation for arithmetic addition. It is a universally quantified function. Similarly,

$$(\forall_x)(\forall_y)(\forall_z)[x(y + z) = (xy + xz)]$$

is a formal expression of the law of distribution of multiplication over addition. In logic, we have two laws of distribution (Section 10–8). In ordinary arithmetic and algebra, there is but one. The statement

$$(\forall_x)(\forall_y)(\forall_z)[x + (yz) = (x + y)(x + z)]$$

is false in arithmetic and algebra. The student should show this by producing a *counter-example*. A counter-example is an instance from the domain adopted for which the theorem or general statement fails.

Suppose a theorem is symbolically expressed by $(\forall_x)\Phi_x$. By **U.I.**, we understand that all elements in the domain have the property Φ. Finding a counter-example is discovering a particular instance, c, for which $\sim\Phi_c$ is true. Generalizing $\sim\Phi_c$, we get $(\exists_x)\sim\Phi_x$. By **Q.N.**, $(\exists_x)\sim\Phi_x \underline{\qquad} \sim(\forall_x)\Phi_x$, which is the contradiction of the theorem. Expressing the matter another way, we can write

1. $(\forall_x)\Phi_x \supset (\Phi_a \cdot \Phi_b \cdot \ldots \cdot \Phi_n)$	(An alf for **U.I.**)	
2. $(\sim\Phi_c)$	(Counter-example)	
3. $(\sim\Phi_c + \sim\Phi_a + \ldots + \sim\Phi_n)$	Add., 2	
4. $\sim(\Phi_a \cdot \Phi_b \cdot \Phi_c \cdot \ldots \cdot \Phi_n)$	D.M., 3	
5. $\sim(\forall_x)\Phi_x$	M.T., 1, 4	

Logic also serves mathematics and science by clarifying the definitions of such important terms as "number," "zero," "one," and so on, and in making more precise the expression of numerical statements.

The problems of logically defining the integers, the character of the integer series, and the natures of zero and one are very difficult ones, involving complex mathematical and philosophical issues that are beyond the scope of this book. The student who wishes to probe into these problems may begin his studies with Bertrand Russell's *Introduction to Mathematical Philosophy*[1] and Gottlob Frege's *Foundations of Arithmetic.*[2]

[1] Bertrand Russell, *Introduction to Mathematical Philosophy* (New York: The Macmillan Co., 1920).

[2] Gottlob Frege, *Foundations of Arithmetic* (New York: Philosophical Library, 1953).

Here we will give logical expression to statements that name numbers of a set, assuming that we know what number or a particular number means. This is an easier task and it is something that can be expressed in the logical apparatus we have already developed.

The statement "There is *at least* one switch in the circuit" can be expressed by

$$(\exists_x)(S_x)$$

where S stands for "switch in the circuit" and the quantifier $(\exists_x)$ is understood in the sense in which it was introduced in Part II. The assertion "There are at least two switches in the circuit" can be logically formulated by

$$(\exists_x)(\exists_y)[S_x \cdot S_y \cdot (x \neq y)]$$

Why is the assertion $(x \neq y)$ included in the formulation? Similarly, the statement "There are at least three holes in the fuselage" can be expressed by

$$(\exists_x)(\exists_y)(\exists_z)[H_x \cdot H_y \cdot H_z \cdot (x \neq y \neq z)]$$

where H stands for "holes in the fuselage."

A statement that there is *no more than* one hole in the fuselage means that, *if* there are two holes in the fuselage, *then* one is identical to the other. Furthermore, the statement does not mean that there is necessarily a hole in the fuselage. Thus, "There is no more than one hole in the fuselage" becomes, in our logical language,

$$(\forall_x)(\forall_y)[H_x \cdot H_y \supset (x = y)]$$

Similarly, "There are no more than two holes in the fuselage" is formulated by

$$(\forall_x)(\forall_y)(\forall_z)\{H_x \cdot H_y \cdot H_z \supset [(x = y) + (y = z) + (z = x)]\}$$

By combining these two sorts of assertions, we can formulate in logical language statements such as "There are *exactly* two switches in the circuit." "There are *exactly* two switches in the circuit" means "There are *at least* two switches in the circuit and there are *no more than* two switches in the circuit." Thus, we express the statement in this way:

$$(\exists_x)(\exists_y)\{S_x \cdot S_y \cdot (x \neq y) \cdot (\forall_z)[S_z \supset (z = x) + (z = y)]\}$$

In a similar manner, the statement "One and only one rat survived the test" can be expressed thus:

$$(\exists_x)\{R_x \cdot S_x \cdot (\forall_y)[R_y S_y \supset (y = x)]\}$$

where R stands for "rat" and S stands for "survived the test." The statement "Every machine in this shop has three moving parts" can be formulated in this manner:

$$(\forall_x)(M_x \supset (\exists_y)(\exists_z)(\exists_w)\{P_y \cdot P_z \cdot P_w \cdot H_{xy} \cdot H_{xz} \cdot H_{xw} \cdot (y \neq z) \cdot$$
$$(z \neq w) \cdot (w \neq y) \cdot (\forall_s)[P_s \cdot H_{rs} \supset (s = y) + (s = z) + (s = w)]\})$$

where M stands for "machine in this shop," P stands for "moving part," and H_{xy} stands for "x has y."

Drawing upon these ideas, we can understand how by using logic a unique individual can be described. Such a description is generally called a *definite description*. "The writer of *Phaedo* is an artist" is such a description. This statement means

1. At least one man wrote *Phaedo*.
2. No more than one man wrote *Phaedo*.
3. That man is an artist.

The logical formula expressing this threefold idea is

$$(\exists_x)\{W_x \cdot (\forall_y)[W_y \supset (y = x)] \cdot A_x\}$$

that is, "At least one man wrote *Phaedo*; and, if any other man wrote *Phaedo*, then he is identical to the first; and that man is an artist," where W stands for "wrote *Phaedo*" and A stands for "is an artist."

By advances of this sort, logic is able to express scientific statements that refer to numbers of things. Much of the discourse in the scientific process involves such numerical statements—"There are two and only two electrons in the helium atom," "At most twelve elements in the periodic table have atomic weights over 200," and "There are three and exactly three kinds of plane triangles in terms of the lengths of their sides." Science talks much about numbers, for its power is based in part on its ability to express the quantitative aspects of factual data. Logic can express exactly the numerical statements so necessary to scientific language.

These are a few of the ways in which logic serves mathematics and, in turn, science in general.

EXERCISE SET 16–2

B

1. In Exercise 5 of Exercise Set 14–2, the student was asked to produce an argument to show that the biconditional ($\supset \subset$) is a reflexive, symmetric, and transitive relation. Exercise 1d of Exercise Set 14–2 required the use of the arithmetic and algebraic equals relation ($=$), which is regarded as reflexive, symmetric, and transitive. Express what you sense to be the difference(s) between $=$ and $\supset \subset$.

2. Write in symbolic form the laws of commutation and association for addition and multiplication in arithmetic and algebra.

3. Consider $(\forall x)(\forall y)(2x + y = 3)$. Is this a statement? Is it true or false? If it is false, give a counter-example. How about $(\exists x)(\exists y)(2x + y = 3)$? How many true substitution instances are there? What is their peculiar characteristic?

4. Proceed as in Exercise 3 for $(\forall x)(x^2 = 4)$ and $(\exists x)(x^2 = 4)$.

5. Among mathematical systems, inconsistent premises are avoided for what reason? The technique of proof by *reductio ad absurdum*, which proceeds by adding to the postulates the contradiction of the statement to be proved, presupposes what about the postulates?

6. Given the equation $\sqrt{3x + 4} = x$, suppose that in solving it we write

$$(\sqrt{3x + 4} = x) \supset (3x + 4 = x^2)$$

$$(3x + 4 = x^2) \supset (x^2 - 3x - 4 = 0)$$

and

$$(x^2 - 3x - 4 = 0) \supset (x = -1)$$

What can you say in assessment of this argument and its statements?

7. Consider $(\exists x)(\exists y)(3x + y = 7)$. Let the domains for x and y be the negative integers, zero, and the positive integers: $\ldots -3, -2, -1, 0, 1, 2, 3, \ldots$ This is a true statement, for $x = 1$ and $y = 4$ satisfy the equation. But so do $x = 2$ and $y = 1$, etc. In other words, a set of *ordered pairs* of values from the domains makes this statement true. Express, then, what a function such as this does in terms of the elements of the domains.

8. Give logical formulas that express the following assertions:

    a. There exist at least two kangaroos.

    b. There are at most two vacuum tubes in the circuit.

    c. All men have at least one eye.

    d. Every student buys at most two books.

    e. Every circle has exactly one center.

    f. Some man has exactly two fingers.

    g. There are three and only three metals in the beaker.

    h. Every man has precisely two legs.

    i. The writer of the *Principia* is a mathematician.

    j. The inventor of the heliocentric system is a Greek who respected Euclid.

    k. There is at least one student who reads Plato, and there are at most four students who read Aristotle.

    l. If there exist exactly two metals that are acids, then at most three substances are alkalies.

16–3. ARGUMENT FORMS IN THE SCIENTIFIC PROCESS

We have illustrated briefly how logic through its argument forms and formal principles serves mathematics and, in turn, serves the scientific process.   The forms and structures of logic are also involved in non-mathematical arguments and inferences in the scientific process.   Since we are not undertaking a thorough survey of so-called "inductive logic," but attempting to suggest what the role of logic, particularly deductive logic, is in the scientific enterprise, the best procedure again will be to proceed by the use of illustrations and examples.

In Section 16–2, we showed that, where mathematical deductions are utilized in the empirical sciences, the formal principles of logic are employed.   Thus, when we begin with a formula for disintegration of uranium,

$$-dM/dt = 4.8 \times 10^{-18}M$$

where 4.8×10^{-18} is the rate of emission of atomic particles from a gram of uranium, M designates mass, and t designates time, and then proceed through such steps as

$$\log (M/M_o) = -4.8 \times 10^{-18}t$$

to the deduced law for the decay of uranium, namely,

$$M = M_o e^{-4.8 \times 10^{-18}t}$$

the steps in the sequence of calculations or deductions are tied together by the conditional connective ($\supset$).   Are they ?

But, even when the inferences in the scientific process are not formulated in mathematical symbols and formulas, the formulas and principles of logic are still employed.   Let us begin with several very simple examples drawn from elementary work in science.   The same logical operations we refer to are, however, also involved in highly complex situations and arguments.

An investigator is confronted with a solution that he conjectures to be sodium hydroxide.   To ascertain whether the solution is, in fact, a base, he inserts a piece of litmus paper.   He observes that the paper does not turn blue.   Whatever the solution may be, he concludes that it is not alkaline.   The reasoning process here may be stated thus: "If the solution is alkaline, then the litmus paper turns blue.   The litmus paper did not turn blue; therefore, the solution is not alkaline."   This argument is in the form *modus tollens* (M.T.).

We have displayed only one logical step in this simple experiment. Let us assume that the investigator continues in a more extensive process of qualitative analysis of the solution.   He reaches a stage in his investigation where he conjectures that the unknown is a chloride.   He proceeds in his analysis by a number of precise steps, namely, $(S_1, S_2, \ldots, S_n)$. These steps are, at the level of logical formulation, joined by conjunction: $(S_1 \cdot S_2 \cdot \ldots \cdot S_n)$.   It is asserted that, if these steps are successful or if the conditions they demand are satisfied, then if the solution is a chloride (q), a precipitate will result (r). But no precipitate results when the test is performed. Thus far, the investigator's reasoning may be symbolically displayed in this way:

1. $\{(S_1 \cdot S_2 \cdot \ldots \cdot S_n) \supset (q \supset r)\}$
2. $\{[(S_1 \cdot S_2 \cdot \ldots \cdot S_n) \cdot (q)] \supset (r)\}$
3. $\{\sim r\}$

Assertion 2 results from the use of an interchange expression for assertion 1. This expression is Exportation. From assertions 2 and 3, by M.T., the investigator concludes

4. $\sim[(S_1 \cdot S_2 \cdot \ldots \cdot S_n) \cdot (q)]$

Although the investigator may be unaware of the argument forms involved in the logical steps he pursues, he may well proceed in this manner: $[\sim(S_1 \cdot S_2 \cdot \ldots \cdot S_n) + (\sim q)]$ is an interchange expression (DeMorgan's Theorem) for $\sim[(S_1 \cdot S_2 \cdot \ldots \cdot S_n) \cdot (q)]$. Reviewing his previous inferences, he thinks, "I have taken steps $(S_1, S_2, \ldots, S_n)$; therefore, the solution is not a chloride." This form of deduction is Disjunctive Syllogism (D.S.).

$$[\sim(S_1 \cdot S_2 \cdot \ldots \cdot S_n) + (\sim q)], [S_1 \cdot S_2 \cdot \ldots \cdot S_n] \vdash [\sim q]$$

Let us illustrate the use of D.S. in another area. Consider an arc gap in an electrical circuit. The spacing between the contacts is 0.050 inch. There is a voltage of 2,000 volts between the contacts. In terms of our past experience with such high-voltage circuits containing gaps, we formulate the statement

1. There is no arc across the gap, or the atmospheric pressure is lower than 6 inches of mercury.

This is a disjunctive statement, and it may be expressed by $(a' + s)$. Such a formulation is, perhaps, a summary of our past experiences with such situations. As a generalization of earlier experience, it is a premiss on the basis of which we now argue about similar situations. Now let us suppose that in a present experimental situation we observe an arc across a gap of 0.050 inch in a 2,000-volt circuit. This observation is expressible in the statement

2. There is an arc across the gap.

In symbols, this is the statement, (a). From premiss 1 and the observational assertion 2, we conclude by D.S. that the atmospheric pressure is lower than 6 inches of mercury; that is, we conclude (s).

Let us consider one more example. Suppose that with respect to a radio transmitter installation, we assert, "If any current in the transmitter surges above 2 amperes, it trips open the circuit breaker in the power line." This statement can be expressed by the logical formula $(s \supset t)$, where s stands for "any current in the transmitter circuit surges above 2 amperes" and t stands for "the current trips open the circuit breaker in the power line." Our knowledge about electrical phenomena leads us, perhaps, to assert a second statement: "If any current trips open the circuit breaker in the power line, it causes the radio transmissions to be cut off." This statement can be symbolized by $(t \supset o)$, where o stands for the statement in the consequent of the hypothetical assertion. When we infer the statement "If any current in the transmitter circuit surges above 2 amperes, it causes the radio transmissions to be cut off," we are employing the valid argument form Hypothetical Syllogism.

If one desires to make assertions like these in such a way as to express the idea that the statements hold for all instances of the sets of phenomena referred to, then the argument form can be expressed in quantified statements:

$$(\forall_x)(S_x \supset T_x)$$
$$\underline{(\forall_x)(T_x \supset O_x)}$$
$$\text{Hence, } (\forall_x)(S_x \supset O_x)$$

where, of course, the S_x, T_x, and O_x are statement functions such as "x is a current in the transmitter circuit that surges above 2 amperes," etc. In order to use an example such as this for the purpose of displaying the use of a logical pattern of argument in the empirical sciences, we have had to leave to the side a whole matrix of details related to electrical and magnetic phenomena. The student will hopefully understand the necessity of ignoring the details in order to set forth clearly the skeleton of the overall structure of the argument employed.

16–4. DEDUCTIVE LOGIC AND THE FORMAL STRUCTURE OF A SCIENTIFIC SYSTEM

In Section 16–1 we remarked that modern science and the structures of knowledge it produces have their footings in two domains: factual data, observations, or sensible phenomena; and logical and mathematical concepts and operations. Let us now consider from another perspective the structure of knowledge in an empirical science, such as Newtonian mechanics. Such a structure of knowledge is neither simply a highly articulated fabric of abstract ideas, nor is it simply an aggregation of unorganized or unrelated data or percepts. Knowledge requires both content (sensory data) and form (organizing concepts).

What is, then, the logical structure of a modern empirical scientific system? First, let us note that an observation of some data is generally expressed in an existential statement, such as "There is an x such that x is a metal and a conductor of electricity." This we can formulate by the logical expression

$$(\exists_x)(M_x C_x)$$

Such a statement is frequently the report of observations or measurements. Reports of this sort often comprise the raw data displayed in charts or lists or plotted on a graphical scheme. As we pointed out in Chapter 15, even these rudimentary experiences of factual data and our reports of them involve a measure of interpretation by the observer or reporter. But, granting this, one footing for scientific knowledge is found in such basic or existential statements as "The steel block is 1.52 inches in length," "The temperature of the wire is 72.7° C.," and "The current in the circuit is 0.52 amperes."

Second, the other anchorage for a structure of scientific knowledge is some abstract concepts or some universal statements (often called *laws*). The raw data or reports of observations in science must be interpreted by some generalizations. Most often these universal statements are expressed in mathematical formulas. For instance, in a certain context where the report "The current in the circuit is 0.52 amperes" is relevant, the law or universal statement invoked for interpretation of the circuit phenomena might be Ohm's Law ($V = I \times R$) or a differential equation expressing voltage drops over the components in the circuit. In another domain, the universal statements might be those of Kepler's formulations for planetary motion; for example, "For all values of x, if x is a planet, then x travels in an elliptical orbit about its sun at one focus." Such a statement of a scientific "law" or hypothesis is generally expressible in a universally quantified logical formula; for instance, $(\forall_x)(P_x \supset E_x)$.

The structure of a modern scientific system is, then, a *union* of some universal statements (laws, hypotheses, principles) and some reports of observations (initial conditions, definitions of parameters, reports of factual data). Symbolically, we can display the logical skeleton of such a system in this way:

Logical Structure of an
Empirical Scientific System

$$\left\{ \begin{array}{l} (\forall_x)\Phi_x \\ \cdot \\ \cdot \\ \cdot \\ (\exists_x)\Psi_x \\ \cdot \\ \cdot \end{array} \right.$$

Universal statements

Existential statements

In general, this is the logical anatomy of the Copernican astronomy, Newtonian mechanics, Bohr's atomism, or Einstein's theory of relativity. (We shall use the device of {. . .} to symbolize a *set* of postulates or principles, where the sorts of statements in the set will be indicated by the presence of $(\forall_x)\Phi_x$ or $(\exists_x)\Psi_x$ inside the brackets.)

Both types of statements—universal and existential—are necessary for a scientific structure of knowledge in the empirical sciences. If we have a set of statements in which each statement is existential (no universal statements are present), we have little more than an aggregation of unconnected reports. The only abstract concepts present are those involved in the reports themselves so as to make the reports meaningful. From such a system, very few deductions can be made. Consider, for example, the number of valid inferences possible in cases where the premises are

Case 1	*Case 2*
$(\exists_x)(A_xB_x)$	$(\exists_x)(A_xB_x)$
$(\exists_x)(B_xC_x)$	$(\exists_x)(C_xD_x)$
Hence, . . .	Hence, . . .

The scientific process could not advance far if science's system of knowledge was built exclusively on existential statements. Moreover, since the inference from "some" to "all" is logically unwarranted, we cannot produce from the existential statements themselves the universal statements we need for relating the reports and for making deductions and predictions. A system of this sort would be infertile, and scientific knowledge would consist of a collection of observations and reports.

On the other hand, if a system consists only of universal statements, $(\forall_x)\Phi_x$, that is, contains no existential statements about observations or initial conditions, we can surely make deductions from it. In general, a lengthy and secure sequence of inferences can be established. But, inasmuch as no existential statements are present, these deductions can have no sure connection with factual data and cannot be tested. Corroboration is impossible, as we suggested earlier. Such a system cannot be a system of knowledge for an *empirical* science. It cannot be used to guide conduct or manipulate the world. A system of this sort can serve for mathematics, but not for mechanics or astronomy. The scientific process as a mode of reflection upon and manipulation of experience would not be possible.

A system $\{(\exists_x)\Psi_x\}$ tends to be simply or purely reportorial. There can be little deduction and therefore little guidance of conduct or control of the world. The scientific process, as we know it, would be impossible. A system $\{(\forall_x)\Phi_x\}$ tends to be empty or purely abstract. Deduction is possible, but it is likely to be unconnected with factual data. And, again, little guidance of conduct or control of the world is possible; and the scientific process, as we know it, would be impossible.

The logical structure of an effective and fertile scientific system, one in which verification and corroboration are possible, and one that can give guidance to human conduct and lead to control of the world, is $\{(\forall_x)\Phi_x, (\exists_x)\Psi_x\}$; that is, it is a combination of universal and existential statements. Process and progress in scientific inquiry and the development of scientific knowledge demand both abstract ideas and concrete data.

EXERCISE SET 16–4

B

1. If a scientific system, $\{(\forall_x)\Phi_x\}$, is inconsistent, how many theorems or statements can be proved? Can you give some sort of symbolic expression to your contention?

2. If a scientific system consists of only three existential statements, $(\exists_x)(A_x)$, $(\exists_y)(B_y)$, and $(\exists_z)(C_z)$, how many validly inferred statements are possible?

3. If a scientific system, $\{(\forall_x)\Phi_x\}$, is inconsistent, can it be decomposed into two consistent systems? Under what condition? Try to give symbolic expression to this situation. Is an inconsistent system, $\{(\forall_x)\Phi_x\}$, "more fertile" than a consistent system, $\{(\forall_y)\Psi_y\}$? In what sense?

16–5. LOGICAL FORMS AND SWITCHING CIRCUITS

We have now discussed a number of the functions that deductive logic performs in the scientific process. It provides the forms and formulations for scientific prediction and is an important factor in the falsification of hypotheses. Deductive logic is used in mathematical deductions; in arguments about substantive matters in the empirical sciences; in expressing relations, numerical statements, and conditional connections; and so on.

Before we close our study, we should at least indicate one of the technical applications of deductive logic. This will illustrate how deductive logic confers upon science power to control some aspects of the world. For this purpose, we choose the application of logic to switches in electrical circuits and to the "adding" mechanisms of digital computers. This is presently one of the most important and widely known uses of formal logic. Here we can outline only a few of the simple steps one can take to move in the direction of interpreting the formulas and operations of logic so as to understand and control switching circuits.

Let us begin by calling attention to a switch that is *normally open* and that closes when a signal (current) flows in a coil and magnetically activates the switch. (Throughout this discussion we are thinking of such relay switches.)

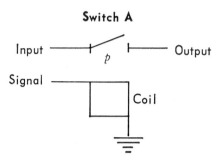

We can denote such a relay switch by, say, *p*. *When the signal activates the coil and switch (designated by value 1), the circuit from the input to the output is closed. When there is no signal activating the coil (designated by the value 0), the circuit between the input and output is broken by the normally open position of the switch.*

We can also have a relay switch that is *normally closed* and that opens upon the activation of the coil.

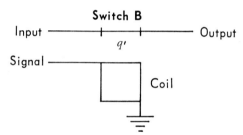

In this case, the signal condition 0 leaves the circuit from input to output closed; but the signal condition 1 opens the switch and breaks the input-to-output line. This type of switching function we can designate by *q′*.

Switch A, normally open (n.o.), under signal condition 1 is designated by *p*. When signal condition 0 obtains (coil not activated), we can denote its status by *p′*. Similarly, in the case of switch B, normally closed (n.c.), which is denoted by *q′*. Under signal condition 0, it can be designated by *q*.

	Signal (Coil) Condition	*Input-Output*	*Symbol*
Normally open switch:	1	closed	p
	0	open	p'
Normally closed switch:	1	open	q'
	0	closed	q

At this point, we have interpreted the sort of symbols we used for statements, $p, q, \ldots$, and the mark for negation ($'$) in terms of switches and their open or closed positions.

Such switches can be connected in series or in parallel. Consider two n.o. switches in series.

For the input-output line to be closed and for a message to travel over it, p must be closed *and* q must be closed. This can be designated by the conjunction (pq). When the signal condition for the coil at p is 1 and the signal condition for the coil at q is 1, then p is closed and q is closed, and the input-output line is closed. This corresponds to the idea that the conjunctive formula (pq) has the value 1, when p separately has the value 1 and q separately has the value 1. The conjunctive formula is, therefore, a logical description for a series circuit. If a n.o. switch r is connected in series with a n.c. switch s, the conjunctive formula describing the circuit is (rs'); and, if both switches are activated by the same coil, we have (rr').

If two n.o. switches are connected in parallel, we have the circuit:

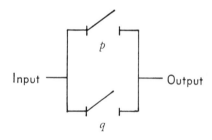

For the input-output line to be closed, p must close *or* q must close. This is describable by the disjunctive formula $(p + q)$. When either the coil activating p or the coil activating q is in the signal condition 1, the input-output line is closed and a message can be transmitted over it. This corresponds to the meaning of the disjunctive formula; namely, if p has the value 1, or q has the value 1, or both have the value 1, then $(p + q)$ has the value 1. The disjunctive formula is a description of a parallel connection between two switches. If we have a parallel connection involving two n.c. switches, v and w, we describe it by the formula $(v' + w')$. If there is a parallel connection between two switches, x and y, one of them n.o. and the other n.c., we have the formula $(x + y')$. The student should draw the schematic diagrams for these last two cases.

If we have three switches in parallel, one of which is n.o. and the other two of which are n.c., the logical formula describing the circuit is $(p + q' + r')$, and so on.

Now we are in a position to write logical formulas for arrays of switches, where some of the connections are parallel and some are series, and where some switches are n.c. while others are n.o. Consider a circuit where we have a n.o. switch, p, in series with a parallel connection between two n.c. switches, q and r.

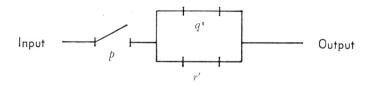

The formula describing this circuit or this switching function is $[(p) \cdot (q' + r')]$. By the use of the truth-table, which is here interpreted as giving the possible conditions for the activation of the three coils, the student should discover and specify under what conditions the input-output line is closed. Under which is it open?

As another example, consider this circuit:

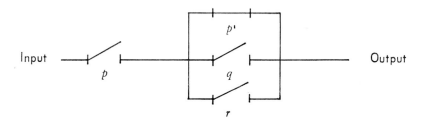

The student should construct the logical formula describing this circuit. What is the significance of one switch being denoted by p, while another in the circuit is denoted by p'? Having arrived at a logical formula that describes the circuit, the student should discover the conditions under which the input-output line can transmit a message.

This topic in the application of logical formulas to switching circuits can be pursued at great length. For example, we can learn to write complex formulas that specify complex circuits, study the problem of simplifying formulas in order to simplify circuits so that we can save hardware, and so forth.

Our discussion has introduced this application in terms of relay switches. In modern machinery and computers, other kinds of switching devices are used: diodes, vacuum tubes, and transistors; but the logical formulas describing the circuitry will, in general, remain the same. The adding mechanisms in digital computers are binary computational systems (values 1 and 0) and consist of arrays of "switching units" that perform functions corresponding to the logical formulas for negation, conjunction, and disjunction. The student should be prepared now, if he so desires, to pursue the topic of the algebra of circuits in connection with computers in such a book as R. K. Richards' *Arithmetic Operations in Digital Computers*[3].

EXERCISE SET 16–5

B

1. Produce a schematic diagram of a switching circuit that corresponds to each of these formulas.

a. $(pq'r')$

b. $[(p + q) \cdot (r + s)]$

c. $[x + y + (zw)]$

d. $[(q + r) \cdot (r) \cdot (s + q')]$

e. $(x'y)$

f. $\{[(p + q) \cdot (r)] + (qp)\}$

g. $\{w' + xyz' + [(xw) \cdot (z + xy')]\}$

h. $[(p + qrs') \cdot (p' + s)]$

i. $(ab'c' + bc' + a'cd + d')$

j. $[p + (p'q) + (p'qr) + (p'qrs)]$

2. Write the logical formulas that express each of these switching circuits.

a.

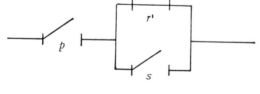

b.

c.

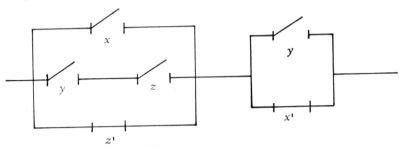

d.

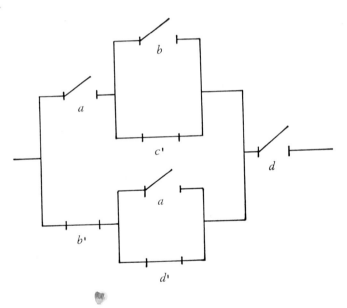

e.

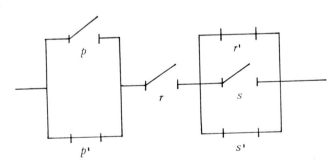

3. Write the truth-tables for the problems in Exercise 1 and determine under what conditions messages can be transmitted over the input-output lines.

4. Do the same for the logical formulas you produced in Exercise 2.

5. Produce the schematic circuit diagram for the formula in Exercise 1g. Produce the circuit diagram for the formula $(w' + x)$. Write the truth-table for each. What do you discover? From this, what do you infer?

6. An effective switching circuit is one that for some conditions of the switches the input-output line can transmit a message, while for others it cannot. Does a tautological formula specify an effective switching circuit? Write a tautological formula and produce the schematic circuit diagram that corresponds to it. Does a self-contradictory logical formula specify an effective switching circuit? (pp') is a simple example. Draw the schematic circuit diagram for (pp'). A logical formula that is sometimes 1 and sometimes 0 is called a *contingent* formula. State the connection between contingent formulas and effective switching circuits. Determine whether the circuits given or described in Exercises 1 and 2 are effective.

7. Construct a schematic circuit diagram for an effective switching circuit involving three n.o. switches and two n.c. switches. Write its logical formula and demonstrate by the truth-table that it is effective. Can the circuit you produced be simplified in any way? If so, write the logical formula for its simplified form.

8. Consider the formula $(x'y + xy + xy'z + z')$. Using the interchange expressions of Part II, simplify this formula as best you can. Draw the schematic circuit diagram for the original formula and for the simplified form. Under what conditions can the switching function, expressed by both formulas, transmit a message on the input-output line? Do the same for

a. $(y' + x)z + (x + y')$

d. $(x + xy + x'yz + x'yz' + xy')$

b. $(x'yz + y'z + z' + x'yzw)$

e. $(xy + xy') \cdot (x'z + x'z') \cdot (z + x')$

c. $(x'yz + xyz + xyzw)$

RECOMMENDED FOR FURTHER STUDY

The four volumes of *The World of Mathematics* (New York, 1956), edited by James R. Newman, can be recommended as a valuable anthology. More specifically, we call attention here to Volume III, Part XI, "Mathematical Truth and the Structure of Mathematics," and Part XII, "The Mathematical Way of Thinking."

Part III, "Development of Various Viewpoints on Foundations [of Mathematics]," of Raymond Wilder's *The Foundations of Mathematics* (New York, 1952) can be heartily recommended for a discussion of intuitionism, formalism, and the Frege-Russell theory on the nature of mathematics and logic.

Ernest Nagel's *The Structure of Science* (New York, 1961) contains a suggestive discussion in Chapter 4, "The Logical Character of Scientific Laws."

The role of mathematics and logic in a particular discipline is revealed in W. H. Watson's *On Understanding Physics* (New York, 1959).

The Rise of Scientific Philosophy (Berkeley, 1956), by Hans Reichenbach, discusses the empirical and rational factors operative in modern science. We call attention specifically to Chapter 6, "The Twofold Nature of Classical Physics."

The student who is interested in pursuing the topic of the application of logic to circuitry and the operations of digital computers can begin his studies with Chapters 2 and 3, "Boolean Algebra Applied to Computer Components" and "Switching Networks," in R. K. Richards' *Arithmetic Operations in Digital Computers* (New York, 1955). From there he can make his way into an extensive literature on circuit algebras, switching networks, and computers.

Volume 28, No. 1, "Jurimetrics," of *Law and Contemporary Problems*, by the Duke University School of Law, discusses the application of symbolic logic to legal documents and arguments.

APPENDIX

Reference List of Interchange Expressions, Simple Argument Forms, and Rules of Inference

Interchange Expressions		Section
1. $(p')' \equiv (p)$	Law of Double Negation (D.N.)	8–5
2. $(pq)' \equiv (p' + q')$ $(p + q)' \equiv (p'q')$	DeMorgan's Rules (D.M.)	8–6
3. $(p \supset q) \equiv (p' + q)$	Definition of the Hypothetical or Conditional (D.C.)	9–1
4. $(p \supset q) \equiv (q' \supset p')$	Law of Transposition (Trans.)	9–2
5. $(p) \equiv (p + p)$ $(p) \equiv (pp)$	Laws of Tautology (Taut.)	8–5
6. $[p \supset\subset q] \equiv [(p \supset q) \cdot (q \supset p)]$ $[p \supset\subset q] \equiv [(pq) + (p'q')]$	Definition of the Biconditional (D.B.)	9–3
7. $(p + q) \equiv (q + p)$ $(pq) \equiv (qp)$	Laws of Commutation (Comm.)	10–1
8. $[(p) + (q + r)] \equiv [(p + q) + (r)]$ $[(p) \cdot (qr)] \equiv [(pq) \cdot (r)]$	Laws of Association (Assoc.)	10–1
9. $[(p) \cdot (q + r)] \equiv [(pq) + (pr)]$ $[(p) + (qr)] \equiv [(p + q) \cdot (p + r)]$	Laws of Distribution (Distr.)	10–2

	Interchange Expressions		*Section*

10. $[(pq) \supset (r)]$ ⎯⎯⎯ $[(p) \supset (q \supset r)]$ Exportation (Exp.)   10–2

11. $[p]$ ⎯⎯⎯ $[(p) + (pq)]$ Absorption (Absorp.)   10–3

   $[p + q]$ ⎯⎯⎯ $[(p) + (p'q)]$

Simple Argument Forms

12. $(pq) \vdash (p)$ Simplification (Simpl.)   10–3

   $(pq) \vdash (q)$

13. $(p) \vdash (p + q)$ Addition (Add.)   10–3

   $(p) \vdash (q + p)$

14. $(p), (q) \vdash (pq)$ Conjunction (Conj.)   10–3

15. $(p + q), (p') \vdash (q)$ Disjunctive Syllogism   10–4
   $(p + q), (q') \vdash (p)$ (D.S.)

16. $(p \supset q), (p) \vdash (q)$ *Modus Ponens* (M.P.)   10–5

17. $(p \supset q), (q') \vdash (p')$ *Modus Tollens* (M.T.)   10–5

18. $(p \supset q), (q \supset r) \vdash (p \supset r)$ Hypothetical Syllogism   10–6
                                    (H.S.)

19. $(p \supset q), (r \supset s), (p + r) \vdash (q + s)$ Constructive Dilemma   10–7
                                    (C.D.)

20. $(p \supset q), (r \supset s), (q' + s') \vdash (p' + r')$ Destructive Dilemma   10–7
                                    (D.D.)

Rules of Inference

21. $(\forall_x)\Phi_x \vdash \Phi_a$ Universal Instantiation   13–5
   $(\forall_x)\Phi_x \vdash \Phi_\alpha$ (**U.I.**)

22. $\Phi_\alpha \vdash (\forall_x)\Phi_x$ Universal Generaliza-   13–5
                                    tion (**U.G.**)

23. $\Phi_a \vdash (\exists_x)\Phi_x$ Existential Generaliza-   13–5
   $\Phi_\alpha \vdash (\exists_x)\Phi_x$ tion (**E.G.**)

24. $(\exists x)\Phi_x \vdash \Phi_a$ Existential Instanti-   13–5
                                              ation (**E.I.**)

Quantifier Negation (Interchange Expressions)

25. $(\forall x)(\Phi_x \supset \Psi_x) \equiv\!\equiv\ \sim(\exists x)(\Phi_x \sim \Psi_x)$ Quantifier Negation   13–4
      $\sim(\forall x)(\Phi_x \supset \Psi_x) \equiv\!\equiv\ (\exists x)(\Phi_x \sim \Psi_x)$ (**Q.N.**)

       $(\forall x)(\Phi_x \supset \sim\Psi_x) \equiv\!\equiv\ \sim(\exists x)(\Phi_x \Psi_x)$

    $\sim(\forall x)(\Phi_x \supset \sim\Psi_x) \equiv\!\equiv\ (\exists x)(\Phi_x \Psi_x)$

Index

Unsystematic: some authors of books cited are included, others not.

263

Adams   Fund. of Gen Log   33,55
Blyth   Mod Intro to Logic 33

Cossier   Lang. & Myth 10
Castell A college Logic 43
Eaton   Symbolism & Truth 22

Frye & Levi Rational Belief 11, 33

Hayakawa   Lang. in Thought & Action 11

Langer   Phil in a New Key   10

Little, Wilson & Moore Applied Logic 43

Morris   Signs, Lang & Beh.   10

Pap   Elements   "Analysis of Meaning" 22

Ruby.   Logic An Intro 11, 33

Russell   Princ of Maths   11
             Prob of Phil   22

Schipper & Schuh 43
Searles   11

Stebbing   Mod Intro to Logic 11

                Bases & Struct of Knowl. 33
Werkmeister Intro to Crit. Thinking th 22, 43

Sidgwick   Fallacies   43

Stuart Chase Guides to Straight Thinking 43

Stebbing   Thinking to Some Purpose 43